Leslie L. Doelle, Eng., M. Arch.

Acoustical Consultant
Associate Professor, University of Montreal
Lecturer, McGill University
Visiting Professor, Laval University

Environmental Acoustics

McGRAW-HILL BOOK COMPANY

New York   St. Louis   San Francisco   Düsseldorf   Johannesburg
Kuala Lumpur   London   Mexico   Montreal   New Delhi
Panama   Rio de Janeiro   Singapore   Sydney   Toronto

This book was set in Laurel by York Graphic Services,
Inc., printed by Halliday Lithograph Corporation, and
bound by A. Horowitz & Son Bookbinders. The designer
was Naomi Auerbach. The editors were William G.
Salo, Jr., and Stanley E. Redka. Teresa F. Leaden
supervised production.

Contents

Preface

In present-day building practice, the enormous increase of noise levels and noise sources means that the acoustical performance of a building will ultimately depend upon the attention given by the architect to acoustical requirements in designing, detailing, specifying, and supervising the project.

Recognizing this fact, the author wrote to a number of practicing architects asking them to describe the particular type and presentation of material on environmental acoustics they would most welcome. The answers pointed almost unanimously to a type of publication which would meet the following requirements:

1. It would be presented in such a way that it could be understood by a reader who had no acoustical experience.
2. It would contain a minimum of mathematical or physical details.
3. It would contain simple and practical recommendations with ample references to actual installations.
4. It would include an illustrated review of the materials and constructions used in practice.
5. It would enable the architect to solve by himself the increasing number of relatively simple acoustical problems encountered in everyday practice, without too much additional reading and without the help of an acoustical expert.

This book has been written with a strict observance of these requirements. It is based upon several years of concurrent teaching at three Canadian schools of architecture and on the large number of acoustical problems solved in a private practice of over 20 years.

Although intended for the architect and the architecture student, the book also will be useful to engineers, interior designers, builders, contractors, promoters, developers, and in general to anyone whose occupation involves him in problems of environmental acoustics. Acoustical experts probably will not find anything new in this book, except perhaps the system of classification and the bibliography.

The book is divided into four parts. Part I introduces the subject and discusses important terms. Part II covers room (or space) acoustics, that is, the acoustical design of auditoriums, such as lecture halls, theaters, concert halls, opera houses, motion-picture theaters, churches, sound studios, and open-air theaters. Part III discusses various aspects and methods of environmental noise control, including sound-insulating walls, floors, doors, windows, and the noise control of auditoriums, residential buildings, hotels, motels, schools, hospitals, offices, and industrial buildings. Part IV is concerned with the execution, supervision, and checking of acoustical works. The Appendixes include tables of sound absorption coefficients of various materials and a detailed selection of wall and floor constructions with their architectural-acoustical characteristics. At the end of each chapter there is a bibliography for further reading. Appendix D lists publications of a more general nature on architectural acoustics.

Most of the drawings and photographs were taken from my own works, obviously because they were readily available, but the works of other acousticians could have served as well or better.

My thanks and acknowledgments are due to a number of people who directly or indirectly contributed to the preparation of this book.

I am greatly indebted to Guy Desbarats, Dean of the School of Architecture, University of Montreal, to John Bland, Director of the School of Architecture, McGill University, and to Paul N. Bourque, Director of the School of Architecture, Laval University, for enabling me to take time out from my teaching duties for the preparation of this book.

I wish to express my sincere appreciation to the National Research Council of Canada, Ottawa, particularly to Dr. Thomas D. Northwood, who kindly permitted me to make use of the results of their extensive acoustical research work.

I am particularly grateful to the National Bureau of Standards and to the U.S. Department of Housing and Urban Development, Washington, D.C., for their permission to use important data on wall and floor constructions published in their excellent book *A Guide to Air-borne, Impact, and Structure-borne Noise Control in Multi-family Dwellings.*

My special thanks are due to Dr. Leo L. Beranek and Robert B. Newman, of Bolt, Beranek, and Newman, Inc., whose extraordinary achievements in all fields of acoustics and superb writings continuously gave me inspiration.

I would like to record my indebtedness to the Acoustical and Insulating Materials Association (previously Acoustical Materials Association) for their excellent publications, which provided several sources for the illustrations in this book.

I record with gratitude the kind cooperation of the Public Information Department of Lincoln Center for the Performing Arts Inc., New York, the Public Relations Departments of the National Arts Center, Ottawa, and Place des Arts, Montreal, and the Management of the Royal Festival Hall, London, for the beautiful photographs they provided.

Credit is due to the following institutions and firms who supplied valuable technical information on several topics: The Carpet and Rug Institute, US Gypsum Co., Canadian Gupsum Co., Johns-Manville Co., Cominco Ltd., Domtar Ltd., New Castle Products, Inc., Pilkington Glass Ltd., The Proudfoot Co., Owens-Corning Fiberglas Corp., The Celotex Corp., Simpson Timber Co., and Amber-Booth Co. The help received from Rupert Gomes of Modernfold of Canada Ltd. is gratefully acknowledged.

All the drawings in this book are the work of Serge Melanson and John Vassiliadis, previously my very capable students and now both graduate architects.

I am particularly grateful to Miss Maureen Anderson for her extraordinary care and attention to the considerable work of reviewing the typescript and for making instructive comments for improvement.

And finally, I must add more than words of gratitude to members of my family whose cooperation made the preparation of this book a real family affair. Thanks to my son, Robert, an electrical engineer, who made outstanding suggestions regarding the technical framework and the style of the book; to my daughter, Judy, who was also my secretary, for taking excellent care of the typing and correspondence; and to my wife, Eva, Librarian of the Blackader Library of Art and Architecture, McGill University, whose arduous research was a great contribution.

Leslie L. Doelle

PART ONE

Introduction

W hile our forefathers lived in relative tranquillity, we are subjected to an incredible increase in the sources of noise and noise intensity, both inside and outside our buildings, often with serious and even harmful effects. At the same time, it has become an accepted practice to replace the conventionally thick and heavy building construction with thin, lightweight, prefabricated—sometimes even movable—building elements. There is also a growing demand for considerably improved hearing conditions in the large number of auditoriums, theaters, concert halls, assembly rooms, churches, and motion-picture theaters being built all over the world. All these elements have contributed to make architectural acoustics an essential discipline in the control of the interior and exterior environment.

CHAPTER ONE

Environmental Acoustics in Architectural Design

1.1 The Scope of Acoustics

Acoustics covers a very wide range, touching upon almost every facet of human experience (Fig. 1.1). Physicians, psychologists, audiologists, and biologists; musicians, composers, and musical-instrument manufacturers; communications, space, and computer scientists; oceanographers; people employed in the radio, television, and recording industries; architects, town planners, and structural, mechanical, electrical, and chemical engineers—these in addition to others—are becoming associated to a greater or lesser extent with some aspect of acoustics.

1.2 Acoustics in Environmental Control

The remarkable growth of the engineering sciences—the development of new sources of power, the invention of synthetic materials, progress in outer-space research and its associated industries, the artificial production and manipulation of light and sound, the increasing degree of automation and mechanization—has contributed to architectural practice to the extent that a building now does much more than provide shelter and protection for its occupants against the thermal, atmospheric, luminous, and sonic fluctuations of the exterior world. Contemporary environmental control can create a complex artificial environment in buildings that will meet all the physical, physiological, and psychological requirements of the occupants. This artificially created synthetic environment is in many respects superior to the natural one. No exterior atmosphere is comparable to an air-conditioned and humidity-controlled room. Lighting fixtures presently available will not only simulate daylight but will create an improved (shadowless) luminous environment indispensable for certain activities. A sound-controlled concert hall or radio studio will provide an acoustical environment that has no precedent in nature.

It is obvious that the architect cannot possess all the qualifications necessary to produce these improved and sometimes highly complex environmental conditions. He will have to consult with mechanical, structural, lighting, acoustical, and sometimes other specialists to meet requirements essential to the safety, health, comfort, satisfaction, and productivity of a building's occupants. But he must have an overall

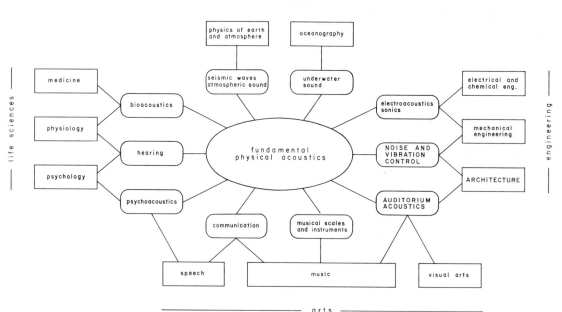

Fig. 1.1   Acoustics and its relation to arts and sciences.

understanding of the environmental disciplines, partly to coordinate the recommendations of his consultants and partly to incorporate their recommendations into architectural drawings and specifications in an efficient manner.

Environmental acoustics, or architectural sound control, constitutes a branch in the environmental control of architectural spaces. It can create an environment, in which ideal listening conditions will be provided both in enclosed spaces and in the open air and the occupants of interior and exterior architectural spaces will be adequately protected against excessive noises and vibrations.

Accordingly, architectural sound control has two goals: (1) To provide the most favorable conditions for the *production, transmission,* and *perception* of desirable sounds (speech or music) inside the rooms used for various listening purposes, or in the open air. This field of architectural sound control, called *room acoustics* or *space acoustics,* will be covered in Part II. (2) The exclusion or reasonable reduction of noises (unwanted sounds) and vibrations. This is termed *noise control* and will be dealt with in Part III.

The problems of room (or space) acoustics and noise control are naturally interrelated and interdependent: they cannot be separated from each other. The control of noise plays an important role in the room-acoustical design of auditoriums. Similarly, room-acoustical problems are involved in the noise control of rooms.

1.3   Acoustical Problems in Contemporary Architectural Design

The architect facing an ever-increasing demand for new residential, institutional, educational, recreational, commercial, and industrial buildings will find an equally increasing number of reasons to be concerned about the overall acoustical performance of his works. The following are the main contributing factors to the architect's acoustical problems:

1. The number of auditoriums (theaters, lecture halls, churches, concert halls, motion-picture theaters, etc.) necessary to meet the requirements of the growing population is substantial. Many of these auditoriums are encountering unprecedented room-acoustical problems. These problems, the solutions to which usually necessitate a considerable amount of research, derive from the need for very large audience capacity, for flexibility and adaptability in the audience-performer relationship (multiform auditoriums), and for different uses (speech, music, film projection, etc.) within the same room (multipurpose auditoriums).

2. Various trends in the basic concept of architectural design may actually be hostile to acoustical privacy. One trend, for instance, advocates that rooms in a building be integrated into visually undivided large spaces without partitions (team-teaching classrooms, landscaped offices, etc). Admittedly, this design concept does create functional and pleasant interiors; however, it conflicts with the noise-control principle of separation between interfering sound sources. Another trend favors general freedom in the architectural layout of buildings, disregarding the principle of locating noisy areas as far as possible from those requiring quiet. All too often is a noisy mechanical-equipment room placed on top of an auditorium, or a gymnasium adjacent to the music department of a school. In such cases the additional cost of noise control would certainly exceed the saving in mechanical installation cost.

3. In the structural and constructional field, in order to save space and cost, thin and lightweight building materials and constructions are increasingly applied. Their use is also due to the present trend in building technology toward eliminating all materials which are not absolutely necessary from the point of view of stability and thermal insulation. Prefabricated elements are being used for exterior and interior walls, partitions, floors, and suspended ceilings. All these constructional elements lack the most important feature of an efficient sound-insulating enclosure, that is, weight. Furthermore, they promote the harmful transmission of noise through gaps and open joints between the elements and by the noise-transmitting characteristics of thin lightweight panels.

4. Buildings are becoming increasingly mechanized. Components of heating, ventilating, and air-conditioning systems (fans, compressors, and cooling towers), work machines (typewriters, office machines, and computers), and laborsaving household appliances (air conditioners, vacuum cleaners, dishwashers, garbage disposers, television and stereo sets)—all unfortunately contribute to the noise pattern of a building. A contemporary building is, in fact, entirely interwoven with a comprehensive network of noise and vibration-transmitting ducts, shafts, and plenums.

5. Since the income potential of underground parking garages in high-rise buildings has been discovered by builders, the mechanical-equipment room, a serious noise source in any building, which in the past was conventionally located in the basement, is now usually built as a penthouse, with high-rental occupancies (penthouse apart-

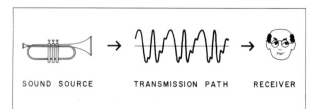

Fig. 1.2 Every acoustical situation has three elements: the source of sound, the path for the transmission, and the receiver.

ments or executive offices) underneath. This may create serious noise and vibration problems.

6. In addition to the interior (mechanical) noises, new, as well as existing, external noise sources are multiplying to a disastrous extent, contributing to what is generally referred to as *noise pollution* of our environment. These external noise sources originate from surface and air transportation (turbojets, supersonic military and civilian aircraft, helicopters, VTOLs, hovercraft, trucks, and diesel engines), posing a serious threat to urban and rural populations alike.

1.4 Source, Path, and Receiver

In any acoustical situation there are three elements to consider (Fig. 1.2): (1) the *sound source*, which can be desirable or undesirable; (2) the *path* for the transmission of sound; and (3) the *receiver*, who may or may not want to listen to the sound.

If the sound is desirable (speech or music), favorable conditions must be provided for its production, transmission, and reception. The sound source must be emphasized by raising it adequately with respect to the listener, and the transmission path must be made more effective by reinforcing sound reflections and by placing the listener as close as possible to the source. In addition, the listener must be relieved of all disturbing or annoying distractions, that is, interior or exterior noises. These measures pertain to both room (or space) acoustics and noise control.

On the other hand, if the sound is undesirable (noise from a neighbor's television set or traffic noise), unfavorable conditions must be provided for the production, transmission, and reception of the disturbance. Measures must be taken to suppress the intensity of the noise at the source; an attempt must be made to move the noise source as far as possible from the receiver. The effectiveness of the transmission path must be reduced as much as possible, probably by the use of barriers which are adequately sound- or vibration-proof, and the receiver must be protected or made tolerant to the disturbance by using masking noise or background music. All these measures belong to the realm of noise control.

BIBLIOGRAPHY[1]

Periodicals

"Beautiful Buildings and Horrible Sounds," *Architectural Forum*, September 1956, pp. 152–157.

Allison, D.: "Acoustics for Modern Interiors," *Architectural Forum*, April 1959, pp. 145–149.

Langdon, F. J.: "The Social and Physical Environment," *J. RIBA*, October 1966, pp. 460–464.

Creighton, H.: "Noise in the External Environment," *J. RIBA*, October 1966, pp. 465–470.

[1] Entries are listed in chronological order because it is believed this will be more helpful to the reader than an alphabetical arrangement.

The auditorium, as a place for listening, developed from the classical open-air theaters, but there is little evidence that the Greeks and Romans gave particular consideration to acoustical principles when they selected natural sites and built open-air theaters.

It is well known that listening conditions outdoors are usually poor, particularly if the audience is seated on a horizontal surface. The difficulties in hearing outdoors are due to (1) the drop of sound energy when sound waves travel in the open air, (2) the considerable sound absorption created by the audience, and (3) the interfering noises originating from various other sources. Outdoors listening conditions can be improved by adding sound-reflective enclosures around the source and by sloping, or raking, the audience area (Fig. 2.1). The ancient Greeks and Romans observed these principles and built their open-air places of assembly accordingly. They had the further advantage that interfering external noises were practically nonexistent in their time.

The schematic layout of a Greek open-air theater (Fig. 2.2) shows the acting area in the middle, the steeply raked audience portion surrounding the acting area, and a longitudinal building used for dressing, storage, and as a background. Later the acting area moved to the front platform, probably to make use of the sound reflections from behind this platform and from the circular central floor area, which was always covered with highly sound-reflective polished marble. The ruins of Greek open-air theaters can still be seen in Athens, Epidaurus, Priene, and Delos.

There is a considerable literature on the acoustics of the ancient open-air theaters, but probably too much credit is given to the Greeks and Romans for acoustical planning. They may well have attempted only to solve the line-of-sight problem and managed at the same time to obtain reasonable hearing conditions. They tried to bring the audience as close as possible to the acting area by shaping the steeply banked seating area in a semicircle, which naturally resulted in at least reasonably good hearing. Apart from this, the performers used large masks, partly to exaggerate their facial expressions and partly to reinforce their vocal power. Later, the Romans flattened the circular orchestra into a semicircle, bringing the audience even closer to the sound source, and built large slanting roofs over the acting area and walls on both sides of it. These measures provided efficient sound reflectors and resulted in an intelligibility which was at least moderately satisfactory in the remote seats.

The theater at Orange, France, built about A.D. 50 by the Romans (Fig. 2.3) is a typical example of the ancient Roman open-air theaters. Seating capacity is around 6,000, the audience area is 340 ft (104 m) in diameter, and there was a large sound-reflective canopy above the acting area.

The first reference to architectural acoustics in recorded history is made by Vitruvius (first century B.C.). In his book *De architectura*, he describes sounding vases (*echeia*) as being used in certain open-air theaters, but no evidence exists that the few vases found near the theaters were used for acoustical purposes.

To provide suitably large spaces for such entertainments as gladiatorial combats, sports events, and chariot races, the Romans built

CHAPTER TWO

A Brief History of Acoustical Ideas

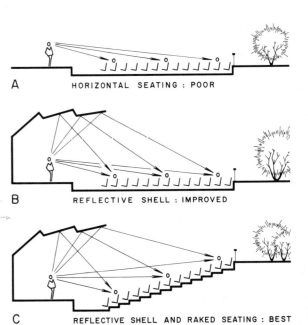

A HORIZONTAL SEATING : POOR

B REFLECTIVE SHELL : IMPROVED

C REFLECTIVE SHELL AND RAKED SEATING : BEST

Fig. 2.1 Listening conditions in the open air (A) without the aid of an electronic sound-amplification system can be improved by the addition of sound-reflective enclosures around the source (B) and by adequately sloping, or raking, the audience area (C).

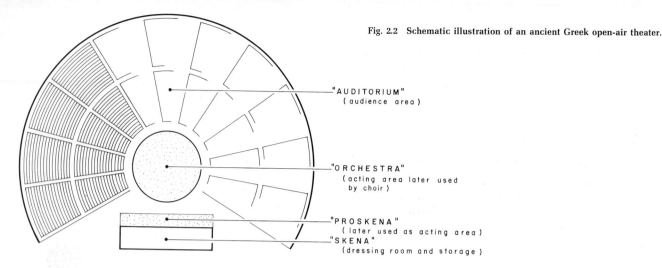

Fig. 2.2 Schematic illustration of an ancient Greek open-air theater.

"AUDITORIUM"
(audience area)

"ORCHESTRA"
(acting area later used
by choir)

"PROSKENA"
(later used as acting area)
"SKENA"
(dressing room and storage)

PLAN

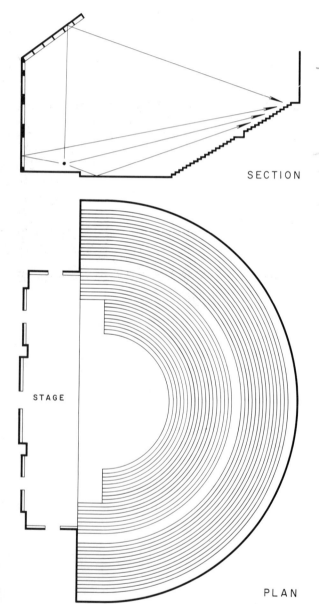

SECTION

STAGE

PLAN

arenas, which can be described as two coupled open-air theaters, open end to open end, surrounding an elliptical or circular acting area in the middle. Modern descendants of the Roman arenas are the sports stadium, the bullfight arena, the circus, and the type of legitimate theater using an arena stage (theater-in-the-round).

After the fall of the Roman Empire the only type of auditorium built during the Middle Ages was the church hall. Since the Middle Ages inherited only an empirical knowledge of the acoustics of enclosed spaces, the acoustical environment of medieval church halls can be characterized by their overwhelming fullness of tone, excessive reverberation, and poor intelligibility.

Another type of auditorium later used by the rapidly developing municipalities of the Middle Ages is the council room, normally contained in the city hall. Examples of council rooms and similar assembly halls also used for judicial, legislative, social, and commercial purposes appear after the eleventh century mainly in Italy (Padua, Vicenza, Venice, and Florence) and in Germany (Goslar, Augsburg, Nuremberg, Ulm, and Münster).

Around the middle of the sixteenth century, strolling professional actors in England used the round, square, or octagonal courtyards of inns as playhouses. The courtyard itself was open to the sky and was used by standing spectators. Along the galleries surrounding the courtyard, the audience occupied seats on benches. The acting area was a square-shaped platform thrust into the courtyard. The gallery above the platform was used for elevated scenes (Fig. 2.4). This type of playhouse, creating an intimate relationship between audience and performers for the first time since the Greek open-air theaters, provided the pattern for the design of several contemporary open (or thrust) stages.

In subsequent centuries, a remarkable number of theaters were built, sometimes with surprisingly large capacities. The Teatro Olimpico at Vicenza (Italy), designed by Palladio, and built from 1579 to 1584, seated an audience of 3,000. The Teatro Farnese at Parma (Italy),

10 0 20 40 60 80 100 FEET
5 0   10   20   30 METERS

Fig. 2.3 The ancient open-air theater at Orange. The steeply banked audience area contributes to excellent direct sound. Sound-reflective surfaces at both sides and above the stage contribute to the natural reinforcement of sound.

designed by Aleotti, and built in 1618, had a capacity of 2,500. Available descriptions do not reveal any particular acoustical deficiencies in these or other auditoriums of the period. The sound absorption provided by the audience and the rich surface decoration resulted in a reasonably well-controlled reverberation time and a uniform distribution of sound energy in these theaters.

From the theaters built after the fifteenth century there developed, in the seventeenth century, the horseshoe-shaped opera house with a large stage area and stage house, and with rings of boxes, or tiers, on top of each other, stacked to the ceiling. These features provided plenty of sound absorption in the audience area and created a short reverberation time, that is, a suitable acoustical environment for the brisk tempo of Italian opera (Fig. 2.5).

The first "scientific" work on room-acoustical phenomena, Athanasius Kircher's *Phonurgia*, appeared in the seventeenth century. It reviews the simple acoustical practice of earlier centuries and can be considered as a contribution to the historical development of architectural acoustics.

Around the beginning of the nineteenth century, the German Ernst F. Friedrich Chladni, in his book *Die Akustik* (Acoustics), made an attempt to explain the phenomenon of reverberation.

Until the beginning of the nineteenth century, the acoustics of enclosed spaces, being almost unknown, was subordinate to other considerations in the design of auditoriums for the performance of music, which in those days meant chiefly churches, opera houses, and ballrooms. The development of church and choral music, opera, and chamber and symphonic music depended in part on the prevailing acoustical conditions of the rooms (public or private) in which it was performed. Every organist was aware, for example, that just as no two organs were ever the same in tone and quality of sound, the acoustics themselves varied from church to church.

Baroque and classical music not written to be played in church was usually performed in the ballrooms of aristocratic patrons of music, some of whom had private orchestras of their own. More intimate music, originally written to be played in smaller rooms, is known as chamber music.

Italian opera, on the other hand, was theatrical and fitted into the acoustical environment of the horseshoe-shaped opera houses of Milan, Munich, London, Paris, and Vienna.

Subsequent composers, from the beginning of the nineteenth century on, had available the concert halls of Vienna, Leipzig, Glasgow, and Basel (Fig. 2.6). Many of these nineteenth-century concert halls represent—even today—the greatest achievements of empirical acoustics before the enormous progress of scientific research in the twentieth century defined and resolved the problems of contemporary room acoustics.

The designers' attitude in the nineteenth century is best reflected in the words of Charles Garnier, architect of the Paris Opera House: "I must explain that I have adopted no principle, that my plan has been based on no theory, and that I leave success or failure to chance alone."[1]

[1]C. Garnier, *Le nouveau Opéra de Paris* . . . , 2 vols., Ducher et Cie, Paris, 1876–1880.

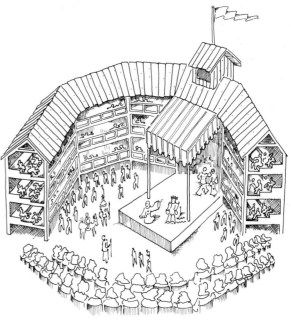

Fig. 2.4 Reconstruction of an Elizabethan playhouse based on contemporary drawings.

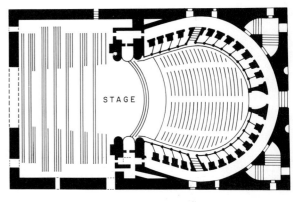

PLAN

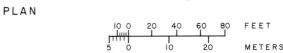

Fig. 2.5 Plan of Teatro San Carlo, Naples (1737), a typical horseshoe-shaped European opera house.

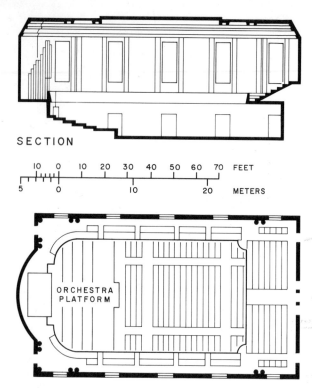

SECTION

10 0 10 20 30 40 50 60 70 FEET

5 0 10 20 METERS

ORCHESTRA
PLATFORM

PLAN

Fig. 2.6 Concert Hall Stadt-Casino, Basel, Switzerland (1876, seating capacity, 1,400), a fine example of a nineteenth-century rectangular music hall, with superb acoustical conditions for the performance of romantic music.

Before the twentieth century, only one auditorium was acoustically planned in the sense that some consideration was given to acoustical requirements. The Festspielhaus in Bayreuth, Germany (Fig. 2.7), was exclusively designed and built for Wagnerian operas. It has no rings of boxes or tiers, and because of this reduced amount of sound-absorptive surfaces, the reverberation time is considerably longer than in the typical European opera houses. In many of the standard proscenium-type theaters (Chap. 7) built all over the world during the twentieth century the fan-shaped layout of the Bayreuth Festspielhaus has been adopted, with the addition of one or several balconies.

In the second half of the nineteenth century the names of Helmholtz, Bell, Weber, and Fechner appeared as important contributors to acoustics. Lord Rayleigh published his classical exposition on *The Theory of Sound;* however, it was not until the twentieth century that Professor W. C. Sabine, of Harvard University, did his pioneer work on room-acoustical design. He first devised the coefficient of sound absorption and arrived at a simple relation between the volume of a room, the amount of sound-absorbing material in it, and its reverberation time (Chap. 4). Sabine thus took auditorium acoustics out of the realm of guesswork and established it as a systematic branch of engineering science.

From this start, the new subject of architectural acoustics advanced rapidly. Acoustical measuring instruments became available, scientists and engineers undertook theoretical and practical research, and the principles of room acoustics became established.

In the 1930s the cinema found its voice. From this date the high-quality recording, amplification, and reproduction of sound began to play an important role in several walks of life—scientific, educational, cultural, and social. The extraordinary development of radio and television broadcasting has presented new acoustical problems and aroused general interest in listening to music.

The mass production and laboratory testing of acoustical materials has supplied the designers of buildings with the necessary means of controlling sound in architectural spaces. The number of auditoriums being built all over the world is very large.

Considering the formidable development of architectural acoustics, it is noticeable that in the first half of the twentieth century progress was more pronounced in the field of room acoustics. However, in view of today's increasingly worsening noise conditions and also because of gradual introduction of thin, lightweight, and prefabricated construction, it is anticipated that in the years to come comparable progress will take place in the other, hitherto neglected, offshoot of environmental acoustics, that is, noise control.

The overall loudness of environmental noise, said a decade ago to be a product of progress, is now, paradoxically, increasing at the same rate at which the amount of human knowledge is growing. This condition will certainly get much worse in the future with the immediate general use of helicopters and jumbo jets and the introduction of supersonic aircraft. At present, and in years to come, the fight against noise pollution of our environment (discussed in detail in Chap. 13) appears to be a most important task. This objective is bound to open new avenues in the history of environmental acoustics.

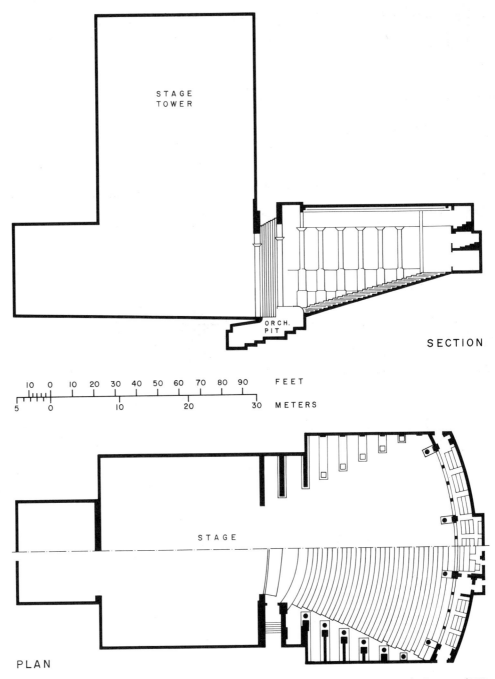

STAGE
TOWER

ORCH.
PIT

SECTION

FEET

METERS

STAGE

PLAN

Fig. 2.7 The Festspielhaus, Bayreuth, Germany (1876, seating capacity, 1,800), built to suit Wagner's style of music.

BIBLIOGRAPHY

Books

Beranek, L. L.: *Music Acoustics and Architecture,* John Wiley & Sons, Inc., New York, 1962, 586 pp.

Sabine, W. C.: *Collected Papers on Acoustics,* Dover Publications, Inc., New York, 1964, 279 pp.

Periodicals

Canac, F.: "On the Acoustics of Grecian and Roman Theaters," *J. RIBA,* July 1949, pp. 412–414.

DeGaetani, T.: "Theater Architecture," *J. AIA,* August 1961, pp. 71–76.

Properties of Sound

Although the intention of this book is to provide practical acoustical guidance for the architect during his design work, a brief discussion of simple theoretical laws of environmental acoustics and basic properties of sound should be helpful and in certain cases even important.

3.1 Origin, Propagation, and Speed of Sound

The word *sound* has two definitions: (1) Physically speaking, it is a fluctuation in pressure, a particle displacement in an elastic medium, like air. This is *objective* sound. (2) Physiologically it is an auditory sensation evoked by the physical fluctuation described above. This is *subjective* sound.

In this book *sound* expresses an auditory sensation passing through the ear and created by fluctuations in air pressure. These fluctuations are usually set up by some vibrating object, for example, the plucked string of a guitar or a struck tuning fork (Fig. 3.1).

Sound-wave motion is created by outward-traveling layers of compression and rarefaction of the air particles, that is, by pressure fluctuations. This is similar to the spread of water waves on the surface of a pond from the point where a stone has been dropped in. The air particles that transmit sound waves do not change their normal positions; they vibrate only about their equilibrium positions, which are their positions when no sound waves are transmitted. The pressure fluctuations are superimposed on the more or less steady atmospheric pressure and are picked up by the ear.

The *speed* of the sound-wave motion at 68°F (20°C) room temperature is about 1,130 ft per sec (344 m per sec). In subsequent discussions it will be shown that it is this relatively low speed of sound that causes acoustical defects, such as long-delayed reflection, echo, and excessive reverberation.

3.2 Frequency, Pitch, Timbre, and Wavelength

The number of displacements or oscillations that a particle undergoes in 1 sec is called *frequency*. Each complete displacement is called a *cycle*. The unit of frequency is the hertz (Hz), which is numerically equal to the cycle per second (cps). If a string undergoes 261 oscillations in 1 sec (261 Hz), it will produce in the eardrum of a listener the subjective tone of middle C. Frequency is an objective physical phenomenon which can be measured by acoustical instruments.

A normal ear responds to sounds within the audio-frequency range of about 20 to 20,000 Hz. This and other frequency ranges of various sound sources are shown in Fig. 3.2. The audio-frequency range varies measurably with different people and different ages, the upper limit decreasing considerably with advancing age. Frequencies higher than 10,000 Hz are of negligible importance for the intelligibility of speech or the enjoyment of music.

Most sounds (speech, music, noise) contain a multitude of frequencies: low-, medium-, and high-frequency components. It is essential, therefore, that acoustical problems be examined throughout the audible frequency spectrum. The standard frequencies selected arbitrarily as representative of significance in environmental acoustics are

125, 250, 500, 1000, 2000, and 4000 Hz

or

128, 256, 512, 1024, 2048, and 4096 Hz

For all practical purposes the two series can be regarded as identical. In the design of spaces which are acoustically particularly sensitive, such as concert halls or radio or recording studios, attention is also given to the frequency one octave below (63 or 64 Hz) and one octave above (8000 or 8192 Hz) the range of standard frequencies.

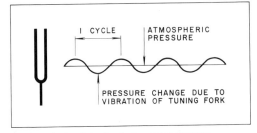

Fig. 3.1 A struck tuning fork creates pressure changes in the air by its vibration and produces sound.

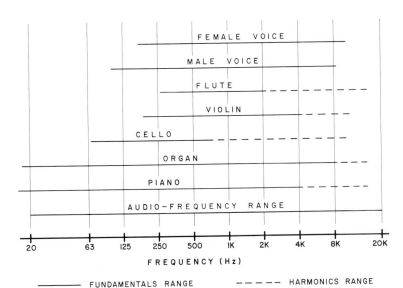

FUNDAMENTALS RANGE   - - - - HARMONICS RANGE

Fig. 3.2 Frequency range of sound sources.

The attribute of an auditory sensation which enables us to order sounds on a scale extending from low to high frequency is called *pitch*. It is the subjective physiological equivalent of frequency. The pitch depends primarily upon the frequency of the sound stimulus: the higher the frequency, the higher the pitch will be.

A sound sensation having pitch is called *tone. Pure tone* (or simple tone) is a sound sensation of a single frequency, characterized by its singleness of pitch. It can be produced by striking a tuning fork or by playing a low note softly on a flute. Most musical sounds do not produce pure tones only but sounds containing several additional frequencies, called *complex tones*. Complex tones are sound sensations characterized by more than one frequency. Whether a person hears a tone as simple or complex depends on his musical experience and listening attitude.

The lowest frequency present in a complex tone is called the *fundamental*; the components of higher frequencies are called *partials* or *overtones*. If the frequencies of the partials are simple integral multiples of the fundamental, they are called *harmonics*. Some musical instruments produce more overtones than others. Different instruments emphasize different overtones. For most musical sounds the pitch of the entire complex tone seems to be the same as that of the fundamental; nevertheless, the overtones add distinctive qualities to the tone.

If we play a G note on the piano, in addition to the fundamental tone, the overtones of several other keys will reach our ears, without the keys actually being played (Fig. 3.3). It is the relative number, prominence, pitch, and intensity of the overtones which contribute to the tone color, or *timbre*, of the musical sounds. A pure tone without overtones sounds empty and uninteresting. Instruments that produce sounds with many overtones sound full and rich. Timbre is the attribute of auditory sensation in terms of which a person can distinguish between sounds that have the same pitch and loudness but are played on different musical instruments.

The distance a sound wave travels during each complete cycle of vibration, that is, the distance between the layers of compression, is called *wavelength*. The following constant relationship exists between wavelength, frequency, and speed of sound:

$$\text{Wavelength} = \frac{\text{speed of sound}}{\text{frequency}}$$

where wavelength is expressed in feet (or meters), speed of sound in feet per second (meters per second), and frequency in hertz.

The wavelength of sound within the frequency range of 20 to 10,000 Hz extends from 56 ft (17 m) to about 1 in. (25 mm). The consideration of the relationship between frequencies and wavelengths is important in the acoustical design of auditoriums. As will be seen later, efficient sound-absorptive, sound-reflective, or diffusive room enclosures must be so designed that their dimensions are comparable to the wavelengths of the frequencies which must be absorbed, reflected, or diffused, respectively.

3.3 Sound Pressure, Sound Intensity, and Loudness

The numerical identification of the quantity of sound (in both the physical and physiological sense) is extremely complex, but since its use is limited in practical architectural design procedures, it can be discussed with maximum simplification.

The fluctuation in the atmospheric pressure caused by the vibration of air particles due to a sound wave is called *sound pressure*. The ear responds to a very wide range of sound pressures, yet the pressures themselves are small.

The standard scale used to measure sound pressure in physical acoustics extends over a wide range, which makes it awkward to deal with. Furthermore, it does not take into account the fact that the ear does not respond equally to changes of sound pressures at all levels of intensity. For these reasons sound pressures are measured on a logarithmic scale, called the *decibel* (dB) *scale*, named in honor of Alexander Graham

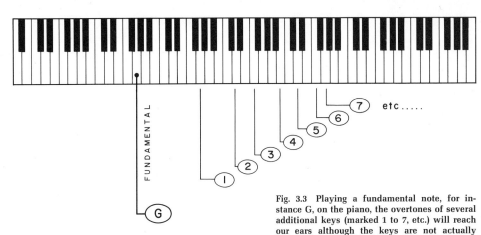

FUNDAMENTAL

G

etc.....

Fig. 3.3 Playing a fundamental note, for instance G, on the piano, the overtones of several additional keys (marked 1 to 7, etc.) will reach our ears although the keys are not actually played. This produces a complex tone.

Bell. The decibel scale fits approximately the human perception of the change of loudness of sound, which is roughly proportional to the logarithm of the sound energy. This implies that sound energies proportional to 10, 100, and 1,000 would produce in the ear effects subjectively proportional to their logarithms, that is, to 1, 2, and 3, respectively. If we multiply numbers of this logarithmic scale by 10, we have established the decibel scale. The unit of this scale, the decibel, is the smallest change in sound pressure that the average ear can detect.

Sound pressure levels are measured by a sound-level meter (Fig. 3.4), consisting of a microphone, amplifier, and output instrument which measures the effective sound pressure level in decibels. Various accessories can be attached to the basic instrument or incorporated into it, according to need, such as a frequency analyzer or graphic recorder. Sound-level meters, manufactured in various sizes and by several firms, can be used for a number of purposes in architectural acoustics. They are important instruments in the evaluation and control of noise and vibration.

Sound pressure levels of representative sounds and noises are shown in Fig. 3.5.

The *sound intensity* in a specified direction at a point is the average rate of sound energy transmitted in the specified direction through a unit area normal to this direction at the point considered. Sound intensity levels are expressed in decibels above a reference level. Multiplying the intensity by 10 at any point in the scale raises the intensity level by 10 dB. A 3-dB change in the intensity level is reasonably perceptible, and a 5-dB change is clearly noticeable. An increase of 10 dB sounds twice as loud, 15 dB means a very appreciable change, and an increase of 20 dB results in a sound very much louder than the original. For practical purposes in environmental noise control, sound pressure levels equal sound intensity levels.

Loudness is the subjective attribute of an auditory sensation in terms of which sounds may be ordered on a scale extending from soft to loud. It is the subjective response to sound pressure and sound intensity. The *phon* is the unit of loudness level, which has been established by extensive psychological testing. The phon scale takes into account the varying sensitivity of the ear to sounds of different frequencies; consequently it is an objective measure.

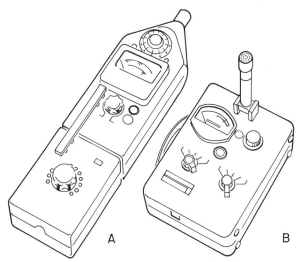

Fig. 3.4 Instruments to measure sound pressure levels: (A) model 2203/1613 sound-level meter and full-octave filter set by Bruel and Kjaer, Copenhagen, Denmark; (B) type 1551-C sound-level meter by General Radio Company, West Concord, Mass.

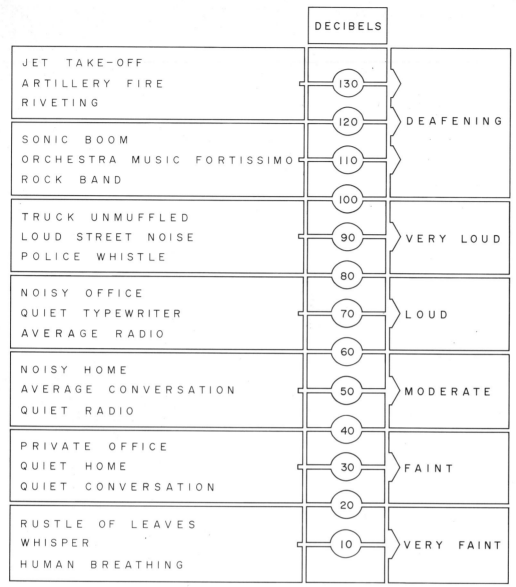

	DECIBELS	
JET TAKE-OFF ARTILLERY FIRE RIVETING	130 120	DEAFENING
SONIC BOOM ORCHESTRA MUSIC FORTISSIMO ROCK BAND	110 100	
TRUCK UNMUFFLED LOUD STREET NOISE POLICE WHISTLE	90 80	VERY LOUD
NOISY OFFICE QUIET TYPEWRITER AVERAGE RADIO	70 60	LOUD
NOISY HOME AVERAGE CONVERSATION QUIET RADIO	50 40	MODERATE
PRIVATE OFFICE QUIET HOME QUIET CONVERSATION	30 20	FAINT
RUSTLE OF LEAVES WHISPER HUMAN BREATHING	10	VERY FAINT

Fig. 3.5 Sound pressure levels of representative sounds and noises.

Figure 3.6 shows the relationship between sound pressure level and relative loudness. Whenever a 10-dB increase in sound pressure level takes place, a doubling in loudness will be noticeable. A 20-dB increase in sound pressure level equals a quadrupling of loudness.

3.4 Acoustical Power of Sound Sources

The average acoustical power generated by all sound sources is surprisingly small. The acoustical power a speaker has to produce in a room to make himself adequately heard varies between 10 and 50 microwatts (μW), depending on the size of the room; consequently the resulting sound pressure is very small.

The minute amount of acoustical power produced by a speaker can be illustrated as follows. The simultaneous loud speech of 4 million people would produce the power necessary to burn a single 40-W bulb. It would require no fewer than 15 million speakers to generate a single horse-power of acoustical energy.

A singing voice or a musical instrument radiates several hundred or even thousands of microwatts of acoustical power. This explains the ease with which a singer or musician can fill the volume of an auditorium that is too large for unamplified speech.

3.5 The Human Ear and Hearing

When alternating pressures of a sound wave reach the outer ear, the vibrations received by the eardrum are multiplied by the small bones in the middle ear and transmitted through a fluid to nerve endings within the inner ear. The nerves finally transmit the impulses to the brain, where the final process of hearing takes place; thus the sensation of sound is created.

The minimum sound pressure level of a sound that is capable of evoking an auditory sensation in the ears of an observer is called the *threshold of audibility.* When the pressure of the sound is increased and the sound becomes louder, it eventually reaches a level at which the sensation of hearing becomes uncomfortable. The minimum sound pressure level of a sound which stimulates the ear to the point at which discomfort gives way to definite pain is called the *threshold of pain.* Between audibility and pain, pressure is increased 1 million times. This shows the extremely wide range of sound pressure to which the ear responds. The curves of the threshold of audibility and the threshold of pain enclose the auditory-sensation area, as shown in Fig. 3.7.

It is noticeable that the ear's sensitivity varies remarkably with sounds of different frequencies. From the curve of threshold of audibility it can be seen that at 1000 Hz a minimum sound pressure level of about 4 dB is necessary to be barely perceived by the ear, while at 63 Hz the ear will not respond to any sound unless its pressure reaches a minimum level of about 35 dB. To a certain degree we are deaf to low-frequency sounds. The reduced sensitivity of our ears in the lower-frequency range is fortunate, as it relieves us of being annoyed by low-frequency sounds within and around us. On the other hand, it is advantageous that the ear is more sensitive to sounds in the frequency range between about 400 and 5000 Hz, which is essential for speech intelligibility and for the full enjoyment of music.

Figure 3.7 also shows a family of curves, known as *equal-loudness contours,* illustrating the subjective responses to various sound pressure levels. It indicates, for instance, that a 32-Hz tone with a sound pressure level of 70 dB, a 125-Hz tone of 40 dB, a 1000-Hz tone of 30 dB, and an 8000-Hz tone of 38 dB sound equally loud, that is, 30 phons, since these values lie on the 30-phon equal-loudness contour.

On the other hand, a 4000-Hz tone having a sound pressure level of only 20 dB sounds as loud as a 63-Hz tone having a sound pressure level of 50 dB. Both have a loudness level of 27 phons. In other words, the ear is less sensitive to low- than to high-frequency sounds.

At low frequencies a given change in sound pressure level produces a much larger change in loudness level than the same change at higher

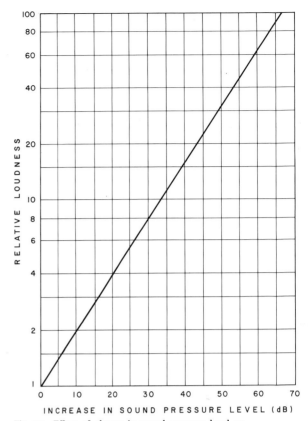

Fig. 3.6 Effect of change in sound pressure level on loudness. An increase of 10 dB in sound pressure level will double the loudness.

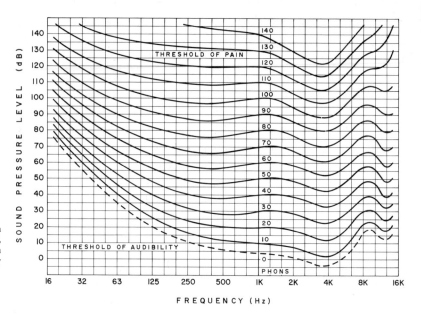

Fig. 3.7 Contours of equal loudness. A 63-Hz tone with a sound pressure level of 53 dB, a 125-Hz tone of 40 dB, a 500-Hz tone of 28 dB, a 1000-Hz tone of 30 dB, and an 8000-Hz tone of 38 dB sound equally loud because they all lie on the 30-dB equal-loudness contour.

frequencies does. The restricted sensitivity of the human ear in the lower frequency range applies only to sounds that are not too loud because to sound pressures of a higher level the ear is almost equally sensitive at all frequencies.

It must be noted that at 1000 Hz the sound pressure levels in decibels are the same as the loudness levels in phons. Figure 3.7 enables us to transpose any single tone from decibels into phons or vice versa; for example, a tone at 4000 Hz at a sound pressure level of 70 dB has a loudness level of about 80 phons.

3.6   Directionality of Sound Sources

Although sound sources radiate sound waves in all directions, in a region free from reflecting surfaces, the intensity of the emitted sound may be most pronounced in one direction. To put it more precisely, the radiation pattern will vary with the frequency of the emitted sound wave. This phenomenon is noticeable with the human voice, with musical instruments, with loudspeakers, and also with many noise sources.

The directionality of the human voice in the horizontal plane is shown in Fig. 3.8. It illustrates that the radiation of high-frequency speech sounds is more pronounced along the longitudinal axis of the sound source, while the distribution of the medium and low frequencies is more uniform in all directions. This can be observed particularly in excessively wide auditoriums where the high-frequency components of speech are not as efficiently radiated to the side seats of the front rows as to the center seats, resulting in a noticeable loss of intelligibility at these side seats. This creates serious problems in the design of open-stage or arena-type theaters (theater-in-the-round), where a performer can face only one section of the audience at a time. Here the use of sound-reflective wall and ceiling surfaces is particularly important to compensate for the loss of the high-frequency components. Experience has shown, however, that in the radiation pattern of the human voice the frequency discrimination is negligible over a total angle of 90° in the forward direction.

3.7 Masking

Although a subdued voice is understandable in a quiet room, it is difficult to understand even a raised voice above the roar of an aircraft engine. This drowning out, or *masking,* occurs because the auditory nerves are unable to carry all the impulses to the brain at one time.

Masking is common in auditoriums of inadequate acoustical design when undesired noises make it difficult or impossible to hear and understand or appreciate the desired sound. In this process the threshold of audibility for one sound, for example, speech in an auditorium, is raised by the presence of another masking sound, for example, street noise or ventilating noise.

Low-frequency sounds produce a considerable masking effect upon high-frequency sounds, particularly if the low-frequency sounds are significantly loud. Excessive low-frequency noises therefore constitute a serious source of interference for speech or music, since they mask the wanted sounds of the entire audio-frequency range. The elimination of low-frequency noises is an important goal in the acoustical design of auditoriums.

High-frequency sounds mask low-frequency sounds to a limited extent because the masking effect is most pronounced when the masking sound has almost the same frequency as the masked sound.

The phenomenon of masking is properly exploited in environmental noise control. If a masking noise is uninterrupted and is not too loud, and if it has no information content, it will become an acceptable *background noise* and will suppress other objectionable intruding noises, making them sound psychologically quieter (Chap. 13). Ventilating and air-conditioning noises, the noise created by uninterrupted traffic flow

Fig. 3.8 Diagrammatic illustration of the directionality of the human voice in the horizontal plane.

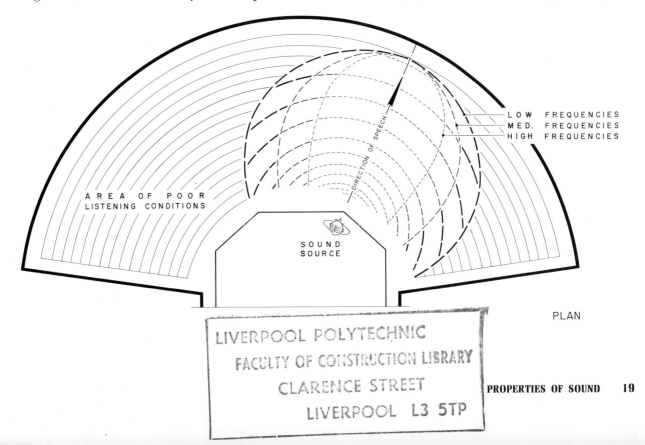

LOW FREQUENCIES
MED. FREQUENCIES
HIGH FREQUENCIES

DIRECTION OF SPEECH

AREA OF POOR
LISTENING CONDITIONS

SOUND
SOURCE

PLAN

PROPERTIES OF SOUND 19

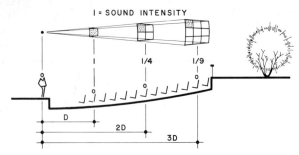

I = SOUND INTENSITY

Fig. 3.9 Inverse-square law. In a free field the intensity of sound at any point is inversely proportional to the square of the distance from the source to that point. For instance, when distance D is tripled, the intensity of sound will be decreased by a factor of 9; it will be I/9.

of a highway, or the sound of a water fountain are good masking-noise sources. Levels of acceptable background noises for various occupancies will be discussed in Chap. 15.

3.8 Sound and Distance

In a field free from reflecting surfaces a sound wave travels outward from its source in a spherical wavefront; consequently, its energy is spread over a continuously extending surface. Since the area of a sphere is proportional to the square of its radius, the intensity of sound at any point is inversely proportional to the square of the distance from the source to that point. This is known as the *inverse-square law* in architectural acoustics (Fig. 3.9), and it explains the inadequate loudness noticeable at the remote seats of very large auditoriums. It must be counterbalanced by placing the audience as close as possible to the sound source.

When there are no reflecting surfaces, the reduction of the sound intensity can be regarded as 6 dB each time the distance from the source is doubled.

BIBLIOGRAPHY

Books

Knudsen, V. O., and C. M. Harris: *Acoustical Designing in Architecture,* John Wiley & Sons, Inc., New York, 1950, chaps. 1 and 2.
Parkin, P. H., and H. R. Humphreys: *Acoustics, Noise and Buildings,* Frederick A. Praeger, Inc., New York, 1958, chap. 1.
Rettinger, M.: *Acoustics,* Chemical Publishing Company, Inc., New York, 1968, chap. 1.

PART TWO

Room (or Space) Acoustics

Sound waves outdoors, traveling from their source in a continuously extending spherical wavefront, rapidly attenuate as the distance from their source increases.

In designing rooms for various purposes, the architect will mostly encounter acoustical problems associated with enclosed spaces. The propagation and behavior of sound waves in enclosed spaces are more complex than in the open air. To follow the rather complicated path of even a single sound wave inside a room requires experience and imagination.

Studying the behavior of sound waves in a room can be simplified if the outwardly spreading layers of compression and rarefaction are replaced by imaginary sound rays, perpendicular to the advancing wavefront, traveling in straight lines in every direction within the space, quite similar to beams of light in optics. This approach in architectural acoustics, which likens the behavior of sound waves to that of light rays, is called *geometric acoustics*. Figure 4.1 illustrates how when sound waves strike the enclosures of a room, a certain portion of their energy will be reflected, absorbed, dispersed, diffracted, or transmitted into adjacent spaces, depending on the acoustical characteristics of the enclosures.

4.1 Sound Reflection

Hard, rigid, and flat surfaces, such as concrete, brick, stone, plaster, or glass, reflect almost all incident sound energy striking them. This phenomenon of sound reflection is quite similar to the well-known reflection of light (sound wave 2 in Fig. 4.1) since the incident and the reflected sound rays lie in the same plane and the angle of the incident sound wave equals the angle of the reflected sound wave (law of reflection). It must be remembered, however, that the wavelengths of sound waves are much larger than those of light rays, and the law of sound reflection is valid only if the wavelengths of the sound waves are small compared to the dimension of the reflecting surfaces. This means that the application of this law must be very critically considered for low-frequency sounds.

Convex reflecting surfaces tend to disperse and concave surfaces tend to concentrate the reflected sound waves in rooms (Fig. 4.2).

In medium- and large-size auditoriums hearing conditions can be considerably improved by the application of large sound reflectors suitably located (Chap. 6).

4.2 Sound Absorption

It is well known that soft, porous materials and fabrics and also people absorb a considerable portion of the sound waves bouncing on them; in other words, they are sound absorbers. By definition, *sound absorption* is the change of sound energy into some other form, usually heat, in passing through a material or on striking a surface (sound wave 3 in Fig. 4.1). The amount of heat produced by the conversion of sound energy is extremely small. The speed of the traveling sound wave is not affected by absorption.

CHAPTER FOUR

Acoustical Phenomena in Enclosed Spaces

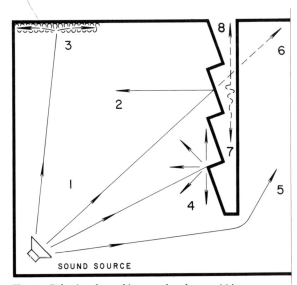

Fig. 4.1 Behavior of sound in an enclosed space: (1) incident or direct sound; (2) reflected sound; (3) sound absorbed by surface treatment; (4) diffused or dispersed sound; (5) diffracted or bent sound; (6) transmitted sound; (7) sound dissipated within the structure; (8) sound conducted by the structure.

PLAN

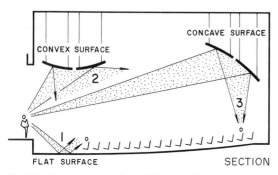

Fig. 4.2 Sound reflection from differently shaped surfaces: (1) uniform reflection; (2) sound dispersion; (3) sound concentration.

Practically all building materials absorb sound to some extent, but successful acoustical control of buildings requires the application of materials with a high degree of sound absorption.

In environmental acoustics the following elements may contribute to sound absorption:

1. Surface treatments of walls, floors, and ceilings

2. Room contents, such as the audience, draperies, upholstered seats, and carpet

3. The air of the space

Various types of sound-absorbing materials and other elements contributing to sound absorption are described in Chap. 5.

How efficient the sound absorption of a material is at a specified frequency is rated by the *sound absorption coefficient*. The sound absorption coefficient of a surface is the fraction of energy of the incident sound absorbed, or not reflected, by the surface. It is denoted by the Greek letter α. The α value can vary between 0 and 1; for example, at 500 Hz if an acoustical material absorbs 65 percent of the energy of incident sound and reflects 35 percent of it, the sound absorption coefficient of this particular material is 0.65. Hard, impermeable interior surfaces, such as brick, masonry, stone, and concrete, normally absorb less than 5 percent of the energy of incident sound waves and reflect 95 percent or more; their absorption coefficient is less than 0.05. On the other hand, thick isolation blankets absorb more than 80 percent of the energy of incident sound; in this case the absorption coefficient is above 0.80. The sound absorption coefficient varies with the angle at which the sound wave impinges on the material and with the frequency. The values of sound absorption coefficients at a certain frequency, as published in architectural-acoustical literature, are averaged over all the angles of incidence at that particular frequency (random incidence).

It is standard practice to list sound-absorption-coefficient values at representative standard frequencies throughout the most important part of the audio-frequency range, that is, at 125, 250, 500, 1000, 2000, and 4000 Hz or at 128, 256, 512, 1024, 2048, and 4096 Hz.

In the architectural-acoustical literature and on information sheets published by manufacturers and dealers, commercial acoustical materials are sometimes characterized by their *noise-reduction coefficient* (NRC), which is the arithmetic average of sound absorption coefficients at the frequencies 250, 500, 1000, and 2000 Hz expressed to the nearest multiple of 0.05. This value is useful in comparing the overall sound absorption of commercial acoustical materials when used for noise-reduction purposes.

The sound absorption of a surface (surface absorption) is measured in *sabins*, formerly called *open-window units*. One sabin represents a surface of 1 sq ft (or 1 sq m) having an absorption coefficient of $\alpha = 1.00$. The surface absorption is obtained by multiplying the area of the surface, in square feet (or square meters), by its sound absorption coefficient. For example, an acoustical treatment extending over an area of $S = 120$ sq ft (11 sq m) and having a sound absorption coefficient of $\alpha = 0.50$ has a surface absorption of $S\alpha = 120 \times 0.50 = 60$ sq ft (or $11 \times$

0.50 = 5.5′ sq m). It was W. C. Sabine who called the unit of surface absorption the open-window unit because it is equivalent in absorption to an identical area of open window, which naturally absorbs 100 percent of the incident sound energy and therefore has an absorption coefficient of 1.0. The open-window unit has been renamed sabin to commemorate Sabine.

The sound absorption provided by persons or exposed objects can be also expressed as a certain number of sabins per person or object. For example, a person in an upholstered theater seat will provide at 500 Hz an absorption of about 4 to 5 sabins. It is more customary, however, to consider the absorption provided by an audience on the basis of occupied floor area, in square feet (or square meters), including aisle widths up to 3.5 ft (1.07 m).

4.3 Sound Diffusion

If the sound pressure is equal in all parts of an auditorium and it is probable that sound waves are traveling in all directions, the sound field is said to be *homogeneous;* in other words, *sound diffusion* or *sound dispersion* prevails in the room (sound wave 4 in Fig. 4.1). Adequate sound diffusion is a necessary acoustical characteristic of certain types of rooms (concert halls, radio and recording studios, and music rooms) because it promotes a uniform distribution of sound, accentuates the natural qualities of music and speech, and prevents the occurrence of undesirable acoustical defects.

Diffusion of sound can be created in several ways (Fig. 4.3):

1. The generous application of surface irregularities and scattering elements, such as pilasters, piers, exposed beams, coffered ceilings, sculptured balcony railings, and serrated enclosures

2. The alternate application of sound-reflective and sound-absorptive surface treatments

3. The irregular and random distribution of differing sound-absorptive treatments

It must be remembered that the overall dimensions of the surface protrusions and of the patches of absorptive treatments must be comparable to the wavelength of every sound wave within the entire audio-frequency range. The projections of the surface irregularities must reach at least one-seventh of the wavelengths of those sound waves which have to be diffused.

4.4 Sound Diffraction

Diffraction is the acoustical phenomenon which causes sound waves to be bent or scattered around such obstacles as corners, columns, walls, and beams (Fig. 4.1, sound wave 5). Diffraction, that is, the bending and scattering of sound waves around obstacles, is more pronounced for low- than for high-frequency sounds, thus proving that the laws of geometric acoustics are inadequate for a precise prediction of the behavior of sound in enclosed spaces because the obstacles usually encountered in room acoustics are too small in comparison to the wavelengths

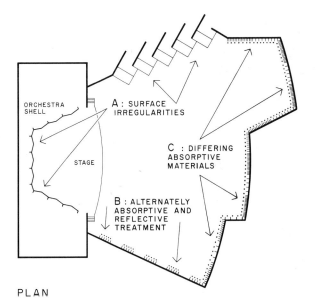

PLAN

Fig. 4.3 Sound diffusion (dispersion), or the uniform distribution of sound energy in auditoriums, can be achieved by the use of (A) surface irregularities, (B) alternately applied sound-absorptive and sound-reflective treatment, or (C) acoustical treatments of differing sound absorption.

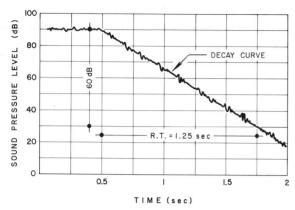

Fig. 4.4 The reverberation time (RT) of a room is defined as the time required for a sound suddenly cut off to decrease by 60 dB.

of the audible sound waves. Although geometric acoustics is a useful approach in dealing with problems related to high-frequency sounds, it is hardly applicable to frequencies below 250 Hz. In other words, low-frequency sounds (of long wavelengths) will not respect the laws of geometric acoustics if they encounter architectural elements of small dimensions. In particular they will not travel in rectilinear directions through an opening and will not diffract, or be scattered by, small-scale architectural elements such as beams, coffers, pilasters, and cornices.

Experience gives ample evidence that deep galleries cast an acoustical shadow on the audience underneath, causing a noticeable loss in high-frequency sounds (with short wavelengths) which do not bend around the protruding balcony edge. This condition creates poor hearing conditions under the balcony. Diffraction, however, lessens this acoustical defect, but only in the lower portion of the audio-frequency range.

4.5 Reverberation

When a steady sound is generated in a room, the sound pressure gradually builds up, and it takes some time (in most rooms about 1 sec) for it to reach its steady-state value.

Similarly, when the source of the sound has stopped, a noticeable time will elapse before the sound dies away (decays) to inaudibility. This prolongation of sound as a result of successive reflections in an enclosed space after the source of sound is turned off is called *reverberation*. It has a distinct effect on hearing conditions in auditoriums because its presence modifies the perception of *transient* sounds, that is, sounds which start or stop suddenly. In the reverberation control of auditoriums it is important to preserve and enhance the transient sounds of speech and music in order to secure the highest intelligibility of speech and the fullest enjoyment of music.

The importance of reverberation control in the acoustical design of auditoriums has necessitated the introduction of a relevant standard of measure, the *reverberation time* (RT). This is the time for the sound pressure level in a room to decrease 60 dB after the sound is stopped (Fig. 4.4).

As mentioned before, Sabine was the first to establish the quantitative relationship between RT, the volume of the room, and the total amount of absorption applied along the enclosures of the room. The Sabine formula, still useful today for a simplified calculation of the RT, is

$$RT = \frac{0.05V}{A + xV}$$

where RT = reverberation time, sec
    V = room volume, cu ft
    A = total room absorption, sq-ft sabins
    x = air absorption coefficient

The air absorption coefficient depends on the temperature and humidity of the air and also on the frequency of the sound.

In the metric system the simplified RT formula is

$$RT = \frac{0.16V}{A + xV}$$

where RT = reverberation time, sec

V = room volume, cu m

A = total room absorption, sq-m sabins

x = air absorption coefficient

The absorption of a surface is found by multiplying its area S by its absorption coefficient α, and the total room absorption A is obtained by the addition of these products with the inclusion of the absorption provided by the audience and other room contents (seats, carpets, draperies, etc.). Thus

$$A = S_1\alpha_1 + S_2\alpha_2 + S_3\alpha_3 + \cdots + S_n\alpha_n$$

where $S_1, \ldots, S_n$ are individual surface areas, in square feet (or square meters), and $\alpha_1, \ldots, \alpha_n$ are their respective absorption coefficients.

Values of the air absorption coefficient x to be considered at and above 1000 Hz only are included in Appendix Table A.1.

The Sabine formula provides a reasonable approximation for the calculation of the RT, and it will enable the architect to perform a quick and easy control as he proceeds in the acoustical design of an auditorium in which the room absorption is moderate. For more precise reverberation calculations for rooms with particular requirements, such as a concert hall or a radio or recording studio, with considerable sound-absorptive treatments, other modified and improved formulas and methods are available; however, they are beyond the scope of this book because their use is outside the normal architectural design practice.

It must be stressed that all the reverberation formulas apply only to auditoriums in which the sound is diffuse; that is, the sound energy is evenly distributed all over the room and therefore the sound dies away in a smooth, even manner, free from disturbing fluctuations. The sound field cannot be considered as diffuse in rooms (1) which have acoustical treatments concentrated in a single area or in very few areas, (2) which have enclosures creating reflected sound concentrations originating from highly reflective domes, curved and acoustically untreated walls, etc., or (3) which have one dimension disproportionately different from the other two. In reality, few auditoriums exist in which the sound field is truly diffuse. For this reason a considerable discrepancy will be observed between measured and calculated RT values in most auditoriums. Fortunately, achieving a perfectly diffuse sound field in a room is not really necessary because under completely diffuse conditions the directional characteristic of the approaching sound waves would fade away.

Since the absorption of various materials and finishes used in the design of auditoriums varies with the frequency, sometimes quite considerably, the RT values naturally vary with the frequency as well. It is therefore essential to specify or calculate the RT for a number of representative frequencies of the audio-frequency range, for example,

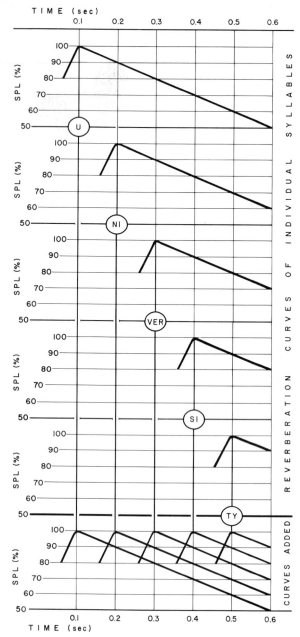

Fig. 4.5 Simplified illustration of the detrimental effect of excessive RT on speech intelligibility; SPL, sound pressure level.

at least at 125, 500, and 2000 Hz. The number of these representative frequencies will depend on the importance attached to acoustical considerations. When an RT value is cited without referring to any particular frequency, it is generally assumed to be the RT at 500 (or 512) Hz.

A sample calculation for the reverberation time of a school auditorium is shown in Chap. 19.

Excessive reverberation creates acoustical conditions under which transient sounds preceding those upon which momentary attention is focused remain perceptible, masking and overlapping subsequent speech or musical sounds.

The unfavorable, often disastrous, acoustical conditions prevailing in highly reverberant auditoriums (mainly cathedrals, such as St. Paul's in London, the cathedrals of Chartres, Paris, Cologne, and Milan, and St. Peter's in Rome) are well known. Speech intelligibility is practically nonexistent in these church auditoriums.

Figure 4.5 illustrates, in a simple fashion, the harmful effect of excessive reverberation on speech intelligibility. In a highly reverberant room, the first syllable *u* of the word university when uttered will die out too slowly, so that when the next syllable *ni* becomes audible, the first syllable *u* maintains about 90 percent of its original level and therefore exercises a masking effect on the second syllable. When the third syllable *ver* is expressed, the first syllable *u* represents about 80 percent and the second syllable *ni* about 90 percent of their original levels, and so on. The excessive reverberation of previously uttered syllables thus blurs the newly spoken ones, seriously reducing speech intelligibility. Under such reverberant conditions both audience and speaker suffer.

Figure 4.6 illustrates the RT curves of five auditoriums, well known for their good acoustics, listed in Table 4.1.

Excessively long RT can easily be detected in an existing auditorium by simply listening, because speech is usually unintelligible and music unenjoyable in such a room. However, if acoustical correction of an existing auditorium is necessary, the correct steps to be taken cannot be determined by listening experience, that is, subjective judgment, alone. Precise acoustical measurements must be conducted to establish the amount of acoustical treatment necessary.

TABLE 4.1 Acoustical Data of Five Auditoriums
In order of decreasing RT

Curve° Auditorium		RT at 500 Hz (occupied), sec	Volume, cu ft (cu m)	Audience capacity
A	Grosser Musikvereins-saal, Vienna	2.1	530,000 (15,000)	1,680
B	Salle Wilfrid Pelletier, Montreal	1.75	936,000 (26,500)	3,000
C	Kresge Auditorium, Cambridge, Mass.	1.5	354,000 (10,200)	1,238
D	Tivoli Koncertsal, Copenhagen	1.3	450,000 (12,740)	1,789
E	Royal Opera House, London	1.1	432,500 (12,240)	2,180

° RT curves are shown in Fig. 4.6.

4.6 Room Resonance

Water poured into a jar creates a gurgling sound, the frequency of which gradually increases as the amount of water in the jar increases. The air in the jar resonates at certain frequencies (like a shower which, by its own resonance, encourages the vocal ambitions of amateur singers). An enclosed room with sound-reflective interior surfaces undesirably accentuates certain frequencies, called the *normal modes of vibration* of the room.

Rooms have a large number of normal modes, depending on their shapes and dimensions. The deleterious effect of the normal modes is particularly noticeable at the lower frequency range, where these modes are unequally distributed. Their detrimental effect can be reduced (1) by acoustically favorable room proportions (Chap. 10), (2) by irregularly laid out room enclosures, (3) by abundantly applied surface irregularities (diffusers), or (4) by the uniform distribution of absorptive elements along the boundary enclosures.

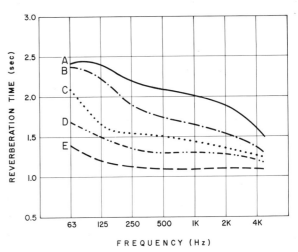

Fig. 4.6 RT curves of five auditoriums, Table 4.1, known for good acoustics.

BIBLIOGRAPHY

Books

Parkin, P. H., and H. R. Humphreys: *Acoustics, Noise and Buildings*, Frederick A. Praeger, Inc., New York, 1958, chap. 2.

Beranek, L. L. (ed.): *Noise Reduction*, McGraw-Hill Book Company, New York, 1960, chap. 11.

The Use of Architectural-acoustical Materials, Acoustical Materials Association, New York, 1963, 36 pp.

CHAPTER FIVE

Sound-absorbing Materials and Constructions

All building materials and surface treatments used in the construction of auditoriums have the capacity to absorb sound to a certain degree. In this chapter, however, only commercial and custom-designed building materials or surface treatments which contribute significantly to the acoustical control of auditoriums or to noise reduction will be considered.

Under special conditions many of the sound-absorptive materials are also successfully used in sound-insulating constructions (Chap. 14), but *sound absorption* should not be confused with *sound insulation*.

On striking any surface, sound is either reflected or absorbed. The sound energy absorbed by an absorbing layer is partially converted into heat but is mostly transmitted to the other side of the layer, unless such transmission is restrained by a backing of an impervious heavy barrier. In other words, a good sound absorber is an efficient sound transmitter, and consequently an inefficient sound insulator. An effective sound-insulating enclosure, on the other hand, will prevent the transmission of sound from one side to the other (Fig. 5.1).

Sound-absorbing materials and constructions used in the acoustical design of auditoriums or for the sound control of noisy rooms can be classified as (1) *porous materials*, (2) *panel* or *membrane absorbers*, and (3) *cavity* (or *Helmholtz*) *resonators*.

Acoustical materials of any of these groups and a combination of these materials (as individually designed acoustical treatments) can be mounted on the room enclosures or suspended in the air as space absorbers. The method of mounting has a considerable effect on the sound absorption of most materials.

5.1 Porous Materials

The basic acoustical characteristic of all *porous materials*, such as fiberboards, soft plasters, mineral wools, and isolation blankets, is a cellular network of interlocking pores. Incident sound energy is converted into heat energy within these pores. The fraction of incident sound thus converted into heat is absorbed, while the remainder, reduced in energy,

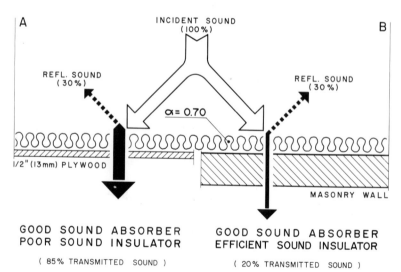

Fig. 5.1 (A) A good absorber ($\alpha = 0.70$) attached to a poor sound insulator, such as plywood, will not prevent the transmission of sound through such an enclosure. (B) Instead of plywood, an effective sound-insulating barrier, such as masonry, should be used to reduce noise transmission through the structure.

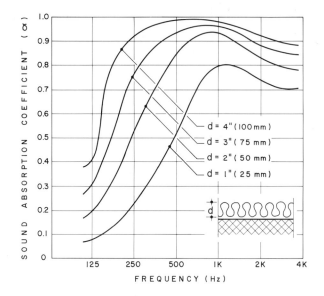

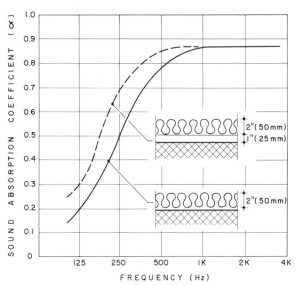

Fig. 5.2 (Above, left) The sound absorption of porous materials increases with thickness, particularly at low frequencies. Sound absorption of Fiberglas blankets with 3.25 lb per cu ft (52 kg per cu m) density and of various thicknesses compared (company measurements). Fig. 5.3 (Above) Sound absorption of a 2-in. (50-mm) mineral-wool blanket installed on rigid backing and on 1-in. (25-mm) framing.

is reflected from the surface of the material. Cellular materials with closed and noninterlocking cells, such as foamed resins, cellular rubbers, and foam glass, are poor sound absorbents.

Figures 5.2 and 5.3 illustrate the following characteristics of porous absorbents: (1) their sound absorption is more efficient at high than at low frequencies, and (2) their acoustical efficiency improves in the low-frequency range with increased thickness and with distance from their solid backing.

Commercial porous materials can be divided into three categories: (1) prefabricated acoustical units, (2) acoustical plasters and sprayed-on materials, and (3) acoustical (isolation) blankets.

5.1.1 Prefabricated Acoustical Units

Various types of perforated, unperforated, fissured, or textured cellulose and mineral-fiber tiles, lay-in panels, and perforated metal pans with absorbent pads constitute typical units in this group (Figs. 5.4 and 5.5). They can be mounted in several ways, according to manufacturers' instructions, for example, cemented to a solid backing, nailed or screwed to a wood framing, or laid in a ceiling suspension system. Special prefabricated units, such as Acoustone Space Units (by US Gypsum Co.), and Geocoustic tiles (by Pittsburgh Corning) used on wall and ceiling surfaces in spaced arrangements or in patches, installed either with cement or with simple mechanical attachments. Their sound absorption exceeds that of standard acoustical tiles because their exposed edges are finished in the same way as their faces (Fig. 5.6). Trade catalogs contain detailed descriptions and information on size, thickness, finish, methods of installation, acoustical efficiency, maintenance, flame resistance, and other important properties of these prefabricated acoustical units. It is imperative that the acoustical properties of products specified in the trade literature be supplied by accredited acoustical laboratories so that pertinent values of their acoustical efficiencies can be compared on an equal basis.

Using prefabricated acoustical units offers several advantages:

1. They have a reliable, factory-guaranteed absorption.

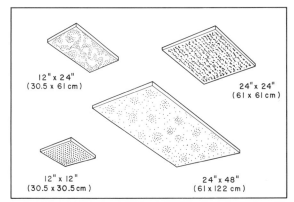

Fig. 5.4 Sizes of typical commercial acoustical tiles.

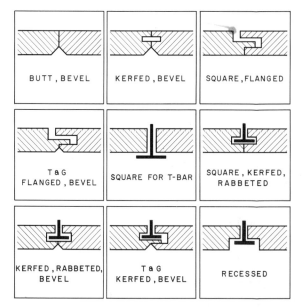

Fig. 5.5 Edge conditions of typical commercial acoustical tiles.

Fig. 5.6 Acoustical control by the use of Acoustone Space Units in a swimming pool in Minneapolis, Minn. (Photograph by Building News, Canadian Gypsum Co., Ltd.)

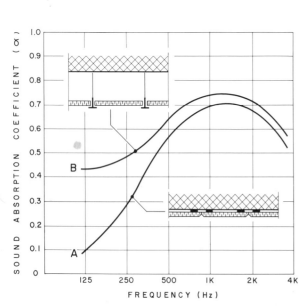

Fig. 5.7 Average absorption of typical acoustical tiles applied with adhesive (A) or in suspension system (B).

2. Installation and maintenance are relatively easy and economical.

3. Some can be redecorated without seriously affecting their absorption.

4. Their use in ceiling systems can be integrated functionally and visually with requirements of lighting, heating, or air conditioning; they assist in noise reduction and offer flexibility in partitioning.

5. If suitably mounted, their absorption can be beneficially increased (Fig. 5.7).

Their application, on the other hand, presents a few problems:

1. It is difficult to conceal the joints between adjacent units.

2. They generally have a soft structure, which would be subjected to mechanical damage if installed at lower levels of the walls.

3. Their aesthetic integration into an individualistic auditorium project poses a formidable task.

4. The use of paint for redecoration purposes may harmfully alter the absorption of most prefabricated acoustical units unless manufacturers' instructions are followed (Fig. 5.8).

The yearly bulletin of the Acoustical and Insulating Materials Association, Park Ridge, Ill., entitled *Performance Data: Architectural-acoustical Materials*, provides up-to-date information on products manufactured by its members, including the largest acoustical-material manufacturers in North America.

Certain concrete blocks and masonry units with lightweight aggregates or properly selected and mixed heavy aggregates, with a relatively porous exposed surface, also make a moderate contribution to sound absorption, particularly at the medium and high frequencies.

5.1.2 Acoustical Plasters and Sprayed-on Materials   These acoustical finishes are used mostly for noise-reduction purposes and sometimes in auditoriums where any other acoustical treatment would be impractical because of the curved or irregular shape of the surface. They are applied in a semiplastic consistency, either by a spray gun or by hand troweling (Sprayed Limpet Asbestos, Zonolite, Vermiculite, Sound Shield, Glatex, Dekoosto, etc.).

Their acoustical efficiency, usually best at the higher frequencies, depends largely on such job conditions as the thickness and composition of the plaster mixture, the amount of binder, the state of the undercoat at the time of application, and the manner in which the finish is applied. In order to obtain the desired acoustical result, it is essential that the job be executed by competent and responsible workmen and that the manufacturers' specifications be followed strictly.

The maintenance of acoustical plasters and sprayed-on finishes (sprayed mineral fiber) certainly offers some difficulties. Redecoration may create serious deterioration of their acoustical properties unless manufacturers' instructions are fully respected.

5.1.3 Acoustical (Isolation) Blankets   Acoustical blankets are manufactured from rock wool, glass fibers, wood fibers, hair felt, etc. Generally installed on a wood or metal framing system, these blankets are used for acoustical purposes in varying thicknesses between 1 and 5 in. (25 and 125 mm). Their absorption increases with thickness, particularly at low frequencies. If space is available, a considerable degree of low-frequency absorption, a characteristic usually missing in other porous absorbents, can be achieved by using a 3- to 5-in. (75- to 125-mm) thick isolation blanket. Since acoustical blankets do not constitute an aesthetically satisfactory finish, they are normally covered with a suitable type of perforated board, wood slats, fly screening, etc., placed over them and fastened to the framing system (Secs. 5.3.2 and 5.3.3).

5.1.4 Carpets and Fabrics   In addition to their traditional role as floor covering, carpets are now being used as versatile acoustical materials because they absorb airborne sounds and noises within the room, they

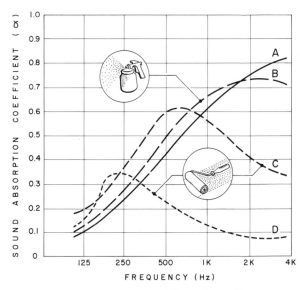

Fig. 5.8 Effect of paint on porous prefabricated acoustical units: (A) untreated surface; (B) one coat of paint applied with spray gun; (C) one coat of paint applied with brush; (D) two coats of paint applied with brush.

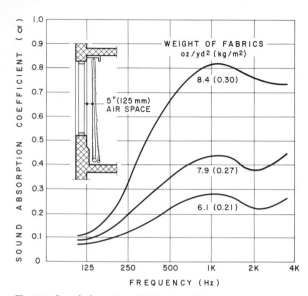

Fig. 5.9 Sound absorption of Fiberglas fabrics varies with the weight of the material. During tests, fabric was tailored to 100 percent fullness with 5 in. (125 mm) air space behind the fabric.

reduce and in some cases almost completely eliminate impact noises from above, and they eliminate surface noises (shuffling of feet, clicking of heels, moving of furniture). Carpets are used for floor and wall covering alike. The following facts have been established by tests conducted on behalf of the Carpet and Rug Institute.

Floor carpeting contributes to sound absorption as follows:

1. The fiber type has practically no effect on sound absorption.

2. Cut piles provide more absorption than loop piles under otherwise identical conditions.

3. With increased pile height and pile weight, in cut-pile fabrics, the sound absorption increases.

4. In loop-pile fabrics when pile height increases, with the density held constant, sound absorption improves; when the pile weight increases, with the pile height constant, sound absorption rises only up to a certain level.

5. The more permeable the backing, the higher the sound absorption.

6. Hair, hair-jute, and foam-rubber pads contribute to higher sound absorption than the less permeable rubber-coated hair-jute, sponge-rubber, and urethane-foam pads.

Carpeting on the floor above contributes to the reduction of impact noises as follows:

1. The heavier the carpet, the higher the protection against impact noise.

2. The thicker the carpet and underlay, the higher the impact-noise insulation.

3. Sponge-rubber pad, which is less efficient for sound absorption, is very effective against impact noises.

4. When the pad is adhered to the carpet, it produces less effective impact-noise insulation than the same layers placed separately.

5. Hair-and-jute pads outperform the all-hair pads; foam-rubber and urethane-foam pads perform extremely well against impact noises.

Wall carpeting contributes to sound absorption as follows:

1. Carpets installed on furred walls are better than carpets glued directly to the wall.

2. Carpets with mineral board, rock wool, styrofoam, or Tectum boards used as fillers between the furring provide higher absorption than those without fillers.

Carpets on walls should be flameproof, as usually required by local building by-laws.

Floor and wall carpeting undoubtedly creates a tranquil atmosphere, a highly desirable feature in our noise-polluted world, offering a hitherto unexplored contribution to psychological noise control.

In addition to light, glare, and solar-heat control, fenestration fabrics and draperies also contribute to sound absorption. The heavier the fabric, the higher the sound absorption (Fig. 5.9). Greater air space between the drapery and backing will beneficially increase low-frequency absorption.

5.2 Panel (or Membrane) Absorbers

The nonperforated *panel*, or *membrane, absorbers* represent the second group of sound-absorbing materials. Any impervious material installed on a solid backing but separated from it by an air space will act as a panel absorber and will vibrate when struck by sound waves. The flexural vibration of the panel will then absorb a certain amount of incident sound energy by converting it into heat energy.

Panels of this sort are efficient low-frequency absorbers. When selected properly, panel absorbers balance the somewhat excessive medium- and high-frequency absorption of porous absorbers and room contents. Thus, panel absorbers contribute to a uniform reverberation characteristic over the entire audio-frequency range. Figure 5.10 illustrates the absorption-frequency characteristics of a ¼-in. (6-mm) plywood panel spaced 3 in. (75 mm) from the wall, with and without porous absorbent in the air space. Using a porous absorber in the air space increases the absorption at low frequencies, broadening the otherwise narrow region of increased absorption.

Among auditorium finishes and constructions the following panel absorbers contribute to low-frequency absorption: wood and hardboard panels, gypsum boards, suspended plaster ceilings, furred-out plasters, rigid plastic boards, windows, glazings, doors, wood floors and platforms, and metal plates (radiators). Because of increased resistance against wear and abrasion, many of these nonperforated panel absorbers are often installed on the lower parts of walls, thereby providing a suitable finish for the dado.

Porous materials spaced away from their solid backing also act as vibrating panel absorbers, favorably contributing to absorption at low frequencies, as shown in Figs. 5.3 and 5.7.

5.3 Cavity (or Helmholtz) Resonators

The *cavity* (or *Helmholtz*) *resonators*, the third and last group of sound absorbents, consist of an enclosed body of air confined within rigid walls and connected by a narrow opening (called the *neck*) to the surrounding space, in which the sound waves travel.

A cavity resonator absorbs maximum sound energy in a narrow region of the low-frequency band. An empty jar or bottle, as described in Sec. 4.6, also acts as a cavity resonator; however, its maximum absorption is confined to a narrow frequency band; that is, it is extremely selective in its absorption.

Cavity resonators can be applied (1) as individual units, (2) as perforated panel resonators, and (3) as slit resonators.

5.3.1 Individual Cavity Resonators
Individual cavity resonators made of empty clay vessels of different sizes were used in medieval Scandinavian churches. Their effective absorption spread between 100 and 400 Hz.

Standard concrete blocks using a regular concrete mixture but with slotted cavities, called Soundblox units, constitute a contemporary version of the cavity resonator. Since they eliminate the need of additionally installed sound-absorptive surface treatment, they offer an economical means for the control of reverberation or noise (Fig. 5.11). The blocks are cast in two series, called type A and type B. Type A units have approximately ¼-in. (6-mm) slots and noncombustible filler elements

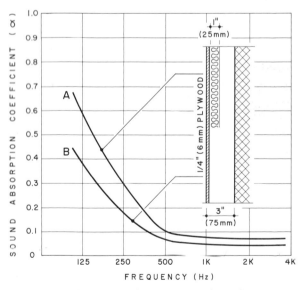

Fig. 5.10 Sound absorption of a ¼-in. (6-mm) plywood panel spaced 3 in. (75 mm) from the wall, with and without an isolation blanket in the air space.

Fig. 5.11 Soundblox units (slotted concrete blocks) used for reverberation control in a computer center, Kansas City, Mo. Radotinsky-Deardorff and Associates, architects. (Photograph by P. D. Steffee.)

in their cavities. In both types the cavities are closed at the top, the slots allowing the closed cavities to act as Helmholtz resonators. The blocks are made in 4-, 6-, and 8-in. thicknesses (10, 15, and 20 cm), all having an 8- by 16-in. (20- by 41-cm) nominal face size. Their maximum sound absorption occurs at low frequencies, decreasing at the higher frequencies (Fig. 5.12). The exposed surfaces of the blocks can be painted, with negligible effect on their absorption. Their great advantage lies in rugged durability, which permits their use in gymnasiums, swimming pools, bowling lanes, industrial plants, mechanical-equipment rooms, transportation terminals, and depressed highways, where the use of conventional soft, that is, nondurable, sound-absorbing materials would be inconceivable.

5.3.2 Perforated Panel Resonators Perforated panels, spaced away from a solid backing, provide a widely used practical application of the cavity-resonator principle. They contain a large number of necks, constituting the perforation of the panel, thus functioning as an array of cavity resonators. The perforations are usually circular (sometimes slotted). The air space behind the perforation forms the undivided body of the resonator, separated into bays by horizontal and vertical elements of the framing system.

Perforated panel resonators do not provide such a selective absorption as single cavity resonators, particularly if an isolation blanket is installed in the air space behind the visually exposed perforated board (Fig. 5.13). If the perforated panel is properly selected, with adequate open area (called *sound transparency*), the isolation blanket increases the overall absorbing efficiency by broadening the frequency region in which considerable absorption can be expected (Fig. 5.14).

The absorption-frequency curves of perforated panel resonators generally show a maximum (peak) value in the medium region of the frequency scale with an apparent drop above 1000 Hz. Therefore, if the same perforated-panel treatment were used extensively in an auditorium, the RT would be unfavorably short at the frequency of the peak absorption value. A reasonably even and uniform reverberation characteristic can be provided if the peak values in the absorption diagram of the perforated-panel treatments are shifted to several different regions of the frequency range. This can be achieved by varying the thickness of the perforated panel; the size and spacing of the holes; the depth of air space behind the perforated panel; the type, thickness, and density of the applied isolation blankets behind the perforated panels; and the spacings between the elements of the furring system.

Various standard commercial panels or boards are available in perforated form, suitable for application as perforated panel absorbers, such as cement-asbestos sheets; hardboards (Masonite); plain, corrugated, and expanded steel or aluminum sheets (Fig. 5.15); rigid plastic sheets and wood and plywood panels; reinforced fiber-glass panels, and plastic-coated steel sheets. Surface treatment of the exposed perforated panels must avoid clogging the holes with paint.

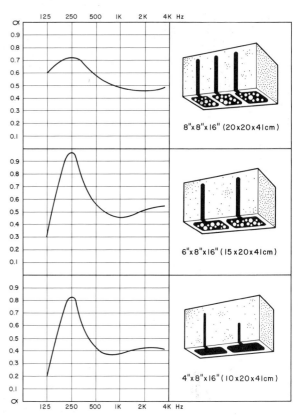

Fig. 5.12 Typical Soundblox units used as individual cavity resonators.

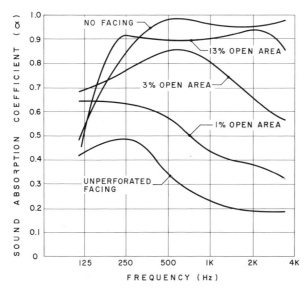

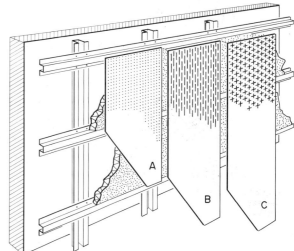

Fig. 5.13 Typical installation of a perforated panel resonator using various types of perforated facings and with an isolation blanket in the air space: (A) perforated board; (B) slotted hardboard; (C) perforated metal or plastic.

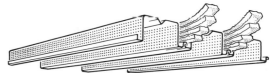

Fig. 5.14 (Left) Sound absorption of perforated panel resonators with isolation blanket in the air space. The open area (sound transparency) of the perforated facing has a considerable effect on the absorption.

Fig. 5.15 (Above) Acoustical steel decks, available in different sizes, with 1.1 lb per cu ft (18 kg per cu m) density glassfiber blankets in the perforated rib webs, make efficient perforated panel resonators. They provide reasonably uniform absorption throughout the standard frequency range.

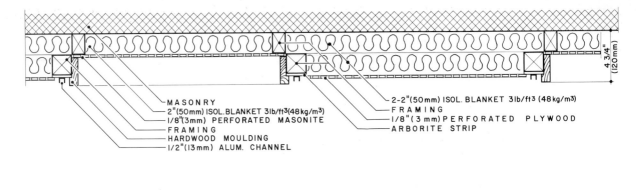

MASONRY
2"(50mm) ISOL.BLANKET 3lb/ft3(48kg/m3)
1/8"(3mm) PERFORATED MASONITE
FRAMING
HARDWOOD MOULDING
1/2"(13mm) ALUM. CHANNEL

2-2"(50mm) ISOL. BLANKET 3lb/ft3 (48kg/m3)
FRAMING
1/8"(3mm) PERFORATED PLYWOOD
ARBORITE STRIP

4 3/4" (120mm)

L I T T L E   T H E A T E R ,   A C A D E M I E   D E   Q U E B E C ,   A M Y O T   V A G I ,   A R C H I T E C T S

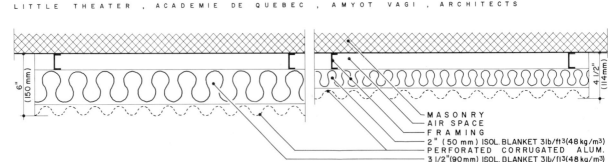

6" (150 mm)

4 1/2" (114mm)

MASONRY
AIR SPACE
FRAMING
2" (50 mm) ISOL. BLANKET 3lb/ft3(48 kg/m3)
PERFORATED CORRUGATED ALUM.
3 1/2"(90mm) ISOL. BLANKET 3lb/ft3(48 kg/m3)

V E R S A I L L E S   T H E A T E R S ,   M O N T R E A L ,   E L I A S O P H   B E R K O W I T Z ,   A R C H I T E C T S

Fig. 5.16 Perforated panel resonators used in various auditoriums. (L. L. Doelle, acoustical consultant.)

Figure 5.16 shows examples of perforated panel resonators applied as acoustical treatment in various auditoriums.

5.3.3 Slit Resonators   In designing auditoriums the desired acoustical effect can often be accomplished by using relatively inexpensive isolation blankets along the room surfaces. However, due to their porosity, isolation blankets need protection against abrasion. This gives the architect an opportunity to design a decorative-protective surface treatment, or screen, with elements of relatively small cross section and with a reasonable spacing to permit sound waves to penetrate between elements of the screen into the porous backing (Fig. 5.17). The protective screen can consist of a system of wood, metal, or rigid plastic slats, cavity blocks, or bricks, with a series of openings, gaps, or exposed slots. The protective screen, with its adequately spaced elements and the isolation blanket behind it, constitutes a slit-resonator absorber. It works like a perforated panel resonator in that it also has a cavity behind the slit-shaped necks created by the spaced elements of the screen. The total open area between the elements, called sound transparency, should constitute at least about 35 percent of the total area of the acoustical treatment (Figs. 5.18 and 5.19).

The popularity of slit resonators in the acoustical control of auditoriums is due to the fact that they offer a wide choice for individual design, although they are more expensive than the commercial, sometimes monotonous standard acoustical materials. Figures 5.20 to 5.22 show additional examples of slit-resonator absorbers, using cavity bricks, special cavity concrete blocks, and wood and steel slats.

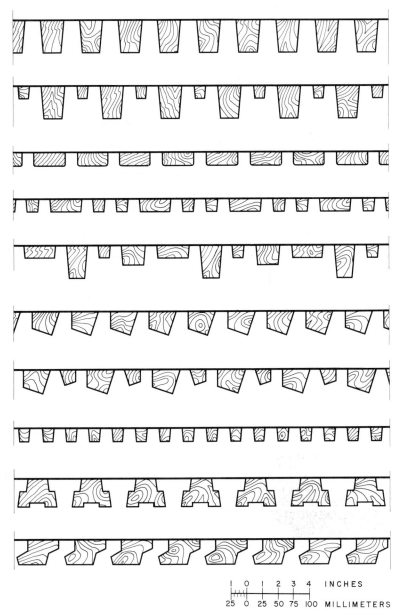

Fig. 5.17 Alternative series of wood slats suitable to protect a relatively soft isolation blanket installed in the cavities of a slit-resonator absorber.

```
I  O  I   2   3   4    INCHES
25 0 25  50  75 100   MILLIMETERS
```

Fig. 5.18 Wood-slatted acoustical treatment used as slit-resonator absorber in a 250-seat lecture hall, Université Laval, Quebec. A sound transparency of 40 percent provides adequate penetration of sound waves between the slats to reach the isolation blanket. (Gauthier and Guité, architects; L. L. Doelle, acoustical consultant.)

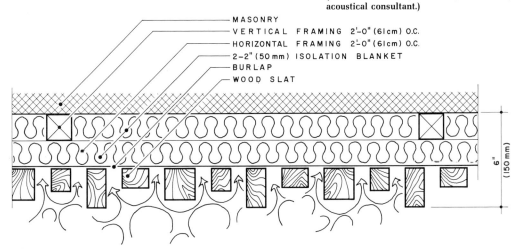

MASONRY
VERTICAL FRAMING 2'-0"(61cm) O.C.
HORIZONTAL FRAMING 2'-0"(61cm) O.C.
2-2"(50mm) ISOLATION BLANKET
BURLAP
WOOD SLAT

6" (150 mm)

40 % SOUND TRANSPARENCY

Fig. 5.19 Wood-slatted treatment in a multipurpose auditorium, Montreal. Eliasoph and Berkowitz, architects; L. L. Doelle, acoustical consultant. (Photograph by Bowe Studio.)

Fig. 5.20 (Opposite, above)   Slit-resonator absorbers used as acoustical treatments in various auditoriums. (L. L. Doelle, acoustical consultant.)

Fig. 5.21 (Opposite, below)   View of the acoustical treatment with open brick and wood slats detailed in Fig. 5.20. (Photograph by Bowe Studio.)

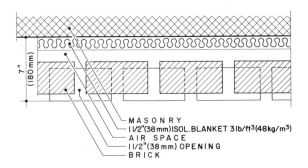

MASONRY
1 1/2"(38 mm)ISOL.BLANKET 3 lb/ft³(48kg/m³)
AIR SPACE
1 1/2"(38mm) OPENING
BRICK

7" (180 mm)

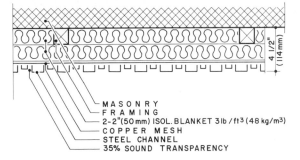

MASONRY
FRAMING
2-2"(50 mm) ISOL. BLANKET 3 lb/ft³(48 kg/m³)
COPPER MESH
STEEL CHANNEL
35% SOUND TRANSPARENCY

4 1/2" (114 mm)

LECTURE HALL , UNIVERSITE LAVAL , QUEBEC
GAUTHIER GUITE , ARCHITECTS

AUDITORIUM , INSTITUT PSYCHIATRIQUE , MONTREAL
BLOUIN BEAUVAIS LUSIGNAN , ARCHITECTS

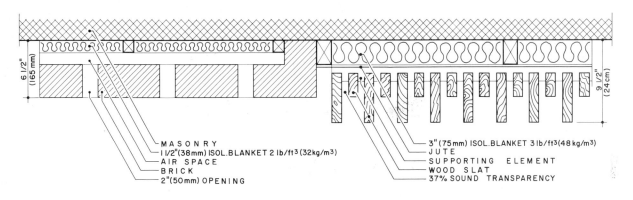

6 1/2" (165 mm)

9 1/2" (24 cm)

MASONRY
1 1/2"(38mm) ISOL.BLANKET 2 lb/ft³ (32kg/m³)
AIR SPACE
BRICK
2"(50mm) OPENING

3"(75mm) ISOL.BLANKET 3 lb/ft³(48kg/m³)
JUTE
SUPPORTING ELEMENT
WOOD SLAT
37% SOUND TRANSPARENCY

SYNAGOGUE , BETH-ZION CONGREGATION , MONTREAL , ROSEN CARUSO VECSEI SHAPIRO WOLFE , ARCHITECTS

Fig. 5.22 Concrete cavity blocks used as slit-resonator absorbers in a 700-seat high-school auditorium, Quebec. (Lemay, Leclerc, and Trahan, architects; L. L. Doelle, acoustical consultant. Photograph by Bowe Studio.)

Several prefabricated slit-resonator absorbers available on the market offer reasonably priced and pleasant surface treatments (Dampa, Luxa-lon, and Linear-Pan).

5.4 Space Absorbers

When the regular boundary enclosures of an auditorium do not provide suitable or adequate area for conventional acoustical treatment, sound-absorbing objects, called *space absorbers* or *functional absorbers,* can be suspended as individual units from the ceiling.

They are easily installed or removed without interfering with existing fixtures or equipment. Since sound waves will probably hit all sides of these absorbers, their absorption is quite powerful compared to standard, commercial acoustical materials. These features make space absorbers a particularly suitable treatment for noisy industrial areas.

Space absorbers are made of perforated sheets (steel, aluminum, hardboard, etc.) in the shape of panels, prisms, cubes, spheres, cylinders, or single or double conical shells and are generally filled or lined with sound-absorbing materials such as rock wool, glass wool, etc. (Fig. 5.23).

The sound absorption of space absorbers is specified as the number of sabins supplied per individual unit. Their acoustical efficiency depends on their spacing. In order to achieve a reasonable amount of room absorption, it is essential that a large number of space absorbers be used within a space. Their distribution requires careful coordination with the lighting layout.

5.5 Variable Absorbers

Since various uses of the same auditorium, as will be seen later, require various RTs, it has long been the aim of architects and acousticians to design special sound-absorbing constructions capable of varying the RT, that is, the acoustical conditions within a room.

Several attempts to do so have been made in the past, particularly in radio studios, where a noticeable change in the RT is frequently necessary. For this purpose various sliding, hinged, movable, and rotatable panels have been constructed that can expose either absorptive or reflective surfaces. Draperies have been installed that can be spread out over walls or be pulled back into suitable pockets, thus arbitrarily increasing or reducing the effective absorptive treatment in a room (Fig. 5.24).

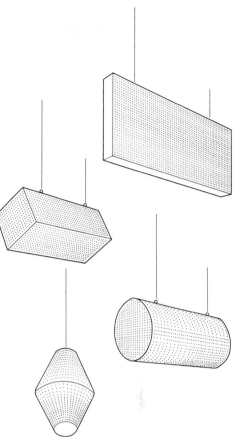

Fig. 5.23 Space absorbers can be suspended as individual units from the ceiling. They are used when the area of the room surfaces is not adequate for conventional acoustical treatment.

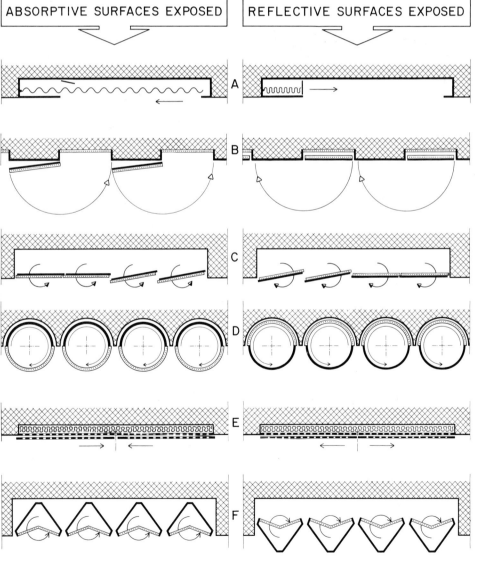

ABSORPTIVE SURFACES EXPOSED   REFLECTIVE SURFACES EXPOSED

Fig. 5.24 Schematic illustration of variable absorbers which provide means for altering the absorption and thus the RT: (A) retractable curtain; (B) hinged panels; (C) rotatable panels; (D) rotatable cylinders; (E) sliding perforated panels; (F) rotatable triangular elements.

The construction of such variable absorbers is justified only if it will be capable of producing a reasonable (at least 20 percent) change of the total absorption over a considerable region of the audio-frequency range.

Experience has given evidence that variable absorption-producing devices are practicable only for rooms which are permanently maintained and serviced by competent personnel, as might be the case for radio and recording studios. It appears, however, that even in studios the control of the RT through conventional variable absorbers will be soon rendered obsolete due to the widely expanding application of electronically operated reverberation control. Its discussion is beyond the scope of this book.

5.6 Air Absorption

It has been mentioned before that besides the various acoustical finishes and room contents, the absorption of the air also contributes to overall room absorption. The air absorption is affected by the temperature and humidity of the air and represents a significant value only at and above 1000 Hz. Values of the air absorption coefficient are given in Appendix Table A.1.

5.7 Sound Absorption of Openings

In calculating the RT of an auditorium, various openings, such as archways, supply and return air grilles, ceiling slots, very deep balconies or boxes, and the proscenium opening, also contribute, sometimes quite considerably, to the overall sound absorption of the room. Since sound absorption coefficients pertinent to these openings are seldom included in tables used for calculations, the architect will have to use his judgment in order to assign realistic absorption values to them.

5.8 Mounting and Distribution of Absorbing Materials

The sound-absorption characteristic of acoustical materials should not be considered as an intrinsic property but as a feature largely dependent on physical properties, installation details, and local conditions. Since the way in which acoustical materials are installed has a marked effect on their absorption properties, comparisons between the absorption coefficients of different materials should be based on data obtained from tests conducted in an accredited laboratory and under identical mounting conditions. Typical mountings used in conducting sound-absorption tests standardized by the Acoustical and Insulating Materials Association are illustrated in Fig. 5.25.

There is no specific type of mounting that can be recommended as optimum for every installation. Various details which have to be considered simultaneously include the following:

1. Physical properties of the acoustical material
2. Strength, surface texture, and location of the room enclosure on which the acoustical material will be installed

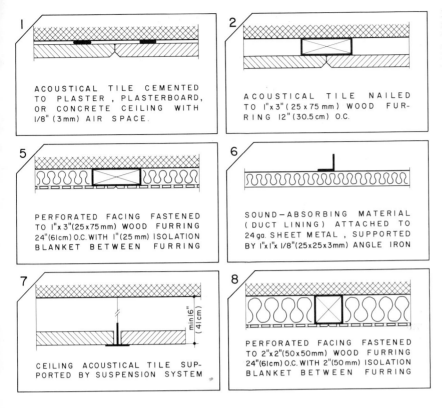

Fig. 5.25 Standard types of mounting for the installation of commercial acoustical materials used in conducting sound-absorption tests standardized by the Acoustical and Insulating Materials Association. Mountings corresponding to missing numbers (3 and 4) are seldom used in architectural acoustics.

3. The space available for the treatment
4. The time required for the labor
5. Probability of removal in the future
6. Costs, etc.

Methods of mounting for an installation on a new construction might be basically different from those feasible in an existing building. The acoustical finishes should be distributed over the room enclosures as uniformly as possible.

5.9 Choice of Sound-absorbing Materials

Since architectural-acoustical materials are supposed to combine the functions of sound absorption and interior finish, it is obvious that in the selection of acoustical finishes a number of considerations other than acoustical must be taken into account simultaneously.

If the main purpose is to achieve a uniform RT over the entire audio-frequency range, finishes must be chosen which will produce a uniform (not necessarily high) absorption characteristic throughout the audio-frequency range. If the application of medium- and high-frequency absorbents (perforated panel resonators or slit-resonator absorbers) is favored, their somewhat excessive medium- and high-frequency absorption can be counterbalanced by the installation of a reasonable number of low-frequency panel absorbers. If acoustically detrimental back reflections (echoes, too long delayed corner reflections) have to be eliminated or avoided, the dangerous reflecting surfaces must be treated with acoustical materials of a highly absorptive character.

The following details should be examined in the selection of sound-absorbing finishes or constructions:

1. Sound absorption coefficients at representative frequencies of the audio-frequency range
2. Appearance (size, edges, joints, color, texture)
3. Fire endurance and resistance to flame spread
4. Installation cost
5. Ease of installation
6. Durability (resistance to impact, mechanical injuries, and abrasion)
7. Light reflectance
8. Maintenance, cleaning, effect of redecoration upon sound absorption, and maintenance cost
9. Job conditions (temperature, humidity during installation, and readiness of backings)
10. Integration of room elements (doors, windows, lighting fixtures, grilles, radiators, etc.) into the acoustical finish
11. Thickness and weight
12. Moisture and condensation resistance once the room is in use
13. Access to suspended ceilings or furred spaces
14. Thermal-insulation value
15. Attraction for vermin, dry rot, fungus
16. Removability (sometimes a temporary requirement to make possible adjustments of isolation blankets)
17. Simultaneous requirement for adequate sound insulation (in case of suspended ceilings and exterior enclosures)

Appendix Table A.1, which lists sound absorption coefficients of common building materials, acoustical materials, and room contents (audience, seats, etc.), will be useful in making simple RT calculations.

5.10 Measurement of Sound Absorption

Various methods for measuring the sound absorption coefficients of acoustical materials are widely discussed in the acoustical literature. Two methods of particular interest are the tube method and the reverberation-chamber method.

5.10.1 Tube Method This method is used to measure the sound absorption coefficients of small samples of acoustical materials for sound waves traveling perpendicular to the surface of the sample. The measurement will give an indication of the sound absorption in the frequency range of about 200 to 3000 Hz.

The method is unsuitable for the overall measurement of sound absorption coefficients because of its limitations. It disregards the fact that sound waves in a room strike the sound-absorbing materials at various angles, and furthermore the size and method of mounting of the test sample have no similarity to actual job conditions. For these reasons, results obtained by the tube method should be used for theoretical work, in the development of new acoustical materials or in the comparison of existing ones, and also for quality control.

5.10.2 Reverberation-chamber Method This method utilizes a bare chamber with a long RT. A large sample or several samples of sound-absorbing material are installed in the chamber, thereby reducing its RT. The sound absorption coefficient of the absorbing material is then calculated from the decrease in the RT of the chamber, created by the sample of the sound-absorbing material.

The size of the test specimen may vary from 60 to 100 sq ft (5.6 to 9.3 sq m), depending on the dimensions of the reverberation chamber. The samples are tested by placing them on the floor, on the walls, or on the ceiling of the chamber. It is essential that the sample be installed in a manner simulating existing or predictable field conditions. Measurements are made at representative frequencies along the audio-frequency range.

The sound absorption coefficient of a sound-absorbing material measured in a reverberation chamber should not be considered as a constant of the material because it will depend on the size of the sample, its position and distribution in the chamber, the way it is mounted, and physical characteristics of the chamber itself. Therefore, values of sound absorption coefficients measured in different laboratories should be compared with caution.

BIBLIOGRAPHY

Books

Parkin, P. H., and H. R. Humphreys: *Acoustics, Noise and Buildings,* Frederick A. Praeger, Inc., New York, 1958, chap. 2.
Beranek, L. L. (ed.): *Noise Reduction,* McGraw-Hill Book Company, New York, 1960, chap. 15.
The Use of Architectural-acoustical Materials, Acoustical Materials Association, New York, 1963, 36 pp.

Periodicals

Harris, C. M.: "Absorption of Sound in Air in the Audio-frequency Range," *J. Acoust. Soc. Am.,* January 1963, pp. 11–17.
Harris, C. M.: "Absorption of Sound in Air versus Humidity and Temperature," *J. Acoust. Soc. Am.,* July 1966, pp. 148–159.
Price, A. J., and K. A. Mulholland: "The Effect of Surface Treatment on Sound-absorbing Materials," *Applied Acoustics,* January 1968, pp. 67–72.
Beranek, L. L.: "Audience and Chair Absorption in Large Halls," *J. Acoust. Soc. Am.,* January 1969, pp. 13–19.
Ford, R. D., and M. West: "The Fundamental Acoustic Parameters of Two Commonly Used Absorbent Materials," *Applied Acoustics,* April 1970, pp. 89–103.
Delany, M. E., and E. N. Barley: "Acoustical Properties of Fibrous Absorbent Materials," *Applied Acoustics,* April 1970, pp. 105–116.

Bulletins and Reports

Sound Conditioning with Carpet, The Carpet and Rug Institute, Inc., New York, 1969, 27 pp.
Performance Data: Architectural-acoustical Materials, Acoustical and Insulating Materials Association Bulletin 30, Park Ridge, Ill., January 1970, 91 pp.

CHAPTER SIX

Acoustical Requirements in Auditorium Design

The design of various types of auditoriums (theaters, lecture halls, churches, concert halls, opera houses, and motion-picture theaters) has become a complex problem in contemporary architectural practice because in addition to its various, sometimes conflicting, aesthetic, functional, technical, artistic, and economical requirements, an auditorium often has to accommodate an unprecedentedly large audience. Furthermore, present standards often mean that the same space must be used for various types of programs (multipurpose auditoriums) and that the capacity of the room must be easily adjustable to momentary needs (multiform auditoriums). These are serious requirements, and it must be remembered that when the audience enters an auditorium, it has the right to expect—quite distinct from the quality of the program itself—comfort, safety, pleasant surroundings, good illumination, proper viewing, and good sound.

Hearing conditions in any auditorium are considerably affected by purely architectural considerations, such as room shape, dimensions, and volume, layout of boundary surfaces, seating arrangement, audience capacity, surface treatments, and materials for interior decoration. Practically every detail within the enclosed space will contribute to a greater or lesser extent to the acoustical performance of the room. The satisfactory solution of acoustical requirements does not curtail or even restrict the architect's freedom of design. Every acoustical problem can be tackled in a number of ways. Present practices in construction and interior decorating permit acoustical principles and requirements to be satisfactorily translated into the language of contemporary architecture.

6.1 Outline of Acoustical Requirements

The following are the requirements for good hearing conditions in an auditorium:

1. There should be adequate loudness in every part of the auditorium, particularly the remote seats.

2. The sound energy should be uniformly distributed (diffused) in the room.

3. Optimum reverberation characteristics should be provided in the auditorium to allow the most favorable reception of the program material by the audience and the most efficient presentation of the program by the performers.

4. The room should be free of such acoustical defects as echoes, long-delayed reflections, flutter echoes, sound concentrations, distortion, sound shadow, and room resonance.

5. Noises and vibrations which would interfere with listening or performing should be excluded or reasonably reduced in every part of the room.

6.2 Adequate Loudness

The problem of providing *adequate loudness*, particularly in medium-size and large auditoriums, results from the energy losses of the traveling sound waves and from excessive absorption by the audience and room

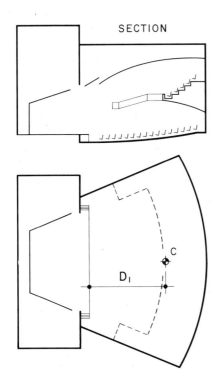

SECTION

FAN-SHAPED PLAN WITH BALCONY

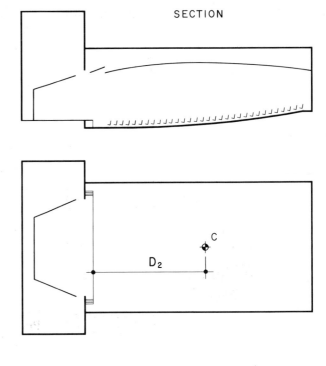

SECTION

RECTANGULAR PLAN WITHOUT BALCONY

Fig. 6.1 In a fan-shaped auditorium with a balcony the audience can be seated closer to the sound source than in a rectangular auditorium of the same capacity without a balcony. C, center of gravity of listening area; D_1, D_2, average distances between sound source and listeners.

contents (upholstered seats, carpets, draperies, etc.). Sound-energy losses can be reduced and adequate loudness can be provided in the following ways.

1. The auditorium should be shaped so that the audience is as close to the sound source as possible, thereby reducing the distance the sound must travel. In larger auditoriums use of a balcony brings more seats closer to the sound source (Fig. 6.1).

2. The sound source should be raised as much as feasible in order to secure a free flow of direct sound waves (those traveling directly from the sound source without reflection) to every listener (Fig. 6.2).

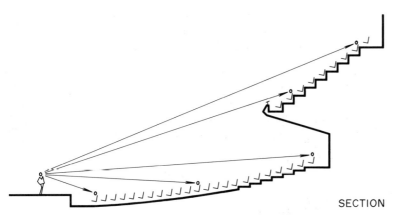

SECTION

Fig. 6.2 When listeners are exposed to ample direct sound waves, loudness benefits.

3. The floor where the audience is seated should be properly ramped, or raked, because sound is more readily absorbed when it travels over the audience at grazing incidence. As a general rule, in the interest

of safety, the gradient along the aisles of sloped auditorium floors should be not more than 1 in 8; however, requirements of local building codes should be consulted. Even if the floor along the aisles is sloped, for practical installation purposes it is customary to use shallow steps under the seats. The audience floor of theaters for live performances, particularly with open or arena stages (Chap. 7), should be stepped (Fig. 6.3).

Fig. 6.3 The stepped audience floor of the 800-seat Théâtre Port-Royal, Montreal, provides an ample flow of direct sounds from the stage to the audience. (David, Barott, and Boulva, architects; Bolt, Beranek, and Newman, acoustical consultants. Photograph by Beaudin-Nobert Inc.)

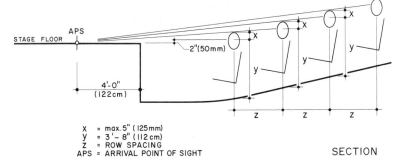

X = max. 5" (125mm)
y = 3'- 8" (112 cm)
z = ROW SPACING
APS = ARRIVAL POINT OF SIGHT

SECTION

Fig. 6.4 Method of establishing good sight lines based on one-row vision.

Figure 6.4 shows a method of establishing the slope of a floor that simultaneously provides good vertical sight lines and a satisfactory flow of direct sound waves to the listeners. It has been assumed that the arrival point of sight (APS) is located on the stage floor 4 ft (122 cm) from the edge of the stage. This will usually result in a floor which is too steep, with the well-known result of excessive room height. A more gentle slope can be achieved by considering any of the following

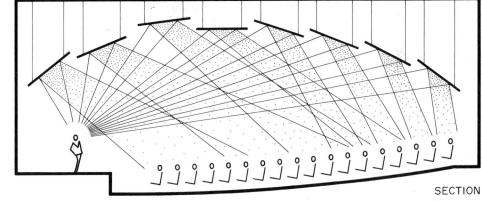

Fig. 6.5 Properly located ceiling reflectors, with progressively increasing sound reflections toward the remote seats, effectively contribute to adequate loudness.

SECTION

compromises: (1) raising the APS to a higher level if this is acceptable, (2) adequately reducing the value of x (explained in Fig. 6.4), or (3) observing two-row vision (instead of one-row vision, which permits unobstructed view over the heads of the spectators in the row immediately ahead) and staggering the seats to allow a view between the heads of the spectators in the row immediately in front.

The usual steep rakes of balconies, applied primarily for visual reasons, normally create satisfactory conditions for the reception of direct sound waves.

4. The sound source should be closely and abundantly surrounded with large sound-reflective surfaces (plaster, gypsum board, plywood, Plexiglas, rigid plastic boards, etc.) in order to supply additional reflected sound energy to every portion of the audience area, particularly to the remote seats (Fig. 6.5). It must be remembered that the dimensions of the reflecting surfaces must be comparable to the wavelengths of the sound waves to be reflected (as pointed out in Chap. 4) and the reflectors must be layed out in such a fashion that the initial time-delay gap between direct and first-reflected sound is relatively short, possibly not exceeding 30 milliseconds (msec), that is, 30/1,000 sec (Fig. 6.6). The angles of the reflective surfaces must be established by the law of sound

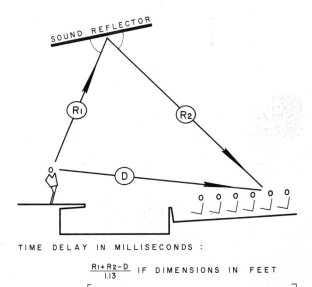

TIME DELAY IN MILLISECONDS :

$$\frac{R_1 + R_2 - D}{1.13} \quad \text{IF DIMENSIONS IN FEET}$$

$$\left[\frac{R_1 + R_2 - D}{0.34} \quad \text{IF DIMENSIONS IN METERS} \right]$$

Fig. 6.6 Reflected sound beneficially reinforces the direct sound if the time delay between them is relatively short, that is, a maximum of 30 msec.

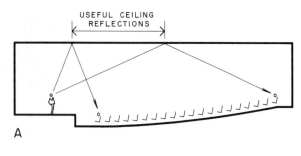

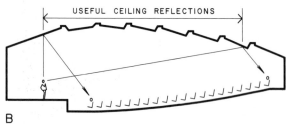

SECTION

Fig. 6.7 A horizontal ceiling (section A) provides only a limited amount of the desirable short-delayed reflections. Properly tilted ceiling surfaces (section B) contribute more to the provision of useful sound reflections, that is, adequate loudness.

reflection (outlined in Chap. 4), and it is essential that good use be made of the ceiling and wall surfaces in order to provide the greatest amount of short-delayed sound reflections (Fig. 6.7). The ceiling and the front portions of the side walls of the auditorium are always suitable surfaces for the accommodation of sound reflectors. In practice, the successful integration of an acoustically efficient system of ceiling and wall reflectors into the overall layout, involving architectural, structural, mechanical, and lighting requirements, is a challenging problem in contemporary auditorium design (Figs. 6.8 to 6.10).

5. The floor area and volume of the auditorium should be kept at a reasonable minimum, thereby shortening the distance that direct and reflected sounds must travel. Table 6.1 lists recommended volume-per-seat values for various types of auditoriums.

TABLE 6.1 Recommended Volume-per-seat Values for Various Types of Auditoriums

| Type of auditorium | Volume per audience seat, cu ft (cu m) | | |
	Min.	Opt.	Max.
Rooms for speech	80	110	150
	(2.3)	(3.1)	(4.3)
Concert halls	220	275	380
	(6.2)	(7.8)	(10.8)
Opera houses	160	200	260
	(4.5)	(5.7)	(7.4)
Roman Catholic churches	200	300	425
	(5.7)	(8.5)	(12)
Protestant churches and synagogues	180	255	320
	(5.1)	(7.2)	(9.1)
Multipurpose auditoriums	180	250	300
	(5.1)	(7.1)	(8.5)
Motion-picture theaters	100	125	180
	(2.8)	(3.5)	(5.1)

Fig. 6.8 The sound-reflective ceiling, a series of tilted panels, in a 350-seat lecture hall, Université de Montréal. (Beauvais and Lusignan, architects; L. L. Doelle, acoustical consultant. Photograph by Bowe Studio.)

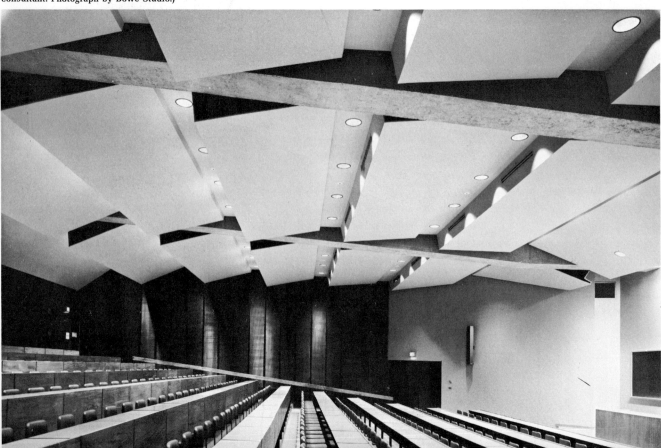

6. Parallelism between opposite (horizontal or vertical) sound-reflective boundary surfaces, particularly close to the sound source, should be avoided, to eliminate undesirable back reflections to the sound source.

7. The audience should occupy those parts of the seating area which are advantageous both for viewing and for hearing. Excessively wide seating areas should be avoided (Fig. 3.8). No aisle should be located along the longitudinal axis of the auditorium, where seeing and listening conditions are most favorable. The acoustical advantage offered by continental seating (without intermediate longitudinal aisles) is quite obvious.

8. If besides the primary sound source, which is normally located at the front part of an auditorium, additional sound sources exist in other parts of the room (for example, in a church), then these sound sources must also be surrounded by sound-reflective surfaces. In every auditorium it is essential that the greatest possible amount of sound energy be emitted from all "sending" positions to all "receiving" areas.

9. In addition to those reflective surfaces which serve to reinforce the direct sound toward the audience, additional reflective surfaces must be provided which direct the sound back to the performers. This is particularly true in auditoriums designed for musical or vocal purposes.

Correctly located sound reflectors, in addition to providing for the required reinforcement of the sound-energy supply, also create an environmental condition known as *space effect*. It is achieved when a listener receives sound from numerous directions, and it is typical of enclosed spaces but entirely missing in open-air theaters.

The measures listed so far will adequately (sometimes surprisingly) improve the loudness in small- and medium-size auditoriums, but they will not perform miracles. A lecturer or actor may talk in such a subdued voice that even listeners nearby have difficulty understanding him. It would be unreasonable to expect the intensity of his faint voice to be raised by natural acoustical measures (without the use of a speech-reinforcement system) to an intelligible level. The first step in the provision for adequate loudness must therefore come from the performer himself: he must speak loudly and understandably, with syllables uttered as clearly and evenly as possible. Proper loudness cannot be provided in an auditorium unless the sound has been properly emitted at the source.

In large auditoriums, even if attention has been given to the points discussed so far, speech level will often be too low for satisfactory hearing conditions. In such cases, and obviously in outdoor locations where no room enclosures exist to provide sufficient reflected sound energy, the installation of a sound-amplification system is nearly always necessary to secure adequate loudness and good sound distribution. This will be discussed in Chap. 11.

6.3 Diffusion of Sound

Section 4.3 describes the ways in which *acoustical diffusion* can be achieved. Two important points must be considered in the effort to provide diffusion in a room: the surface irregularities (exposed structural elements, coffered ceilings, serrated enclosures, protruding boxes, sculptured surface decorations, deep window reveals, etc.) must be abundantly applied, and they must be reasonably large (Figs. 6.11 and 6.12).

Fig. 6.11 Large-scale sound-diffusive surface irregularities integrated into the sound-reflective stage enclosures in a 1,000-seat multipurpose auditorium in Quebec. (Amyot and Vagi, architects; L. L. Doelle, acoustical consultant. Photograph by Legare & Kedl.)

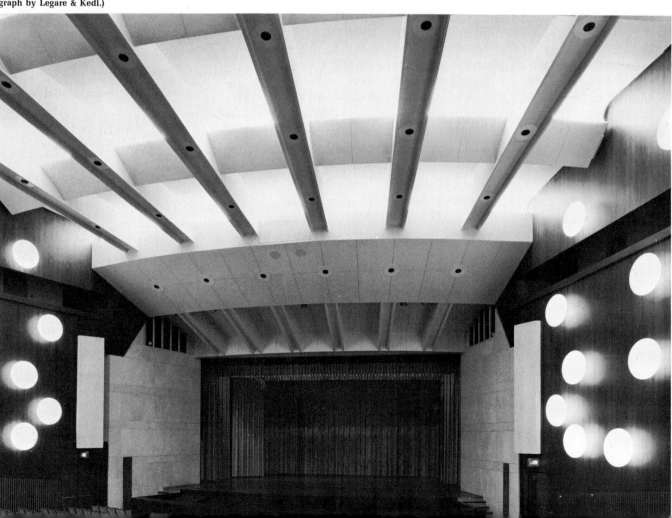

Fig. 6.12 The serrated layout of sound-reflective ceiling panels provides beneficial diffusion in this 300-seat lecture hall, Université de Montréal. (Beauvais and Lusignan, architects; L. L. Doelle, acoustical consultant. Photograph by Bowe Studio.)

For reasons of economy and aesthetics, particularly in small rooms, the application of surface irregularities is often difficult. In such cases the random distribution of absorbing material or the alternate application of sound-reflective and sound-absorptive treatment are other means of promoting diffusion. The use of acoustical diffusers is particularly important for concert halls, opera houses, radio and recording studios, and music rooms (Fig. 6.13).

The beneficial effect of acoustical diffusers upon the acoustical conditions of auditoriums is quite remarkable. When a considerable number of properly sized surface irregularities have been installed in rooms with rather excessive RTs, hearing conditions are greatly improved.

6.4 Control of Reverberation

Orators, actors, musicians, singers—in fact all performers in an auditorium—will expect the sound generated at the source not to die away or diminish quickly but to persist for some moments. In other words, an auditorium should react to desirable sounds just as a musical instrument would, enhancing and prolonging the original sound. This prolongation of sound as a result of successive reflections in an enclosed space after the source of sound has been turned off is called *reverberation;* it has a distinct effect on hearing conditions, as described in Chap. 4.

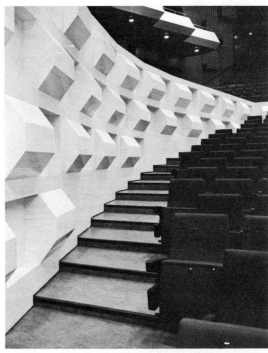

Fig. 6.13 Marble diffusers in the 2,232-seat Groote Zaal of Rotterdam's De Doelen concert-hall complex. (Kraaijvanger, Kraaijvanger, and Fledderus, architects; C. W. A. Kosten and P. A. de Lange, acoustical consultants. Photograph by W. van Suchtelen.)

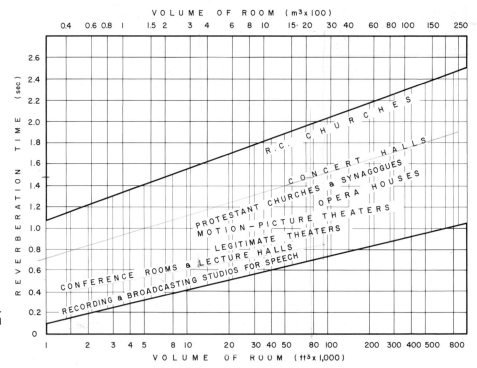

VOLUME OF ROOM (m³ x 100)

VOLUME OF ROOM (ft³ x 1,000)

Fig. 6.14 Approximate range of optimum mid-frequency (500 to 1000 Hz) RTs for fully occupied rooms of various volumes and functions.

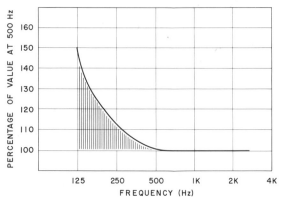

Fig. 6.15 Recommended variation of RT with frequency. At frequencies lower than 500 Hz, the RT should increase according to the values inside the shaded area.

Optimum reverberation characteristics of a room, depending on its volume and function, implies (1) favorable RT-vs.-frequency characteristics, (2) advantageous ratio of reflected to direct sound reaching the audience, and (3) optimum growth and decay of sound.

The control of RT is an important step in the acoustical design of auditoriums, but it is secondary to a careful analysis of room shape and proper distribution of reflected sound energy. The optimum RT of auditoriums can be represented by a series of curves specifying ideal values related to the volume and function of the room in question.

Figure 6.14 gives a range of optimum reverberation times of auditoriums plotted against their volumes, as recommended by various authors. They apply to the mid-frequency range of 500 to 1000 Hz. These values serve as a reliable basis for good hearing conditions in auditoriums. Experience shows that excessive variation of RT at frequencies other than the mid-frequency value will create unsatisfactory hearing conditions. Various RT-vs.-frequency curves have been suggested; a flat curve above 500 Hz is generally recommended. For music, a curve rising to about 1.5 times the 500-Hz value at 125 Hz is proposed, while for speech the curve should remain flat down to 125 Hz. This is shown in Fig. 6.15. For multipurpose auditoriums, the RT-vs.-frequency curve below 500 Hz may lie anywhere between these limits. A deviation of about 5 to 10 percent from a selected optimum RT value is generally considered acceptable, particularly in auditoriums with a high degree of diffusion. Figure 6.14 clearly indicates that rooms used for speech require a shorter RT than rooms of the same volume used for musical or vocal purposes.

In the acoustical design of an auditorium, once the optimum RT at the mid-frequency range has been selected and the RT-vs.-frequency relationship below 500 Hz decided upon, the reverberation control consists of establishing the total amount of room absorption to be supplied by the acoustical finishes, occupants, room contents, etc., in order to produce the selected value of RT. For the simplified RT calculation of moderately sized rooms with economically applied sound-absorbing treatments (as in most cases), the formula discussed in Chap. 4 can be used:

$$RT = \begin{cases} \dfrac{0.05V}{A + xV} & \text{English system} \\[2ex] \dfrac{0.16V}{A + xV} & \text{metric system} \end{cases}$$

where RT = reverberation time, sec

$\quad$ V = room volume, cu ft (cu m)

$\quad$ A = total room absorption, sq-ft sabins (sq-m sabins)

$\quad$ x = air absorption coefficient (see Appendix Table A.1)

This formula clearly shows that the larger the room volume, the longer the RT, and the more absorption is introduced into the room, the shorter the RT will be. The formula also suggests that the RT can be changed within the same auditorium by increasing or decreasing the room volume (for example, by lowering or raising a movable ceiling) or by using variable absorbers (Chap. 5). A sample RT calculation is given in Chap. 19.

Since the absorption of various materials and finishes used in the design of auditoriums normally varies with frequency, the RT values also vary with frequency. It is therefore essential to specify and calculate the RT for a number of representative frequencies of the audio-frequency range. As noted earlier, reference to an RT value without mentioning any particular frequency generally means the RT at 500 Hz.

In selecting acoustical finishes a number of considerations must be taken into account simultaneously; they have already been listed in Sec. 5.9.

In almost every auditorium the audience provides most of the absorption, about 5 sq-ft (0.45 sq-m) sabins per person. When attendance fluctuates widely, hearing conditions should also be satisfactory in the partial or even total absence of an audience. The most effective way of achieving this, though certainly not cheap, is to replace the possible loss of audience absorption by upholstered seats, with the underneath side of the seats also absorptive.

As a general rule, sound-absorbing materials should be installed along those boundary surfaces of the auditorium which are liable to produce such acoustical defects as echoes, flutter echoes, long-delayed reflections, and sound concentrations. The acoustical treatment should go first on the rear wall (opposite the sound source), then on those portions of the side walls which are furthest from the source or along the perimeter of the ceiling. There is no justification for placing a sound-absorbing surface along the middle portion of an auditorium ceiling because the primary function of this area should be to supply short-delayed sound reflections to the listeners.

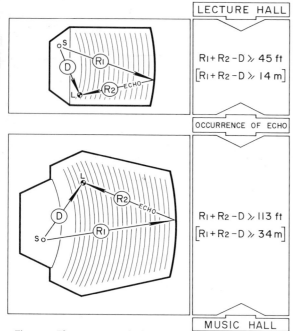

Fig. 6.16 The occurrence of echo in auditoriums. S, sound source; L, listener; D, direct sound; R_1, R_2, reflected sounds.

The reverberation calculation, the selection, and distribution of acoustical finishes in a larger auditorium, depending on the degree of importance attached to acoustical considerations, normally call for the services of an acoustician, in order to avoid inefficient and ill-sited acoustical finishes.

Since in designing an auditorium the architect normally strives for an individual solution, standard commercial sound-absorbing materials are seldom used in practice. Figures 5.16 to 5.21 illustrate examples of custom-designed acoustical treatments used successfully in reverberation control.

6.5 Elimination of Room-acoustical Defects

Besides providing for positive acoustical attributes, such as adequate loudness, uniform distribution of sound energy, and optimum reverberation time, it is essential that potential room-acoustical defects be eliminated. The most common acoustical defects which can impair and sometimes even destroy otherwise acceptable acoustical conditions will be described briefly.

6.5.1 Echo Probably the most serious room-acoustical defect, *echo* is noticeable when the sound is being reflected from any boundary surface with sufficient magnitude and delay to be perceived as a sound distinct from that traveling directly from source to listener. Echo occurs (Fig. 6.16) if a minimum interval of $\frac{1}{25}$ sec (for speech) to $\frac{1}{10}$ sec (for music) elapses between the perception of the direct and reflected sounds originating from the same source. Since the speed of sound is about 1,130 ft per sec (344 m per sec), the critical time intervals specified above correspond to path differences of minimum 45 ft (14 m) for speech or 113 ft (34 m) for music between direct and reflected sounds. A

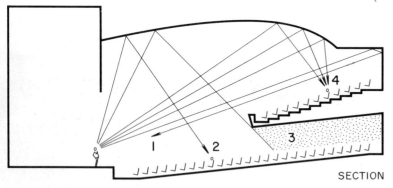

Fig. 6.17 Acoustical defects in an auditorium. (1) echo; (2) long-delayed reflection; (3) sound shadow; (4) sound concentration.

SECTION

sound-reflective rear wall, opposite the sound source, is a potential echo-producing surface in an auditorium unless it is acoustically treated or is under a deep balcony (Fig. 6.17, sound wave 1).

Echo should not be confused with reverberation. Echo is the distinct and highly undesirable repetition of the original sound; reverberation, within reasonable limits, is the beneficial extension or prolongation of the sound.

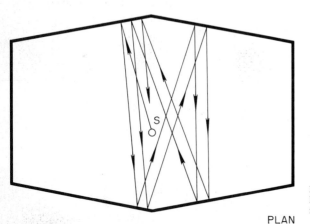

Fig. 6.18 Flutter echo can occur between nonparallel sound-reflective surfaces if the sound source S is located between them.

PLAN

6.5.2 Long-delayed Reflection

Long-delayed reflection is a defect similar to echo except that the time delay between the perception of direct and reflected sounds is somewhat less (Fig. 6.17, sound wave 2).

6.5.3 Flutter Echo

A flutter echo consists of a rapid succession of noticeable small echoes and is observed when a short burst of sound, such as a clap or shot, is produced between parallel sound-reflective surfaces, even though the other pair of opposite enclosures in the room consists of nonparallel, absorbent, or diffusive surfaces. Elimination of parallelism between opposite reflecting surfaces is one way to avoid flutter echoes. No flutter echo will be noticeable if the sound source is not located between the critical parallel surfaces.

Flutter echo can also occur between nonparallel sound-reflective surfaces (Fig. 6.18) if the sound source is located between these surfaces.

Echoes, long-delayed reflections, and flutter echoes can be prevented by installing sound-absorbing materials along the defect-producing reflective surfaces. If using acoustical finishes along these critical areas is not feasible, they should be rendered diffusive or tilted, in order to produce beneficial short-delayed reflections (Fig. 6.19).

6.5.4 Sound Concentration

Sound concentrations, sometimes referred to as "hot spots," are caused by sound reflections from concave surfaces. The intensity of sound at hot spots is unnaturally high and always occurs at the expense of other listening areas, or "dead spots," where hearing conditions are poor (Fig. 6.17, sound wave 4). The presence of hot and dead spots creates a nonuniform distribution of sound energy in the room. The elimination of this phenomenon is important in room acoustics.

Large, unbroken concave enclosures, particularly those having a large radius of curvature, should be eliminated or treated with efficient sound-absorbing materials (Fig. 6.20). If large concave surfaces cannot be avoided or acoustical treatment is not feasible, these concave surfaces should be laid out in such a manner that they focus in space outside or above the audience area.

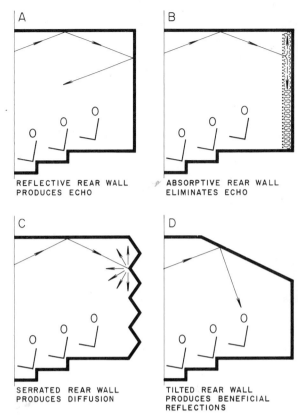

Fig. 6.19 Sound-reflective rear wall (A), liable to produce echo, should be treated acoustically (B), rendered diffusive (C), or tilted to produce beneficial short-delayed reflections (D).

Fig. 6.20 Undesirable sound concentration in the 700-seat curvilinear church of Ville d'Anjou, Quebec, has been avoided by the use of sound-absorbing cavity blocks along the curved side wall. (A. Blouin, architect; L. L. Doelle, acoustical consultant. Photograph by M. Corbeau.)

Fig. 6.21   The use of shallow balconies in the 3,000-seat Salle Wilfrid Pelletier, Montreal, keeps the under-balcony seats entirely free from acoustical shadow. (Affleck, Desbarats, Dimakopoulos, Lebensold, Michaud, and Sise, architects; Bolt, Beranek, Newman, and N. Pappas and Associates, acoustical consultants. Photograph by Studio Lausanne Co.)

A suitably selected and properly installed sound-amplification system can reduce the detrimental acoustical effects of echoes, long-delayed reflections, flutter echoes, and sound concentrations, but it can never overcome them completely.

6.5.5   Coupled Spaces   If an auditorium is connected to an adjacent reverberant space (such as a vestibule, stairwell, corridor, stage tower, or baptistry) by means of open doorways, the two rooms will form coupled spaces. As long as the air spaces of the coupled rooms are interconnected, an inflow of reverberant sound into the auditorium from the adjacent space will be noticeable, although reverberation might have been properly controlled in the auditorium. This phenomenon will be particularly disturbing to people seated close to the open doorways, no matter how much consideration has been given to the reverberation control of the room.

The undesirable effect of coupled spaces can be overcome by adequate acoustical separation between the coupled spaces, by providing approximately the same RT in both spaces or by reducing the RT of both.

6.5.6   Distortion   Distortion is an undesirable change in the quality of musical sound due to the uneven or excessive sound absorption of the boundary surfaces at different frequencies. It can be avoided if the applied acoustical finishes have balanced absorption characteristics over the entire audio-frequency range.

6.5.7 Room Resonance   Room resonance, sometimes called *coloration*, occurs when certain sounds within a narrow band of frequency tend to sound louder than other frequencies. This acoustical defect is more serious in small rooms than in larger ones. Its elimination is of particular importance in the design of radio and recording studios, where the sound is picked up by microphones.

6.5.8 Sound Shadow   The phenomenon of sound shadow is noticeable under a balcony which protrudes too far into the air space of an auditorium (Fig. 6.17, sound wave 3). Such under-balcony spaces, with a depth exceeding twice the height, should be avoided, since they will prevent the remote seats underneath from receiving an adequate amount of direct and reflected sounds, thus creating poor audibility in this portion of the listening area (Fig. 6.21).

6.5.9 Whispering Gallery   High frequencies of sound have a tendency to "creep" along large concave surfaces, such as hemispherical domes (St. Paul's Cathedral, London; Royal Theater, Copenhagen). A very soft sound like a whisper uttered close to such a dome will be surprisingly audible at the opposite side. A whispering gallery is amusing and often harmless, but it cannot be considered a desirable contribution to good acoustics.

6.6 Noise and Vibration Control

This subject is discussed in detail in Part III.

BIBLIOGRAPHY

Periodicals

Northwood, T. D.: "Acoustical Factors in Architectural Design," *J. RAIC*, November 1954, pp. 397–399.
"Design for Hearing," *Progressive Architecture*, May 1959, pp. 143–205.
Doelle, L. L.: "Acoustic Finishes in Auditoria," *The Canadian Architect*, March 1961, pp. 71–75.
Newman, R. B., and W. J. Cavanaugh: "Acoustics," in J. H. Callender (ed.), *Time-saver Standards*, 4th ed., McGraw-Hill Book Company, New York, 1966, pp. 636–641.
Doelle, L. L.: "Auditorium Acoustics," *Architecture Canada*, October 1967, pp. 35–44.
McGuinness, W. J.: "Adjusting Auditoriums Acoustically," *Progressive Architecture*, March 1968, p. 166.
Jordan, V. L.: "Room Acoustics and Architectural Acoustics Development in Recent Years," *Applied Acoustics*, January 1969, pp. 59–81.

Digests

Northwood, T. D.: *Acoustical Factors in Architectural Design*, National Research Council, Ottawa, Technical Paper 23, November 1954, 3 pp.
Northwood, T. D.: *Room Acoustics: Design for Listening*, National Research Council, Ottawa, Canadian Building Digest 92, August 1967, 4 pp.

CHAPTER SEVEN

Acoustical Design of Rooms for Speech

In the acoustical design of auditoriums used primarily for speech, intelligibility must be given top priority. If a space is used for theatrical performances, the audience rightfully expects to understand every single word uttered by the performers. Similarly, in lecture halls and classrooms, when, for example, new terminology is introduced or a foreign language is spoken, sometimes by lecturers not trained in diction, listening conditions should obviously be as good as acoustical skill can make them.

Speech sounds contain vowels and consonants, woven into an individual pattern of predominant tones, sometimes called *formants*. These formants, consisting mostly of vowels, endow a person's voice with distinctive characteristics, contributing to the basic tone of speech. Vowels emphasize the natural qualities of speech. Intelligibility, however, also depends on the proper recognition of consonant sounds, which are often short sounds of very high frequency in rapid succession and with a limited acoustical power compared to vowels. The preservation of both vowels and consonant sounds is therefore important in achieving favorable speech acoustics.

The physical and acoustical features of an auditorium, such as size and shape, reverberation characteristics, and prevailing noise conditions, have an influence on the way a speaker will talk and on the transmission and perception of the spoken word in the room.

In the absence of a sound-amplification system the larger an auditorium is, the more effort a speaker must exert in order to make himself understood in every part of the room, particularly at the remote seats.

Proper reverberation reinforces the loudness of speech, but excessive reverberation harms intelligibility by blurring and masking newly spoken syllables by the still audible reverberation of previously uttered syllables. Under such reverberant conditions a speaker, besides being annoyed, will also be inclined to speak more softly and slowly and articulate more than he otherwise would.

7.1 Speech Acoustics in Auditoriums

To provide the desirable degree of intelligibility and to enable an audience to appreciate subtleties or dramatic effects of the speaker—whether actor, preacher, or politician—the general requirements described in Chap. 6 must be met. In addition, particular attention should be paid to the following points.

1. The paths of direct sound waves should be as short as possible to reduce sound-energy losses in the air. This requires a compact room shape with a short distance between sound source and listeners and with a volume-per-seat value of about 80 to 150 cu ft (2.3 to 4.3 cu m), preferably nearer the lower figure. It follows from the RT formula that, other conditions being equal, the lower the volume-per-seat value, the less acoustical treatment will be required to provide the same RT.

2. Unamplified speech sound traveling directly from source to listener is hardly understandable beyond about 30 to 40 ft (9 to 12 m). It is therefore essential that short-delayed sound reflections from reflective surfaces arrive at the listener's position with a path difference of not

more than about 30 to 35 ft (9 to 10.5 m), corresponding to a time-delay gap of about 30 msec.

3. The seats should be laid out in such a pattern that they fall within an angle of about 140° from the position of the speaker (Fig. 7.1). This is necessary to preserve high-frequency speech sounds, which would lose power outside this angle because of their directional characteristics. In the interest of ample direct sound supply, such obstructing elements as columns or deep under-balcony spaces should be avoided.

4. The RT of the auditorium should be as close as possible to the ideal value throughout the entire audio-frequency range, as shown in Fig. 6.14. It must be noted, however, as suggested in this figure, that achievement of a short RT alone is no guarantee of good hearing conditions in rooms used for speech. The acoustical finishes applied in the room should have uniform absorption characteristics between 250 and 8000 Hz to prevent excessive absorption of vowel or consonant sounds within this frequency range.

5. The control of noise is fundamental in the acoustical design of rooms used for speech. At frequencies from 125 to 4000 Hz intelligibility is seriously affected by the signal-to-noise ratio (a term borrowed from electrical engineering), that is, the ratio of the level of the speech signal to that of the background, or ambient, noise. If the signal-to-noise ratio is sufficiently large, intelligibility improves. When the speech level is too low, it is partially submerged in the background noise and intelligibility suffers. It is difficult to establish a straightforward criterion for an ideal signal-to-noise ratio because noises of various characteristics mask speech sounds to a different extent, depending not only on the intensity level of the background noise but also on its information content. The interfering background noise may, for example, consist of speech (coming from an exterior source), which will make it very difficult to concentrate on the speech being given in the auditorium. In this case the interfering ambient noise will be extremely distracting, no matter how faint the intruding speech sounds are. Acceptable levels of background noises in various rooms are listed in Chap. 15.

Speech intelligibility in an auditorium can be determined quantitatively by articulation testing, which will be discussed in Chap. 19.

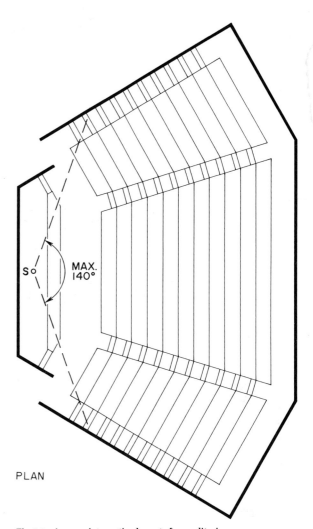

Fig. 7.1 Appropriate seating layout of an auditorium for speech with seats within an angle of about 140° from the position of the speaker S.

7.2 Theaters

Acoustical problems in the architectural design of legitimate theaters are constantly increasing because of fundamental changes taking place in theater design. Actors, soloists, musicians, choreographers, producers, stage designers, and theater technicians all expect revolutionary changes, or at least considerable innovation, from the architect in order to satisfy new concepts. Evaluating their individualistic and sometimes conflicting requirements during the design period places more responsibility on the architect.

In the layout of a theater auditorium the following design and functional considerations will affect acoustical conditions:
1. Shape of audience area and seating capacity
2. Size of acting area

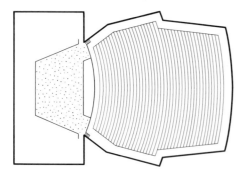

PROSCENIUM STAGE

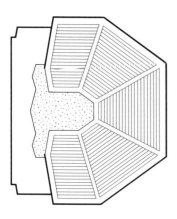

OPEN STAGE

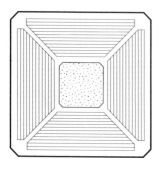

ARENA STAGE

[······] PERFORMING AREA   [||||||||||] AUDIENCE AREA

Fig. 7.2 Basic stage forms used in theater design.

3. Type and scale of production envisaged and priorities of use

4. Audience-performer relationship

The seating capacity of an auditorium is usually established by a compromise between economics, which presses for more seats, and audience-performer satisfaction, which places intimacy above large capacity. The larger the audience capacity, the greater the distance between acting area and remote seats and the more difficult it is for adequately loud unamplified speech to reach these seats.

A large cast obviously requires a wider acting and audience area, which in turn increases the difficulty of providing satisfactory direct and reflected sound energy from every part of the acting area to every member of the audience.

Once the theater is in operation, the client usually does not hesitate to put it to multiple use, that is, live stage performances, concerts, ballets, films, or social gatherings. Each activity has its own visual and acoustical limitations. For example, a live theater performance calls for a short RT and a relatively small audience. A symphony concert requires a much longer RT but can accommodate an audience of any size. Unfortunately these visual and acoustical ideals must be ignored once the auditorium is put to multiple use, thus narrowing the range of acoustical or visual experience.

The relationship of the performing area (sound source) to the audience area (receivers), a crucial factor in theater acoustics, is normally set according to one of the following four basic stage forms or a combination of them (Fig. 7.2):

1. Proscenium stage
2. Open stage
3. Arena stage
4. Adaptable stage

In a theater with a *proscenium stage* (also called a picture-frame stage or an enclosed stage) the performing area is at one end of the auditorium, with the audience observing through the frame of the proscenium opening. This stage form developed from the performing area of the ancient Greek and Roman open-air theater and was stimulated by the popularity of opera, with its continuously increasing demand for colorful stage settings. It separates performers from the audience and poses several acoustical problems.

1. Since the audience can face the performing area from one side only, it is difficult to seat a large audience close to the proscenium opening. Therefore the distance between actors and remote seats is often excessive; satisfactory loudness at remote seats will be hard to achieve without speech reinforcement.

2. Lighting fixtures, multiple access to the performing area, and the stage sets make it difficult or almost impossible to find room around the performing area for a reasonable number of large sound reflectors, which are essential for adequate loudness.

3. The flies, indispensable for accommodating the elaborate stage and lighting equipment essential for the big splashy settings of proscenium productions, dissipate too much of the sound energy created in the acting area.

4. In an attempt to seat a large audience not too far from the stage, one or several balconies may be planned, requiring a considerable

vertical space. For this reason the lowest level of audience floor (orchestra level, or pit) is usually inadequately sloped, or raked, resulting in impaired visual and acoustical conditions there. The resulting excessive height may contribute to an unfavorably long RT. Balconies that are too deep also create acoustical shadow.

In an *end stage*, an alternative to the proscenium stage, the acting area is as wide as the front portion of the audience area. Here the emphasized separation between audience and performers by the proscenium opening is less noticeable.

Figure 7.3 shows examples of theaters with proscenium stages, and Table 7.1 lists some theaters with proscenium or end stage. Figures 7.4 and 7.5 show the interiors of two theaters with proscenium stage.

TABLE 7.1   Theaters with Proscenium or End Stage
(Listed Chronologically)

Name	Location	Completion date	Seating capacity
Nationaltheater	Mannheim, Germany	1957	1,200
Community Theater	Midland, Tex.	1957	400
Belgrade Theater	Coventry, England	1958	910
Stadttheater	Lünen, Germany	1958	765
Mermaid Theater	London, England	1959	508
Royalty Theater	London, England	1960	997
Community Theater	Western Springs, Ill.	1961	417
Civic Theater	Johannesburg, South Africa	1962	1,120
Ashcroft Theater	Croydon, England	1962	750
Stadttheater	Krefeld, Germany	1963	832
Congress Theater	Eastbourne, England	1963	1,678
Pheonix Theater	Leicester, England	1963	275
Playhouse	Nottingham, England	1963	756
New York State Theater, Lincoln Center	New York, N.Y.	1964	2,729
Playhouse	Oxford, England	1964	700
Nuffield Theater	Southampton, England	1964	500
Theater Center	Canberra, Australia	1964	1,200
Yvonne Arnaud Theater	Guilford, England	1965	568
University Theater	Manchester, England	1965	300
Stadttheater	Wuppertal, Germany	1966	750
Abbey Theater	Dublin, Ireland	1966	628
Imperial Theater	Tokyo, Japan	1966	1,950
Théâtre, Maison de la Culture	Amiens, France	1966	1,070
Stadttheater	Schweinfurt, Germany	1966	750
Théâtre Port-Royal	Montreal, Quebec	1967	800
Mechanic Theater	Baltimore, Md.	1967	1,800
Confederation Theater	Charlottetown, Prince Edward Island	1967	970
City Theater	Helsinki, Finland	1967	920
Théâtre, Maison de la Culture	Grenoble, France	1967	1,200
Northcott Theater	Exeter, England	1968	433
University College Theater	London, England	1968	599
Forum Theater	Billingham, England	1968	643
Abbey Theater	St. Albans, England	1968	240
Playhouse, Krannert Center	Urbana-Champaign, Ill.	1968	678
Gateway Theater	Chester, England	1968	500
Playhouse	Weston super Mare, England	1969	368
Theater, Eton College	Eton, England	1969	410
Juilliard Theater, Lincoln Center	New York, N.Y.	1969	1,026
Camberwell Civic Center	Victoria, Australia	1970	500
SGIO Theater	Brisbane, Australia	1970	619
Shaw Theater	Camden, England	1970	458
Theater, John F. Kennedy Center	Washington, D.C.	1971	1,100
Drama Center, Opera House	Sydney, Australia	1971	750

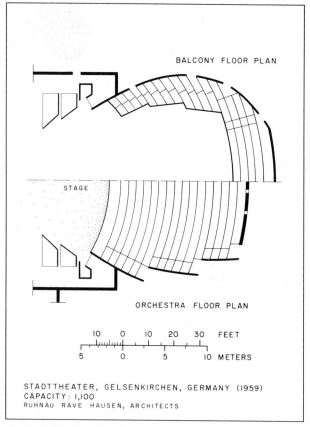

BALCONY FLOOR PLAN

STAGE

ORCHESTRA FLOOR PLAN

10   0   10   20   30   FEET
5   0   5   10   METERS

STADTTHEATER, GELSENKIRCHEN, GERMANY (1959)
CAPACITY: 1,100
RUHNAU RAVE HAUSEN, ARCHITECTS

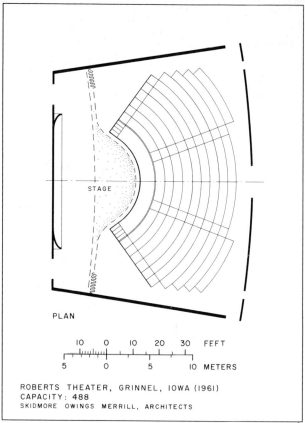

STAGE

PLAN

10   0   10   20   30   FEET
5   0   5   10   METERS

ROBERTS THEATER, GRINNEL, IOWA (1961)
CAPACITY: 488
SKIDMORE OWINGS MERRILL, ARCHITECTS

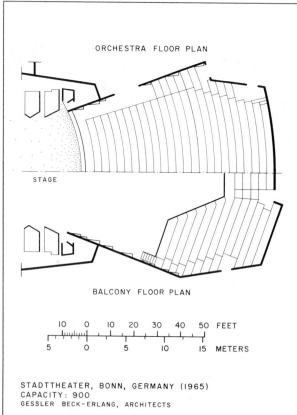

ORCHESTRA FLOOR PLAN

STAGE

BALCONY FLOOR PLAN

10   0   10   20   30   40   50   FEET
5   0   5   10   15   METERS

STADTTHEATER, BONN, GERMANY (1965)
CAPACITY: 900
GESSLER BECK-ERLANG, ARCHITECTS

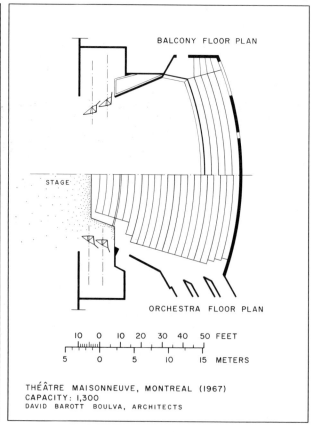

BALCONY FLOOR PLAN

STAGE

ORCHESTRA FLOOR PLAN

10   0   10   20   30   40   50   FEET
5   0   5   10   15   METERS

THÉÂTRE MAISONNEUVE, MONTREAL (1967)
CAPACITY: 1,300
DAVID BAROTT BOULVA, ARCHITECTS

Fig. 7.3 Four examples of theaters with proscenium stages.

Fig. 7.4 (opposite, above)   Interior of the 1,300-seat Théâtre Maisonneuve, Montreal (1967). (David, Barott, and Boulva, architects; Bolt, Beranek, and Newman, acoustical consultants. Photograph by G. Lalumière.)

Fig. 7.5 (opposite, below)   Auditorium of the 1,026-seat Juilliard Theater; Lincoln Center, New York City (1969). (Belluschi, Catalano, and Westermann, architects; H. Keilholz, acoustical consultant. Photograph by E. Stoller Associates.)

In theaters with an *open stage* (also called a thrust stage or an Elizabethan stage), the main performing area projects into the audience and is surrounded by it on several sides. While performers and audience are contained within the same space, some acting can also take place behind openings of the back wall of the stage. Developed from the Elizabethan stages, this stage form creates an intimate and sometimes embarrassingly close relationship between performers and audience and poses a few serious acoustical problems.

The first problem is inherent in the layout of open stages: the audience to some extent encircles the performing area, and consequently the actors, at least for parts of the play, have their backs to one section of the audience or another. As explained in Fig. 3.8, the directional characteristics of speech sound impair intelligibility along sections of the audience momentarily "neglected" by an actor. In addition to the unfavorable visual and acoustical effects of this condition, it also makes an increasing demand on the performers' acting technique and calls for considerable experience and professional skill, from performer and producer alike. Another difficulty arises because the need for an elaborate system of stage lighting fixtures, accesses, vomitories, etc., above and around the central stage makes it practically impossible to accommodate sound-reflective enclosures around the stage.

On the other hand, the close relationship between performers and audience alleviates some of the acoustical problems normal for theaters with a proscenium stage. The increased intimacy of open stages permits accommodation of a large number of spectators close to the stage: an audience of 1,000 to 2,000 can be seated around an open stage, none more than 55 to 60 ft (17 to 19 m) from the stage, and probably no seat further than 15 to 18 rows from the front. In a proscenium theater of the same capacity the distance between the stage and the remotest seat would be 100 to 120 ft (30 to 37 m).

In several proscenium theaters the area occupied by the front rows of the audience can be transformed into an apron stage, making it possible to use these theaters also for open-stage productions (Fig. 7.6). Figures 7.7 and 7.8 illustrate and Table 7.2 lists some examples of theaters with open stages.

The *arena stage* (also called a central stage or theater-in-the-round) developed from the radial layout of classical amphitheaters and certainly goes back to a circle of primitive people gathered around their dancers. Like the open stage, this form eliminates separation between performers and audience. The popularity of arena stages is to some extent attributable to the low cost of production: very simple scenery is needed, and any hall can accommodate this type of stage with relative ease. Since the layout of an arena stage is a further continuation of the open-stage concept, acoustical problems associated with open stages, as described above, apply also to arena stages.

Figure 7.9 shows an example and Table 7.3 enumerates some theaters with arena stages.

In the three types of performer-audience relationship described so far, acting area and audience area are more or less fixed. This means that in the sound-source–transmission-path–receiver sequence (Chap. 1)

Fig. 7.6 Interior of the 1,140-seat auditorium of the Vivian Beaumont Theater, with the stage in its thrust position, Lincoln Center, New York City (1965). (E. Saarinen and Associates, architects; J. Mielziner, collaborating designer. Photograph by E. Stoller Associates.)

the positions of these three elements are nearly constant. In contemporary theater practice, with continuously changing aesthetic needs, these three types of performer-audience relationship are often considered too traditional and restrictive. It is becoming increasingly necessary to make fundamental transformations in the relationship between actors and spectators, not only for a particular play but several times during a performance. This transformation in *adaptable theaters* (or *multiform theaters*) can be accomplished by manual or electromechanical means so that the position, shape, and size of the acting area and its relationship to the audience area can be changed, almost without limit.

TABLE 7.2 Theaters with Open Stages (Listed Chronologically)

Name	Location	Completion date	Seating capacity
Tyrone Guthrie Theater	Minneapolis, Minn.	1963	1,437
Theater	Atlanta, Ga.	1966	768
Alley Theater	Houston, Tex.	1967	800
Wehr Theater	Milwaukee, Wis.	1969	526
Gulbenkian Theater, University of Kent	Canterbury, England	1969	342
National Theater	London, England	1972	1,165

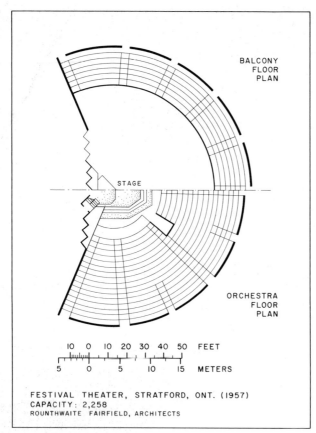

BALCONY
FLOOR
PLAN

STAGE

ORCHESTRA
FLOOR
PLAN

10 0 10 20 30 40 50 FEET
5   0   5   10   15 METERS

FESTIVAL THEATER, STRATFORD, ONT. (1957)
CAPACITY: 2,258
ROUNTHWAITE FAIRFIELD, ARCHITECTS

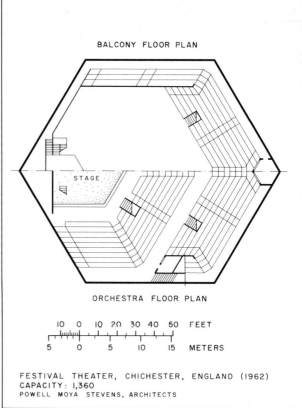

BALCONY FLOOR PLAN

STAGE

ORCHESTRA FLOOR PLAN

10 0 10 20 30 40 50 FEET
5   0   5   10   15 METERS

FESTIVAL THEATER, CHICHESTER, ENGLAND (1962)
CAPACITY: 1,360
POWELL MOYA STEVENS, ARCHITECTS

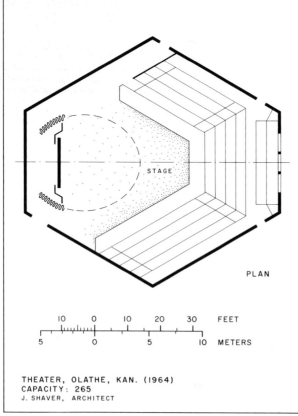

STAGE

PLAN

10   0   10   20   30 FEET
5   0   5   10 METERS

THEATER, OLATHE, KAN. (1964)
CAPACITY: 265
J. SHAVER, ARCHITECT

BALCONY
FLOOR
PLAN

STAGE

ORCHESTRA
FLOOR
PLAN

10 0 10 20 30 40 50 FEET
5   0   5   10   15 METERS

THEATER, NATIONAL ARTS CENTER, OTTAWA (1969)
CAPACITY: 800
AFFLECK DESBARATS DIMAKOPOULOS LEBENSOLD SISE, ARCH.

Fig. 7.7 Theaters with open stages.

Fig. 7.8 Interior of the 800-seat theater with open stage, National Arts Center, Ottawa. (Affleck, Desbarats, Dimakopoulos, Lebensold, and Sise, architects; N. Pappas and Associates, acoustical consultants. Photograph by J. Evans.)

PLAN

TABLE 7.3 Theaters with Arena Stages (Listed Chronologically)

Name	Location	Completion date	Seating capacity
Ring Theater	Coral Gables, Fla.	1950	400
Teatro Sant'Erasmo	Milan, Italy	1953	232
Théâtre en Rond	Paris, France	1954	305
Arena Stage	Washington, D.C.	1961	752
Victoria Theater	Stoke on Trent, England	1962	343
Melodyland Theater	Anaheim, Calif.	1963	3,000
Octagon Theater	Bolton, England	1967	422
Arena Theater	Houston, Tex.	1967	300
Tupton Hall Theater	Derbyshire, England	1969	230

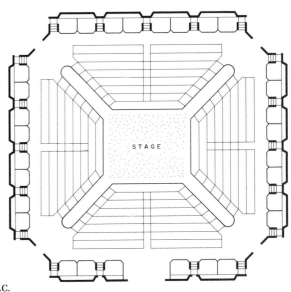

Fig. 7.9 Arena stage in Washington, D.C. (1961, capacity; 752). (H. Weese and Associates, architect.)

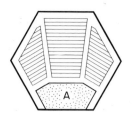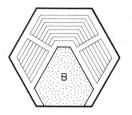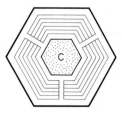

Fig. 7.10 Adaptable stage in a theater auditorium used as (A) end stage; (B) open stage; and (C) arena stage.

Obviously an acoustical transformation (in the sound-source–transmission-path–receiver sequence) is necessary as often as a positional transformation takes place in the relationship between performing area and audience area. This can be achieved to some extent by means of variable absorbers (Chap. 5), that is, by transforming sound-reflective surfaces into sound-absorbing ones, and vice versa, as the need may be. However, it must be stressed that this type of acoustical transformation requires acoustically and professionally qualified personnel, seldom available (for financial reasons) in the routine operation of adaptable, rather experimental theaters. It is therefore recommended that adaptable theaters be restricted to spaces below a seating capacity of 500.

Figure 7.10 illustrates a theater with an adaptable stage, and Table 7.4 lists some examples.

In the acoustical design of theaters, in addition to the requirements outlined in Chap. 6 and in preceding parts of this chapter, attention should be given to the control of exterior and interior sounds (footstep noises and mechanical noises). This measure will increase the signal-to-noise ratio; that is, it will reduce the masking effect of interfering noises on faint speech sounds.

If the same theater will be used for productions requiring different RTs, using variable absorbers around the audience area is recommended.

TABLE 7.4 Theaters with Adaptable Stages (Listed Chronologically)

Name	Location	Completion date	Seating capacity
Loeb Drama Center	Cambridge, Mass.	1960	588
Questors Theater	Ealing, London, England	1964	478
Crescent Theater	Birmingham, England	1964	288
Loretto Hilton Center	Webster Grove, Mo.	1965	1,200
Experimental Theater	Austin, Tex.	1965	350
Theater, Knox College	Galesburg, Ill.	1965	350
Northcott Theater	Exeter, England	1967	583
Experimental Theater	Grenoble, France	1967	538
Studio Theater, Maison de la Culture	Rennes, France	1968	500
Studio Theater, National Arts Center	Ottawa, Ontario	1969	300
Theater	Birmingham, Ala.	1969	370
Gulbenkian Theater, University of Hull	Hull, England	1969	200
Cockpit Theater	Marylebone, London, England	1970	177
Studio Playhouse, John F. Kennedy Center	Washington, D.C.	1971	510
Winter Garden Theater	London, England	1971	911

In the interest of providing sufficient direct sound to every member of the audience, the acting area of proscenium stages is normally raised to about 3 ft 6 in. (106 cm) above the floor level of the first row of spectators. Open and arena stages are elevated less than this; sometimes the height coincides with the floor level of the first row. In this case the audience floor must be steeply raked, for both visual and acoustical reasons.

A carefully laid-out, unobtrusive high-quality sound-amplification system is almost indispensable in any theater with an open or arena stage in order to alleviate the acoustical problems created by the directional characteristics of speech. Such a system includes a ring of microphones around the perimeter of the stage, suspended overhead or hidden along the stage floor. If the actor faces a particular section of the audience, his voice will be picked up by the microphones located right in front of him and fed into loudspeakers radiating the electronically amplified sound in the opposite (neglected) direction. A sound-amplification system will be needed in any theater if the audience capacity exceeds about 800 to 1,000.

Figures 7.11 and 7.12 illustrate details of the 770-seat proscenium theater, Bishop's University, Lennoxville, Quebec.

7.3 Lecture Halls and Classrooms

Lecture halls of educational institutions, sometimes termed *amphitheaters* and normally seating more than about 100 persons, should be designed in accordance with the relevant acoustical principles discussed above in order to secure the most favorable conditions for speech intelligibility. The requirements for an optimum room shape and size, for an adequate and correctly directed supply of short-delayed sound reflections, for the provision of a short RT, for full elimination of possible acoustical defects, and for efficient noise control should be carefully observed. The optical and acoustical requirements in lecture halls are in complete agreement: suitable room proportion and shape will contribute to good viewing and good hearing. In the RT calculation of lecture halls it is reasonable to assume about one-half to two-thirds of the audience capacity, because of a relatively wide fluctuation in attendance.

In the interest of excluding exterior noise, lecture halls today are seldom designed with natural light and ventilation. This necessitates a complex ceiling, incorporating mechanical and lighting components into the sound-reflective ceiling.

Figures 7.13 and 7.14 show details of a 130-seat lecture hall at Université Laval, Quebec, and Fig. 7.15 shows a close-up of a sound-reflective ceiling panel in the same lecture hall, providing additional short-delayed sound reflections for listeners farthest away from the podium.

The exact purpose of a lecture hall should be ascertained well in advance because rooms to be used for demonstrations or for audio-visual education require particular care in their acoustical design and detailing.

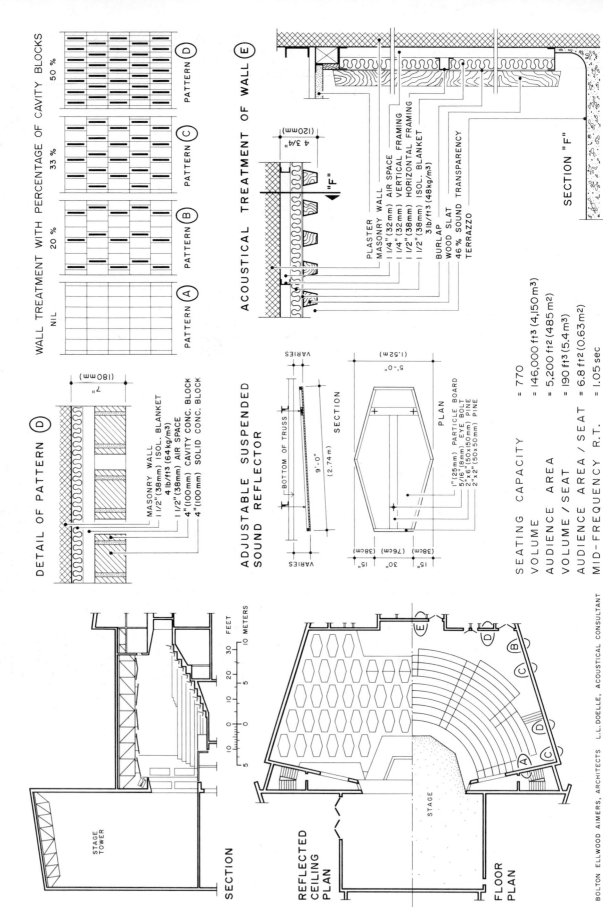

WALL TREATMENT WITH PERCENTAGE OF CAVITY BLOCKS

PATTERN Ⓐ — NIL
PATTERN Ⓑ — 20 %
PATTERN Ⓒ — 33 %
PATTERN Ⓓ — 50 %

DETAIL OF PATTERN Ⓓ

7" (180 mm)

MASONRY WALL
1 1/2" (38 mm) ISOL. BLANKET 4 lb/ft3 (64 kg/m3)
1 1/2" (38 mm) AIR SPACE
4" (100 mm) CAVITY CONC. BLOCK
4" (100 mm) SOLID CONC. BLOCK

ACOUSTICAL TREATMENT OF WALL Ⓔ

4 3/4" (120 mm)

"F"

PLASTER
MASONRY WALL
1 1/4" (32 mm) AIR SPACE
1 1/4" (32 mm) VERTICAL FRAMING
1 1/2" (38 mm) HORIZONTAL FRAMING
1 1/2" (38 mm) ISOL. BLANKET 3 lb/ft3 (48 kg/m3)
BURLAP
WOOD SLAT
46 % SOUND TRANSPARENCY
TERRAZZO

SECTION "F"

ADJUSTABLE SUSPENDED SOUND REFLECTOR

BOTTOM OF TRUSS
VARIES
VARIES
9'-0" (2.74 m)

SECTION

5'-0" (1.52 m)

PLAN

15" 30" 15"
(38cm) (76cm) (38cm)

1" (25 mm) PARTICLE BOARD
5/16" (8 mm) EYE BOLT
2" x 6" (50 x 150 mm) PINE
2" x 2" (50 x 50 mm) PINE

SEATING CAPACITY = 770
VOLUME = 146,000 ft3 (4,150 m3)
AUDIENCE AREA = 5,200 ft2 (485 m2)
VOLUME / SEAT = 190 ft3 (5.4 m3)
AUDIENCE AREA / SEAT = 6.8 ft2 (0.63 m2)
MID-FREQUENCY R.T. = 1.05 sec

SECTION

STAGE TOWER

FEET / METERS

REFLECTED CEILING PLAN

FLOOR PLAN

STAGE

BOLTON ELLWOOD AIMERS, ARCHITECTS   L.L.DOELLE, ACOUSTICAL CONSULTANT

Fig. 7.11   Theater, Bishop's University, Lennoxville, Quebec (1968).

Fig. 7.12 Interior of the 770-seat theater, Bishop's University, Lennoxville, Quebec. (Bolton, Ellwood, and Aimers, architects; L. L. Doelle, acoustical consultant. Photograph by Bowe Studio.)

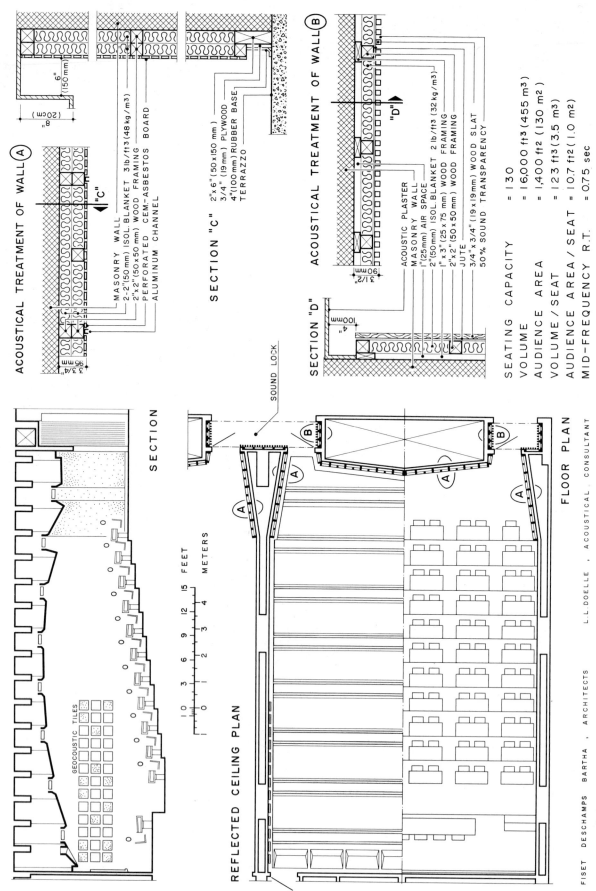

ACOUSTICAL TREATMENT OF WALL (A)

MASONRY WALL
2-2"(50 mm) ISOL. BLANKET 3 lb/ft3 (48 kg/m3)
2"x 2"(50 x 50 mm) WOOD FRAMING
PERFORATED CEM.-ASBESTOS BOARD
ALUMINUM CHANNEL

SECTION "C"
2"x 6" (50 x 150 mm)
3/4" (19 mm) PLYWOOD
4"(100 mm) RUBBER BASE
TERRAZZO

ACOUSTICAL TREATMENT OF WALL (B)

ACOUSTIC PLASTER
MASONRY WALL
1"(25 mm) AIR SPACE
2"(50 mm) ISOL. BLANKET 2 lb/ft3 (32 kg/m3)
1"x 3" (25 x 75 mm) WOOD FRAMING
2"x 2" (50 x 50 mm) WOOD FRAMING
JUTE
3/4"x 3/4" (19 x 19mm) WOOD SLAT
50 % SOUND TRANSPARENCY

SECTION "D"

SEATING CAPACITY   = 130
VOLUME   = 16,000 ft3 (455 m3)
AUDIENCE AREA   = 1,400 ft2 (130 m2)
VOLUME / SEAT   = 123 ft3 (3.5 m3)
AUDIENCE AREA / SEAT   = 10.7 ft2 (1.0 m2)
MID-FREQUENCY R.T.   = 0.75 sec

SECTION

FEET
METERS

GEOCOUSTIC TILES

REFLECTED CEILING PLAN

SOUND LOCK

FLOOR PLAN

FISET DESCHAMPS BARTHA , ARCHITECTS   L.L. DOELLE , ACOUSTICAL CONSULTANT

Fig. 7.13 Lecture hall, Université Laval, Quebec (1964).

Fig. 7.14 Interior of a 130-seat lecture hall, Université Laval, Quebec. (Fiset, Deschamps, and Bartha, architects; L. L. Doelle, acoustical consultant. Photograph by Legare & Kedl.)

Fig. 7.15 Close-up of a sound-reflective ceiling panel in the lecture hall in Fig. 7.13. (Photograph by Legare & Kedl.)

Fig. 7.16 Structural, mechanical, electrical, audio-visual, and acoustical requirements incorporated in the front portion of a 350-seat lecture hall, Université de Montréal. (Beauvais and Lusignan, architects; L. L. Doelle, acoustical consultant. Photograph by Bowe Studio.)

The shape and volume of audio-visual lecture rooms, factors considerably affecting hearing conditions, are influenced by the viewing geometry of the room, that is, the horizontal and vertical envelopes of good sight lines. The viewing geometry, in turn, depends upon the equipment to be used (front vs. rear-screen film projector, overhead projector, television projector, sound-recording and reproducing units, television camera pick-up, etc.). The additional integration of such typical elements as desk, demonstration table, chalkboard, projection screens, microphone, loudspeakers, and remote-control unit at the front portion of the lecture room into the system of sound-reflective room enclosures will certainly require the utmost attention from the outset (Fig. 7.16).

Lecture halls with volumes of up to about 15,000 to 20,000 cu ft (425 to 570 cu m) or for an audience of up to about 150 to 200 will not require a sound-amplification system if their acoustical design is based on the principles and recommendations discussed so far. In any case, use of a sound-amplification system in a lecture hall should be avoided as long as the size of the hall enables the lecturer to project sufficient unamplified sound from the front to every member of his audience. Using loudspeakers in a lecture hall psychologically separates lecturer and audience because questions and comments raised from the floor (unequipped with microphones) will not be properly understood by the lecturer.

For rectangular lecture rooms with a modest capacity, a diagonal seating layout is particularly recommended. It automatically eliminates undesirable parallelism between walls at the podium and utilizes the splayed front walls as sound reflectors (Fig. 7.17).

Classrooms with rectangular shapes, level floors, and floor areas normally between about 600 and 1,000 sq ft (56 to 93 sq m) seldom create any serious acoustical problems. The rear wall opposite the lecturer, even if acoustically untreated, causes no audible acoustical defect (such as echo or long-delayed reflection) because the length of the classroom is small and the usual bulletin boards, wall tables, and built-in book shelves and cupboards dissipate and diffuse a considerable fraction of the incident sound.

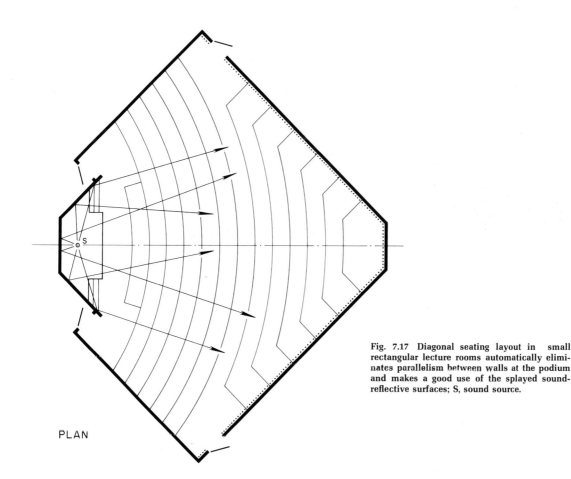

PLAN

Fig. 7.17 Diagonal seating layout in small rectangular lecture rooms automatically eliminates parallelism between walls at the podium and makes a good use of the splayed sound-reflective surfaces; S, sound source.

The RT of fully occupied classrooms should be approximately 0.6 to 0.8 sec at the mid-frequency, depending on the volume. In most cases this requirement is fulfilled if the rooms are occupied, well furnished with built-in shelves, bulletin boards, cupboards, etc., and if lightweight, prefabricated building panels (plaster board, dry-wall construction, suspended ceiling), large glazed areas, luminous fixtures, etc., are installed in the classroom. If additional absorbent treatment seems necessary, it should be installed along the perimeter of the ceiling or in the upper parts of the side and rear walls. No matter how many additional absorbent finishes are required in a classroom, the middle of the ceiling should always be kept reflective to provide uniform sound-energy distribution, originating from any part of the room.

Acoustical aspects of the design of team-teaching classrooms and divisible auditoriums are discussed in Chap. 17.

7.4 Assembly Halls and Congress Halls

In the use of assembly halls in educational buildings (school auditoriums) or in other large establishments (office or factory) and in congress halls, priority is usually given to specific sound programs, such as lectures, panel discussions, symposia, amateur theatricals, debates, vocational or political meetings, and congresses. All these functions require primarily the intelligibility of the spoken word. In the acoustical design of these auditoriums the use of upholstered seats and carpeted aisles and a reasonable compromise in RT (close to speech requirements) is recommended. Usually accommodating a large audience, they should always be equipped with a high-quality speech-reinforcement system, providing uniform coverage along the entire seating area.

7.5 Conference Rooms, Courtrooms, and Chambers for Local and National Government

From an acoustical point of view, auditoriums in which administrative, debating, judicial, and legislative activities take place, have the following requirements in common: high intelligibility of speech must receive top priority, and excellent hearing conditions are required since speech originates from different positions in the room.

The requirement for a low volume-per-seat value, recommended at 80 to 150 cu ft (2.3 to 4.3 cu m) in Sec. 6.2, unfortunately conflicts with the aim of achieving a dignified and impressive interior in many of these rooms. Even in conference rooms and courtrooms, with their relatively lower ceiling heights, the achievement of a low volume-per-seat value is practically impossible. In parliament chambers this figure often reaches a value of 350 to 500 cu ft (10 to 14 cu m) at capacity attendance; it may rise to as high as 1,000 cu ft (28 cu m) for low attendance, not infrequent in the history of legislative assemblies. Under such conditions rather poor speech intelligibility can be expected.

Seating arrangements obviously vary in these halls according to architectural layout, capacity, and purpose of the room; however, members of the participating audience should face each other, within the limits of possibility. Since semicircular and horseshoe-shaped floor areas meet this requirement best, attention should be given to the elimination of back reflections and sound concentrations from curved boundary surfaces.

The following requirements should be strictly observed, in addition to those already dealt with, in the acoustical design of conference rooms, courtrooms, and chambers for local or national government:

1. Greatest economy in floor area and volume
2. Minimum ceiling height
3. Reflective and dispersive ceiling treatment
4. Steeply sloped or stepped seating and raised dais
5. Short RT as required in auditoriums for speech, particularly if sound recording will take place in the room, for example, in courtrooms
6. Soft floor finish, particularly along the aisles
7. Fixed and highly absorbent (upholstered) seating
8. Selection of a high-quality speech-reinforcement system if one is required by the room volume
9. Total exclusion of exterior noise, in view of the fact that these auditoriums are usually located in the noisiest districts of the city
10. Achievement of low background-noise level (Chap. 15), particularly if no sound-amplification system will be used

When these auditoriums are provided with space for public attendance, it should take the form of a secluded seating area (gallery), suitably separated from the main floor area. This public area should be treated acoustically as "dead" as possible with highly absorbing acoustical finishes all around, carpeted floors, and upholstered seats.

7.6 Arenas and Coliseums

The acoustical design of arenas and coliseums is included here because although a multitude of activities normally takes place in these spaces, the achievement of intelligibility for the spoken word transmitted through a public-address system is of great importance.

The activities taking place in these auditoriums are often serious noise producers, which will disturb not only the participants and spectators within the halls but constitute objectionable sources of interference to nearby rooms as well. The acoustical finishes used in these auditoriums should therefore serve two purposes: they should contribute to a short RT, and at the same time they should reduce the prevailing noise level within the hall. The acoustical finishes installed will contribute to noise reduction within the space only and will not prevent the penetration of noise into adjacent areas. The problem of noise insulation must be resolved independently. This can be achieved by surrounding the noisy hall with barriers that provide adequate insulation against noise and vibration generated in the hall or by locating the noisy auditorium as far as possible from rooms requiring a quiet environment. Methods of noise control by means of sensible architectural planning will be discussed in Chap. 13.

Because of functional requirements, opposite boundary surfaces of these auditoriums are usually parallel, often giving rise to harmful acoustical phenomena, such as excessive reverberation and flutter echoes. Since a marked deviation from the rectangular room shape is seldom justified in these auditoriums, the proper distribution of sound-absorbing materials and abundant application of surface irregularities (exposed structural elements, recesses, splays, serrations, etc.) is imperative.

Huge arenas (coliseums) are frequently constructed to be used for a wide range of programs and to accommodate a vast audience. In such cases various (often conflicting) acoustical requirements have to be blended into a single concept, resulting at best in a reasonable compromise only. These huge auditoriums are far too large to provide satisfactory hearing conditions for unamplified sound. The installation of a sound-amplification system, which will produce uniform sound coverage and undistorted sound in every part of the seating area, is therefore indispensable.

BIBLIOGRAPHY

Books

Parkin, P. H., and H. R. Humphreys: *Acoustics, Noise and Buildings*, Frederick A. Praeger, Inc., New York, 1958, chap. 3.

Burris-Meyer, H., and E. C. Cole: *Theaters and Auditoriums*, 2d ed., Reinhold Publishing Corporation, New York, 1964, 376 pp.

Duncan, C. J. (ed.): *Modern Lecture Theaters*, Oriel Press, Ltd., Newcastle upon Tyne, 1966, 340 pp.

Nicoll, A.: *The Development of the Theater*, 5th ed., George G. Harrap & Co., Ltd., London, 1966, 292 pp.

Theater Planning, parts 1 and 2, reprinted from *The Architects' Journal*, distributed by the Association of British Theater Technicians, London, 1967.

Joseph, S.: *New Theater Forms*, Sir Isaac Pitman & Sons, Ltd., London, 1968, 144 pp.

Bentham, F.: *New Theaters in Britain*, Whitefriars Press, Ltd., London, 1970, 142 pp.

Periodicals

Newman, R. B.: "Making the Theater Work," *Architectural Forum*, June 1960, pp. 102–103.

"Theaters," *Progressive Architecture*, February 1962, pp. 96–132.

Wilke, H.: "Audio-Visual Systems for Large Group Instruction," *Architectural Record*, October 1962, pp. 172–175.

Cavanaugh, W. J.: "School Auditorium," *Sound*, January-February 1963, pp. 19–27.

Leacroft, R.: "Actor and Audience," *J. RIBA*, April 1963, pp. 145–155; May 1963, pp. 195–204.

Glasstone, V.: "Auditoria Galore," *Architectural Design*, November 1963, pp. 547–556.

"The Changing Practice: Theaters," *Progressive Architecture*, October 1965, pp. 160–221.

"Teaching Machine for Drama," *The Architectural Forum*, April 1969, pp. 78–84.

Ham, R.: "Theater Design in Britain," *Architectural Design*, July 1970, pp. 352–357.

"Theater Inflation," *Progressive Architecture*, December 1970, pp. 48–78, 114.

CHAPTER EIGHT

W hile the acoustical efficiency of rooms for speech can be judged quite accurately by means of speech-intelligibility tests (Chap. 19), evaluating the room-acoustical qualities of auditoriums used for musical performances is more difficult. A speech-intelligibility test is an objective rating method, but the acoustical qualities of halls for music are often assessed on the basis of subjective comments by musicians, conductors, music lovers, and music teachers, whose assessments, if influenced by their emotions, are sometimes debatable.

8.1 Room-acoustical Attributes Affecting the Quality of Music

The shape and volume of an auditorium, its audience capacity and attendance, and surface acoustical treatments all contribute to certain room-acoustical characteristics which noticeably affect the sound quality of music performed in the hall.

If the music gives the impression of being performed in a small, intimate hall, the auditorium is said to have *acoustical intimacy*. Usually it is neither possible nor necessary for the auditorium to be limited in size to achieve this intimacy. If the initial time-delay gap, that is, the time interval between direct sound received by a listener and the first reflection from any boundary surface of the room (Chap. 6) is shorter than 20 msec (20/1,000 sec), corresponding to a path difference of 23 ft (7.0 m), and the direct sound is not too faint, the room will be found to be acoustically intimate. Acoustical intimacy is one of the most desirable features of an auditorium used primarily for music.

If an auditorium has a large volume relative to its audience capacity, with predominantly sound-reflective enclosures, it is said to be *live*. A live hall has a relatively long RT, particularly at the middle and high frequencies, resulting in a full, sustained tone at these frequencies. A hall with a relatively small volume compared to its audience capacity, with enclosures which are highly sound-absorptive, is said to be *dead* or *dry*. A dry hall has a short RT, and music played in it will sound uninteresting and dull. On the other hand, when the room has a relatively long RT at the lower frequencies (below about 250 Hz), it has the fine acoustical quality of *warmth*, resulting in a rich bass. If the RT is adequately controlled over the entire audio-frequency range, a pleasant *fullness of tone* will be noticeable. Excessive fullness of tone makes the sound blurred and unenjoyable.

In a hall which is not too large, which is properly ramped or stepped, which provides the audience with a satisfactory amount of direct and reflected sound, and in which the RT is properly controlled, the beneficial phenomenon of *loudness* will prevail.

If the sounds of the different musical instruments played simultaneously in an orchestra are easily distinguishable, and if every sound within a rapid passage is heard separately, the room is said to possess *definition* or *clarity*. Good definition will prevail if a considerable amount of short-delayed reflections have been provided for, if the room has a relatively small volume with a short RT, and if the listeners are close enough to the sound source. Definition and fullness of tone are

Acoustical Design of Rooms for Music

normally inversely related; that is, a room with a high degree of definition usually has a short RT and vice versa.

If reflected sound waves approach the listener from every direction in approximately equal amounts, the result is *diffusion*. A relatively long RT and ample wall and surface irregularities promote diffusion, a highly desirable room-acoustical characteristic in auditoriums for music.

Another important room-acoustical feature of a hall used for music is *balance*. It can be achieved by numerous sound-reflective and sound-diffusive surfaces around the sound source to strengthen and improve the balance between the various sections of the orchestra, as well as between the orchestra and soloists. The control of balance, of course, is also a responsibility of the conductor.

If musical sounds are well mixed before they reach the listener, so that they are perceived as harmonious, the sending end of the auditorium is said to have good *blend*. The reflective and diffusive orchestra enclosures control blend. If an orchestra platform or orchestra pit is too wide, it will lack a good blend.

If the musicians and soloists have the ability to perform in unison so that the entire orchestra sounds like a well-rehearsed and coordinated unit, the music hall is said to possess *ensemble*. Undoubtedly, ensemble is controlled primarily by the conductor; however, it is also enhanced by a well-proportioned and suitably raked stage floor and by stage enclosures that project the sounds from one side of the platform to the other.

Freedom from noise, that is, the reduction of exterior and interior noises to inaudibility or at least to an acceptable minimum, is one of the most important requisites in auditoriums for music. Another essential room-acoustical quality is the complete *freedom from acoustical defects*, such as echo, sound concentration, distortion, and sound shadow.

8.2 Effects of Room Acoustics on Music

Room-acoustical attributes exercise a marked influence on the various stages of the musical process, that is, on composition, on performance (production), and on listening.

As already outlined in Chap. 2, the music of early composers was largely influenced by the acoustical setting of the room in which their work was composed or performed. Composers of church music, throughout the centuries, have exploited the beneficial effect of fullness of tone upon their music, a room-acoustical feature characteristic of churches. Baroque and classical music were scaled to relatively small, rectangular halls, ballrooms, or theaters. They had reflective enclosures producing a high degree of acoustical intimacy with short RT and excellent definition, ideal for baroque and classical music. Composers of European operas envisaged the Italian type of opera house, which required a high degree of definition and a relatively short RT. The symphonies of the romantic period and the operas of Wagner were all composed for auditoriums that possessed remarkable intimacy and fullness of tone. Since the beginning of the present century, however, music is no longer composed in terms of the acoustical qualities of existing halls. In fact, auditoriums of our times have to satisfy an ever-increasing number of musical-acoustical requirements in order to provide an optimum acoustical environment for the performance of music.

Since the appreciation of music can never be dissociated from the acoustical environment of the room in which it is performed, musicians or soloists normally adjust their performance to the acoustical qualities of the auditorium in which they are playing. They are fully aware that their success does not depend solely on them but to a great extent on the acoustical features of the room. Before selecting a tempo they must check the prevailing room-acoustical features such as intimacy, fullness of tone, definition, diffusion, balance, and blend. Rehearsals also serve the purpose of familiarizing performers with the important musical-acoustical qualities of the hall. When fully respected, these room-acoustical characteristics enhance the performance, but they can result in poor performance when disregarded. Conductors always adjust to the acoustical characteristics of the hall in question.

Both the audience and the music critic are greatly influenced by the acoustical qualities of the auditorium in their evaluation of a musical performance, in their approval or disapproval of the music, and in deciding whether the hall is suitable for the performance of music.

Naturally the selection of a concert program and the size of an orchestra depend in part on basic room-acoustical attributes of the concert hall. No conductor would think of presenting Bach's Brandenburg Concertos in a highly reverberant auditorium or performing Brahms in a dead hall.

Extensive research continues, to ascertain and evaluate the audience's preferences and the optimum acoustical environment for music of different periods and styles. These investigations make it clear that music requires a definitely longer RT than speech, mainly because musical sounds last longer than the syllables of speech, and a reasonable degree of blurring and overlapping in musical sounds is often considered acceptable and sometimes even desirable. At mid-frequency, for various styles of music, it has been found that an RT somewhat above 1.0 sec is ideal for baroque music, 1.5 sec is recommended for classical and modern music, and somewhat above 2.0 sec is preferable for romantic music. The most favorable compromise for fully occupied music halls to be used primarily but not exclusively for the performance of music is about 1.7 sec at the mid-frequency range. For opera houses in which the intelligibility of the libretto is of advantage (when sung in the language of the audience), an RT of 1.2 to 1.4 sec is recommended.

8.3 Acoustical Considerations in the Architectural Design of Musical Auditoriums

The growing range of aesthetic, structural, mechanical, electrical, functional, musical-acoustical, and financial requirements in the architectural design of auditoriums for music is formidable. The acoustical problems encountered apply often to auditoriums of unusual size and shape.

In addition to the general requirements outlined in Chap. 6, consideration should be given to the following points.

1. Since no music hall is built for one specific type or style of music, the RT must always be a meticulously established compromise. A carefully controlled RT will increase fullness of tone and will help loudness,

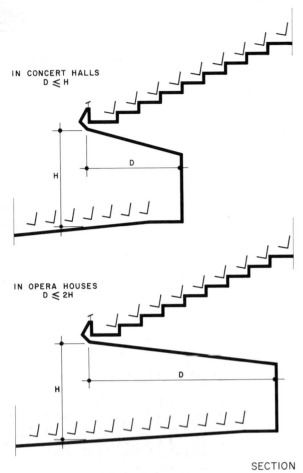

IN CONCERT HALLS
D ≤ H

IN OPERA HOUSES
D ≤ 2H

SECTION

Fig. 8.1 Balconies recommended for music halls.

definition, and diffusion. However, the establishing of an ideal RT alone is no guarantee that a hall will be acoustically excellent for the performance of music; it is a contributing factor only.

2. Definition will be satisfactory if the initial time-delay gap (Chap. 6) does not exceed 20 msec; if the direct sound is loud enough relative to the reverberant sound, that is, listeners are reasonably close to the sound source; and if there is no echo.

3. Providing an adequate supply and distribution of bass tones over a large audience area (above 2,500 seats) is a serious acoustical problem, in part because the fundamentals of several musical instruments (double bass, harp, etc.) are relatively weak and most of the time only their harmonics are heard.

4. To achieve uniform quality of sound over the entire seating area balconies should not protrude too deeply into the air space of the room (Fig. 8.1), listeners should have unobstructed sight lines so that they receive ample direct sound, the room should be of reasonable size and proportion, and concave enclosures should be avoided.

5. Echo will be particularly noticeable if the RT is short and diffusion is inadequate. The longer the RT in a room, the less trouble can be expected from echo. The longer RT will "cover up" the single intrusions of an echo. In checking echo-producing spots, it should always be borne in mind that the acoustical design of rooms is a three-dimensional problem.

6. The frequencies of sounds involved in the acoustics of music halls extend over a considerably wider range than those for speech, from about 30 Hz for certain musical instruments to about 12,000 Hz, including those high-frequency components of musical sounds which characterize some musical instruments.

7. Particular attention is required to control noises and vibrations originating from the heating, ventilating, and air-conditioning systems; from nearby spaces; mechanical and electrical rooms; and from surface, underground, and air transportation. Masking noise, a good feature in residential and other buildings, should be reduced to an absolute minimum (Chap. 15) to avoid interference with pianissimo notes.

8.4 Floor Shapes

The shape of the floor in an auditorium used for music certainly affects the sound-source–transmission-path–receiver sequence (Chap. 1). It is therefore essential to determine the shape before details of the design are considered. The floor shapes of auditoriums used for music usually derive from one or a combination of shapes, briefly described below.

The *rectangular* floor shape (Fig. 8.2) is a historical one with a remarkable tradition and is still used with success. The fine concert halls of the nineteenth and early twentieth centuries—the Grosser Musikvereinssaal, Vienna; St. Andrew's Hall, Glasgow; the Concertgebouw, Amsterdam; the Stadt-Casino, Basel; and Symphony Hall, Boston—all have rectangular floor shapes. These and some contemporary examples are listed in Table 8.1. Cross reflections between parallel walls contribute to increased fullness of tone, a highly desirable room-acoustical feature for music halls.

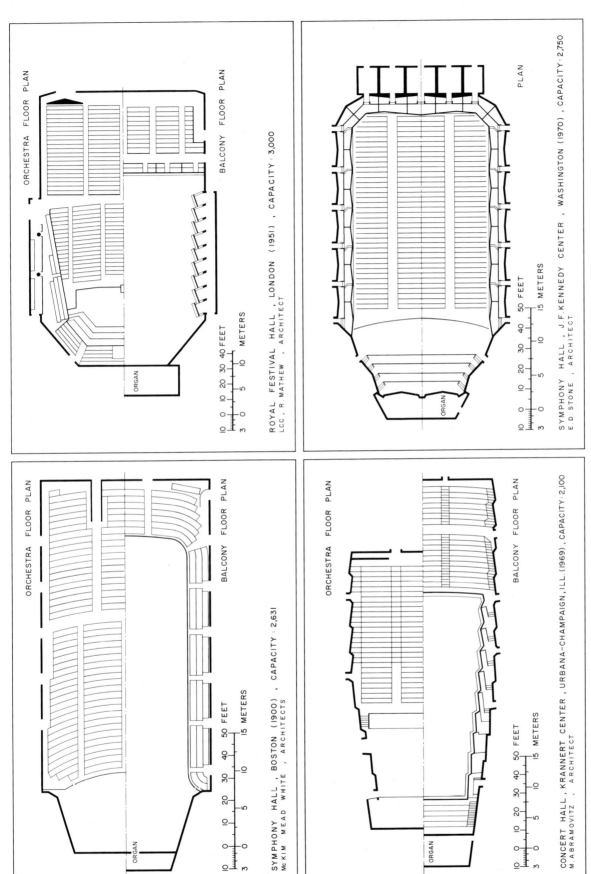

ORCHESTRA FLOOR PLAN

BALCONY FLOOR PLAN

ORGAN

ROYAL FESTIVAL HALL , LONDON (1951) , CAPACITY: 3,000
LCC, R MATHEW , ARCHITECT

10 20 30 40 FEET
METERS
10 0 10
3 0 5 10

PLAN

ORGAN

SYMPHONY HALL , J.F.KENNEDY CENTER , WASHINGTON (1970) , CAPACITY: 2,750
E. D. STONE , ARCHITECT

50 FEET
10 20 30 40
15 METERS
10 0 10
3 0 5 10

ORCHESTRA FLOOR PLAN

BALCONY FLOOR PLAN

ORGAN

SYMPHONY HALL , BOSTON (1900) , CAPACITY : 2,631
McKIM MEAD WHITE , ARCHITECTS

50 FEET
15 METERS
10 20 30 40
10 0 10
3 0 5

ORCHESTRA FLOOR PLAN

BALCONY FLOOR PLAN

ORGAN

CONCERT HALL , KRANNERT CENTER , URBANA-CHAMPAIGN, ILL. (1969) , CAPACITY: 2,100
M. ABRAMOVITZ , ARCHITECT

50 FEET
10 20 30 40
15 METERS
10 0 10
3 0 5

Fig. 8.2 Auditoriums for music with rectangular floor plans.

TABLE 8.1   Architectural-acoustical Data of Concert Halls
In order of increasing seating capacity

Name and year of completion	Floor shape°	Volume V, cu ft (cu m)	Seating capacity	V per audience seat, cu ft (cu m)	Mid-frequency RT, sec
Grande Salle de Concerts, Paris, France, 1963	F	425,000 (12,000)	937	455 (12.8)	2.0†
Konserttisali, Turku, Finland, 1953	F	340,000 (9,600)	1,002	339 (9.6)	1.6
Salle Musica, La Chaux-de-Fonds, Switzerland, 1955	R	240,000 (6,800)	1,032	233 (6.6)	1.6
Radiohuset, Studio l, Copenhagen, Denmark, 1945	F	420,000 (11,890)	1,093	384 (10.9)	1.5
Herkulessaal, Munich, Germany, 1953	R	495,000 (14,000)	1,200	412 (11.7)	2.0
Konzertsaal, Musikhochschule, Berlin, Germany, 1954	R	340,000 (9,600)	1,340	254 (7.2)	1.65
Konserthus, Göteborg, Sweden, 1935	F	420,000 (11,900)	1,371	306 (8.7)	1.7
Beethovenhalle, Bonn, Germany, 1959	I	555,400 (15,700)	1,407	395 (11.2)	1.7
Kulttuuritalo, Helsinki, Finland, 1957	F	354,000 (10,000)	1,500	236 (6.7)	1.05
Grosser Tonhallesaal, Zurich, Switzerland, 1895	R	402,500 (11,400)	1,546	260 (7.4)	1.6
Grosser Musikvereinssaal, Vienna, Austria, 1870	R	530,000 (15,000)	1,680	315 (8.9)	2.1
Tivoli Koncertsal, Copenhagen, Denmark, 1956	F	450,000 (12,740)	1,789	252 (7.1)	1.3
Concert Hall, Chiba, Japan, 1965	I	495,000 (14,000)	1,800	275 (7.8)	1.6
Severance Hall, Cleveland, Ohio, 1930	H	554,000 (15,700)	1,890	289 (8.2)	1.7
Philharmonic Hall, Liverpool, England, 1939	F	479,000 (13,500)	1,955	245 (6.9)	1.5
Liederhalle, Grosser Saal, Stuttgart, Germany, 1956	I	565,000 (16,000)	2,000	283 (8.1)	1.7
Neues Festspielhaus, Salzburg, Austria, 1960	F	460,000 (13,000)	2,160	212 (6.0)	1.5
Colston Hall, Bristol, England, 1951	R	475,000 (13,450)	2,180	218 (6.2)	1.7
Concertgebouw, Amsterdam, Netherlands, 1887	R	663,000 (18,700)	2,206	301 (8.5)	2.0
Philharmonie, Berlin, Germany, 1963	I	890,000 (25,000)	2,218	400 (11.3)	2.0
Grote Zaal, De Doelen, Rotterdam, Netherlands, 1966	I	990,000 (28,000)	2,232	440 (12.5)	2.0†
St. Andrew's Hall, Glasgow, Scotland, 1874	R	810,000 (23,000)	2,500	325 (9.2)	1.9
Free Trade Hall, Manchester, England, 1951	R	545,000 (15,400)	2,569	212 (6.0)	1.6
Symphony Hall, Boston, Mass., 1900	R	662,000 (18,740)	2,631	252 (7.1)	1.8
F. R. Mann Concert Hall, Tel Aviv, Israel, 1957	F	750,000 (21,200)	2,715	276 (7.8)	1.55
Jubilee Auditoriums, Edmonton, Alberta, and Calgary, Alberta, 1957	F	759,000 (21,480)	2,731	278 (7.9)	1.42
Carnegie Hall, New York, N.Y., 1891	H	857,000 (24,250)	2,760	311 (8.8)	1.7
Queen Elizabeth Theater, Vancouver, British Columbia, 1959	I	592,000 (16,750)	2,800	211 (5.6)	1.5
Philharmonic Hall, Lincoln Center, New York, N.Y., 1962	I	865,000 (24,500)	2,836	306 (8.7)	2.0
Kleinhans Music Hall, Buffalo, N.Y., 1940	F	644,000 (18,220)	2,839	227 (6.4)	1.32
Academy of Music, Philadelphia, Pa., 1857	H	555,000 (15,700)	2,984	186 (5.3)	1.4
Royal Festival Hall, London, England, 1951	R	775,000 (22,000)	3,000	258 (7.3)	1.5
Binyanei Ha'oomah, Jerusalem, Israel, 1960	F	873,000 (24,700)	3,142	278 (7.9)	1.75
Tanglewood Music Shed, Lenox, Mass., 1938	F	1,500,000 (42,450)	6,000	250 (7.1)	2.05
Royal Albert Hall, London, England, 1871	C	3,060,000 (86,600)	6,080	503 (14.2)	2.3†

°R = rectangular, F = fan-shaped, H = horseshoe-shaped, C = curvilinear, I = irregular.
†Estimated.

The *fan-shaped* floor brings the audience closer to the sound source, permitting the construction of balconies (Fig. 8.3). The curved rear wall and the curved balcony front, unless acoustically treated or rendered diffusive, are likely to create echoes or sound concentrations.

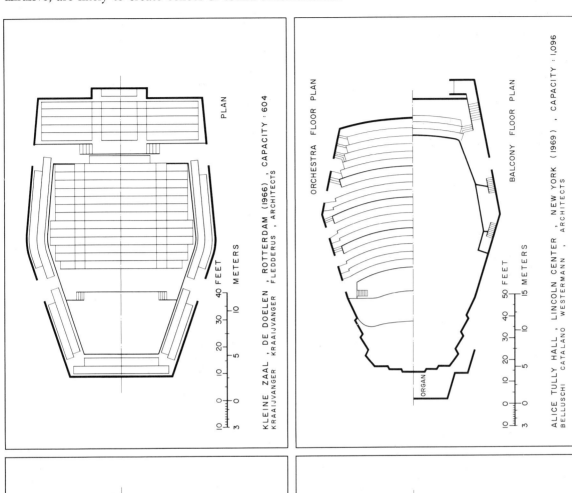

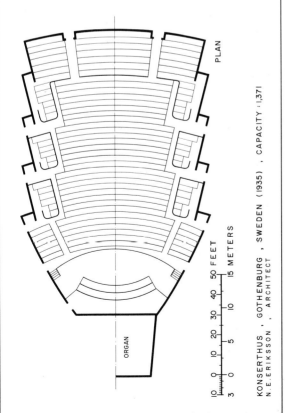

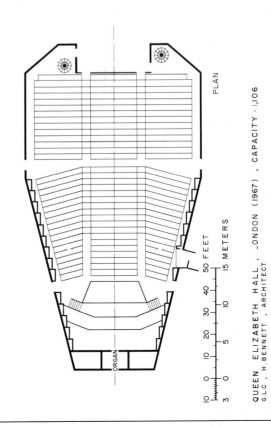

Fig. 8.3 Auditoriums for music with fan-shaped floor plans.

The *horseshoe-shaped* floor plan represents the traditional layout of opera houses. The characteristic feature of this floor shape is rings of boxes on top of each other. Even without interior sound-absorptive surface treatments these boxes contribute efficiently to sound absorption, providing a relatively short RT suitable for the rapid passages of European opera but too short for orchestral performances. Figure 8.4 illustrates a classical and a contemporary example of a horseshoe-shaped opera house.

The *curvilinear* floor shape is normally associated with a dome roof of excessive height. Unless treated acoustically, curvilinear enclosures may create echoes, long-delayed reflections, and sound concentrations, all of which can contribute to an excessively long RT. For these reasons the curvilinear floor should be avoided. The Royal Albert Hall in London, which has a curvilinear floor shape, was noted for its acoustical deficiencies. After 1968, when 109 suspended fiber-glass "saucers," 6 to 12 ft (1.83 to 3.65 m) in diameter, were installed, there has been a considerable acoustical improvement.

The *irregular* floor shape can bring the audience unusually close to the sound source. It can secure acoustical intimacy and definition, since surfaces used to produce short-delayed reflections can be easily integrated into the overall architectural design. The irregular layout gives an opportunity for the random distribution of absorbent elements and diffusive surface irregularities. The free relationship between audience area and platform offers wide scope in design and increased fulfillment of several musical-acoustical requirements. From an acoustical point of view, this floor shape presents hitherto unexplored advantages. Figure 8.5 illustrates music halls with irregular floor shapes. One, the Phil-

Fig. 8.4 Auditoriums for music with horseshoe-shaped floor plans.

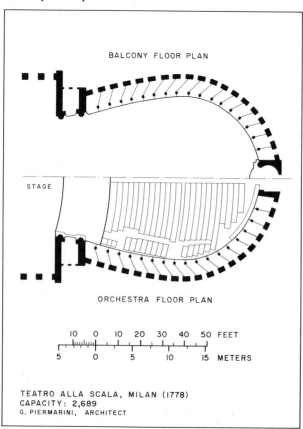

BALCONY FLOOR PLAN

STAGE

ORCHESTRA FLOOR PLAN

```
10    0    10   20   30   40   50 FEET
 |‖‖‖|‖‖‖|    |    |    |    |
 5    0    5         10        15 METERS
```

TEATRO ALLA SCALA, MILAN (1778)
CAPACITY: 2,689
G. PIERMARINI, ARCHITECT

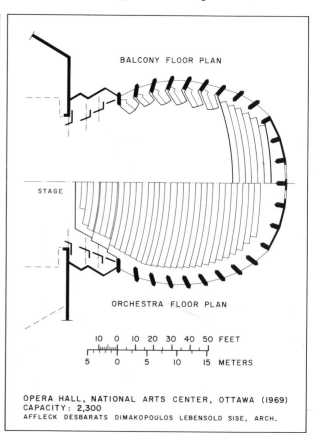

BALCONY FLOOR PLAN

STAGE

ORCHESTRA FLOOR PLAN

```
10    0    10   20   30   40   50 FEET
 |‖‖‖|‖‖‖|    |    |    |    |
 5    0    5         10        15 METERS
```

OPERA HALL, NATIONAL ARTS CENTER, OTTAWA (1969)
CAPACITY: 2,300
AFFLECK DESBARATS DIMAKOPOULOS LEBENSOLD SISE, ARCH.

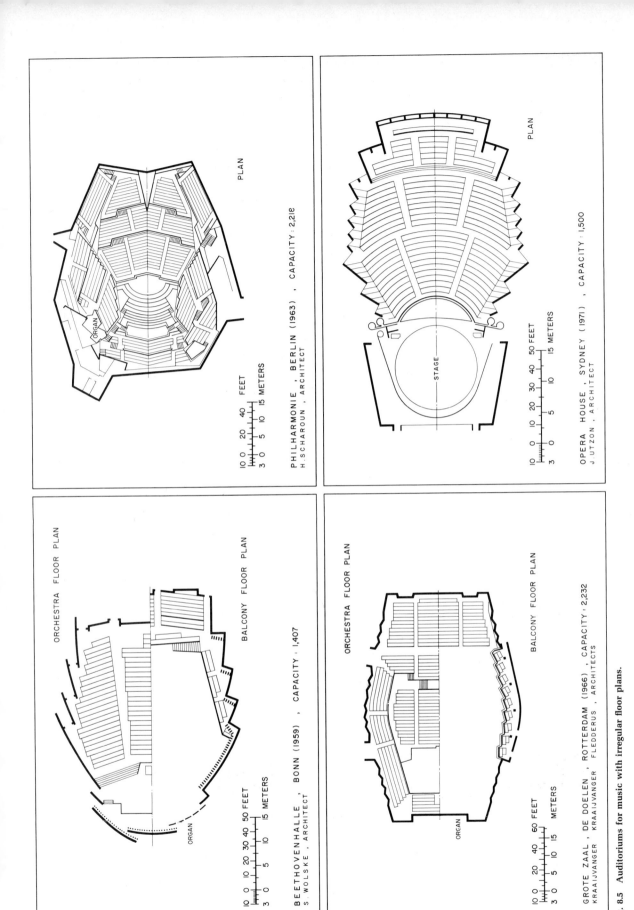

PHILHARMONIE , BERLIN (1963) , CAPACITY: 2,218
H.SCHAROUN , ARCHITECT

PLAN

10 0 20 40 FEET
3 0 5 10 15 METERS

OPERA HOUSE , SYDNEY (1971) , CAPACITY: 1,500
J.UTZON , ARCHITECT

PLAN

STAGE

10 0 10 20 30 40 50 FEET
3 0 5 10 15 METERS

ORCHESTRA FLOOR PLAN

BALCONY FLOOR PLAN

ORGAN

BEETHOVENHALLE , BONN (1959) , CAPACITY: 1,407
S. WOLSKE , ARCHITECT

10 0 10 20 30 40 50 FEET
3 0 5 10 15 METERS

ORCHESTRA FLOOR PLAN

BALCONY FLOOR PLAN

ORGAN

GROTE ZAAL , DE DOELEN , ROTTERDAM (1966) , CAPACITY: 2,232
KRAAIJVANGER KRAAIJVANGER FLEDDERUS , ARCHITECTS

10 0 20 40 60 FEET
3 0 5 10 15 METERS

Fig. 8.5 Auditoriums for music with irregular floor plans.

Fig. 8.6 Interior of the 1,680-seat Grosser Musikvereinssaal, Vienna (1870), with rectangular floor plan, considered one of the finest concert halls of Europe. (T. R. von Hansen, architect. Photograph by C. Till-Borchardt.)

harmonie, in Berlin, is built with three-dimensional irregularity. The orchestra platform is almost surrounded by the audience, which eliminates the need for a reflective orchestra shell, otherwise a necessity in a large concert hall. Ten large plastic reflectors, suspended from the ceiling above the platform, are substituted for the shell. Philharmonic Hall, New York, one of the finest concert halls ever built, is another example of irregular floor shape. Some acoustical modifications were applied to the hall because of grossly exaggerated acoustical problems after its opening in 1962.

8.5 Concert Halls

In a good concert hall audience and musicians are contained within the same space with no separating structure (proscenium wall) between them. There is no specific room shape which can be considered as being ideal for a concert hall. At present, the fan-shaped and irregular layouts seem to be preferred, provided that proper attention is given to the acoustical requirements outlined above. However, the rectangular shape is still favored by those who prefer to follow traditional and successful methods rather than risk experimentation (Fig. 8.6).

The use of a balcony (or balconies) in large concert halls is often advantageous because it brings the audience closer to the platform, it is relatively easy to supply short-delayed reflections to the steeply raked seats of the balconies, and sound waves do not reach the rows of the balcony at grazing incidence as they do along the main seating area. To provide satisfactory hearing conditions under a balcony, see the recommendations illustrated in Fig. 8.1.

The achievement of a highly desirable long RT in large concert halls is difficult. It is therefore imperative that use of a sound-absorptive surface treatment (even along the rear wall, opposite the orchestra podium) be given critical consideration and either reduced to a minimum or avoided altogether. In particular circumstances one might have to avoid acoustical treatment entirely and rely on audience absorption, which in any case is excessive. This may result in echoes reflected from the rear wall during rehearsals when audience absorption is missing. However, the echoes normally disappear during a performance due to audience absorption, particularly at capacity attendance.

In a concert hall with a volume of less than 900,000 cu ft (25,000 cu m), the use of a sound-amplification system, even though it is installed in the hall, should be avoided. All room-acoustical problems in such halls should be resolved by architectural-acoustical means. The recommended volume-per-seat values for concert halls are given in Table 6.1.

In designing the *orchestra platform*, the following are the main points to remember.

1. The floor area should be based on the space requirements of musicians, their instruments, conductor, and soloists. Each musician will need about 12 to 15 sq ft (1.1 to 1.4 sq m) and each member of the chorus 3 to 4 sq ft (0.3 to 0.4 sq m) of floor area.

2. Close musician-listener relationship should be achieved with excellent horizontal and vertical sight clearance from every part of the

audience area, in order to provide loudness, intimacy, and definition. A good view of all musical instruments from every part of the audience area, that is, a proper raking of the orchestra platform, is a prerequisite of satisfactory hearing conditions and one which is surprisingly neglected in many concert halls.

3. The orchestra platform should be neither too deep nor too wide. A maximum depth of about 30 ft (9 m) and a maximum width of about 60 ft (18 m) is recommended for the performing area of the orchestra alone. The depth added by a chorus should not exceed about 10 ft (3 m) at the back or to either side. A sensible raking and platform width-to-depth proportion should provide appropriate loudness, diffusion, balance, blend, and ensemble.

4. Surrounding enclosures should have reflective treatment and be laid out so that they enhance the projection of sound into the audience area and reduce undesirable sound absorption at the source.

5. The level of the platform should be elevated high enough above the audience floor level to provide ample direct sound to every listener. The floor should be constructed with at least a 20-in. (50-cm) deep resonant space underneath, in order to enhance instrumental bass radiation and reduce the overpowering sounds of percussion instruments.

6. The spatial relationship between platform and organ installation should be close.

7. The orchestra platform should have good horizontal and vertical access to instrument stores for quick and unhampered delivery of instruments to and from the platform.

8. Structural, mechanical, and electrical requirements should be coordinated with acoustical needs.

In a multipurpose auditorium an *orchestra shell* is a vital element of the platform; it serves the following functions:

1. It balances the acoustical energy of various sections of the orchestra and creates a rich and full orchestral tone.

2. It prevents the dissipation of sound energy through the flies and wings and projects the sound into the listening area.

3. It counteracts the directional characteristics of individual musical instruments and blends them into a whole.

4. It can reduce (or absorb) the sound of the particularly loud sections of the orchestra like the tympani and brass and thus prevent them from drowning out low-energy sections like the woodwinds and strings.

5. It enables members of the orchestra to hear each other and themselves better.

6. It accommodates lighting fixtures and establishes permanent microphone locations.

The size and structure of an orchestra shell should be easily adaptable to the spatial requirements of various instruments or performing groups—from soloists and chamber orchestras to full-size symphony orchestras and large choirs. Different materials, such as wood, plywood, hardboard, metal, plaster, and reinforced fiber glass, can be used for the construction.

Elements of the shell should be capable of being installed easily and quickly and stored in the flies or in off-stage (understage) areas, and they should have high durability and strength without excessive weight.

Fig. 8.7 (below) Interior of the 3,000-seat Royal Festival Hall, London (1951). (London County Council, R. Mathew, architect; H. Bagenal, acoustical consultant, in collaboration with the Building Research Station. Photograph by Greater London Council, Photographic Department of Architecture & Civic Design.)

Fig. 8.8 (opposite, above) Interior of the 604-seat Kleine Zaal of Rotterdam's De Doelen concert-hall complex (1966). (Kraaijvanger, Kraaijvanger, and Fledderus, architects; C. W. A. Kosten and P. A. de Lange, acoustical consultants. Photograph by W. van Suchtelen.)

Fig. 8.9 (opposite, below) Interior of the 1,106-seat Queen Elizabeth Hall, London (1967). (Greater London Council, H. Bennett, architect; H. Creighton and P. H. Parker, acoustical consultants, in collaboration with the Building Research Station. Photograph by Greater London Council, Photographic Department of Architecture & Civic Design.)

An orchestra shell with adjustable elements can regulate the proportion of direct to reflected sound energy, contributing to the acoustical adjustment, or tuning, of a concert hall.

Table 8.1 lists architectural-acoustical data of concert halls, compiled from sometimes conflicting data, and additional examples of concert halls are given in Table 8.2. Figures 8.7 to 8.12 illustrate the interiors of outstanding concert halls of the last decade.

TABLE 8.2 Some Recent Concert Halls
In order of increasing seating capacity

Name	Location	Completion date	Seating capacity
Recital Hall, Skidmore College	Saratoga Springs, N.Y.	1970	242
Paul Recital Hall, Lincoln Center	New York, N.Y.	1969	278
Purcell Hall	London, England	1967	372
Hopkins Center	Hanover, N.H.	1962	900
Concert Hall, Benedicta Arts Center	St. Joseph, Mo.	1964	1,000
Concert Hall	Albuquerque, N. Mex.	1964	2,100
Uihlein Hall, Milwaukee Center for the Performing Arts	Milwaukee, Wis.	1969	2,327
Concert Hall, Opera House	Sydney, Australia	1971	2,800
Jesse H. Jones Hall	Houston, Tex.	1966	3,000
Performing Arts Center	Saratoga Springs, N.Y.	1966	5,100

8.6 Opera Houses

Strictly speaking, an opera house is the combination of a legitimate theater and a concert hall; consequently the pertinent recommendations discussed in the present and previous chapters should be followed.

An opera performance relies heavily upon colorful settings and scenery to be stored in and manipulated from the flies or the wings. Therefore, opera houses use proscenium stages, with the obvious consequence of separation between performers and spectators. This, however, should not create any acoustical problem since the power of the singers' voices will provide adequate loudness as long as the audience does not exceed 1,500. In opera houses of larger capacities (above 1,500), however, performers will obviously need more powerful voices.

The traditional horseshoe-shaped European type of opera house, with its highly absorbent rings of boxes and its relatively short RT (about 1.2 sec), still suggests the best architectural layout for European operas, as illustrated in Fig. 8.4.

The Festspeilhaus, Bayreuth, was constructed primarily to meet the needs of Wagner's musical style (Fig. 2.7). The tiers of balconies were eliminated, creating an RT of 1.55 sec (with capacity audience), with high fullness of tone and reduced definition, rather unsuitable for European operas.

Fig. 8.10 (opposite, above) Interior of the 1,096-seat Alice Tully Hall, Lincoln Center, New York City (1969). (Belluschi, Catalano, and Westermann, architects; H. Keilholz, acoustical consultant. Photograph by E. Stoller Associates.)

Fig. 8.11 (opposite, below) Interior of the 2,232-seat Grote Zaal, De Doelen concert-hall complex, Rotterdam (1966). (Kraaijvanger, Kraaijvanger, and Fledderus, architects; C. W. A. Kosten and P. A. de Lange, acoustical consultants. Photograph by W. van Suchtelen.)

Fig. 8.12 (above) Interior of the 2,836-seat Philharmonic Hall, Lincoln Center, New York City (1962). (M. Abramovitz, architect; Bolt, Beranek, Newman, and H. Keilholz, acoustical consultants. Photograph by S. Spirito.)

The performing area of any auditorium used for the production of operas and musicals needs an *orchestra pit* with sufficient floor area for 35 to 50 musicians. Each musician in the pit needs a floor area of about 10 to 14 sq ft (0.95 to 1.3 sq m). The floor level of the orchestra pit should be about 8 ft (2.5 m) below stage floor level to provide sufficient headroom for the musicians. To secure an adequate balance between orchestra and singers, the projecting forestage should not cover more than about one-third of the orchestra-pit floor area. The layout of the floor and walls of the orchestra pit should permit adequate projection of sound from orchestra pit into the audience area.

Considerable flexibility is desirable in the use of the orchestra pit. Its area and volume should be adjustable to suit orchestras of different sizes and to secure balance within the orchestra. In addition, it should be possible to cover the orchestra pit with portable sections, either to extend the audience floor or to form a forestage (apron stage). This adaptibility can be mechanized, with the forestage on a lift which can be sunk to extend the audience floor level or to form an orchestra pit, as the requirement may be.

The stage floor of most old European opera houses was raked in order to improve spectator's and conductor's viewing and to accentuate the perspective of the painted scenery. This condition, however beneficial acoustically in enhancing the supply of direct sound waves from singers to listeners, is a hindrance for ballet dancers and makes it awkward to handle scenery. In a contemporary opera house, in spite of acoustical advantage, there is no visual justification for a raked stage floor, as sight lines should be satisfactory without raking.

In the relationship between the audience area and stage house, coupled spaces should be eliminated. The stage house, however, should not be rendered too dead or singers will be deprived of its helpful reverberant environment.

In opera houses provision for an apron stage protruding into the audience area is recommended, to reduce the average distance between singers and audience and render the ceiling reflectors more effective in the supply of short-delayed reflections to the audience.

Recommended volume-per-seat values for European type opera houses are given in Table 6.1. Table 8.3 lists architectural-acoustical data of opera houses compiled from various sources. Figures 8.13 to 8.15 illustrate the interiors of two recently built opera houses that are acoustically highly successful.

8.7 Rehearsal Rooms, Band Rooms, Practice Booths, and Listening Booths

Achieving the required room acoustics in these relatively small rooms is naturally much easier than in concert halls or opera houses. Suitably shaped room enclosures, provision for adequate diffusion, well-controlled RT, carefully selected and well-distributed acoustical finishes, and a high degree of noise control will produce acoustically efficient rehearsal rooms. If excellent acoustical conditions are expected, the

Fig. 8.13 (opposite) Interior of the 2,300-seat Opera Hall, National Arts Center, Ottawa (1969). (Affleck, Desbarats, Dimakopoulos, Lebensold, and Sise, architects; Bolt, Beranek, and Newman, acoustical consultants. Photograph by J. Evans.)

TABLE 8.3 Architectural-acoustical Data of Opera Houses

In order of increasing seating capacity

Name and year of completion	Floor shape°	Volume V of audience area, cu ft (cu m)	Audience capacity (+ standees)	V per audience seat, cu ft (cu m)	Mid-frequency RT, sec
Opernhaus, Cologne, Germany, 1957	F	305,000 (8,650)	1,346	225 (6.4)	1.6
Staatsoper, Berlin, Germany, 1742, 1954	H	247,000 (7,000)	1,488	166 (4.7)	1.0
Staatsoper, Hamburg, Germany, 1955	F	343,000 (9,700)	1,650	208 (5.9)	1.25
Staatsoper, Vienna, Austria, 1869, 1955	H	376,000 (10,660)	1,658 (+560)	195 (5.5)	1.45
Staatsoper, Leipzig, East Germany, 1960	F	340,000 (9,600)	1,700	201 (5.7)	1.45
Festspielhaus, Bayreuth, Germany, 1876	R	364,000 (10,300)	1,800	202 (5.7)	1.55
Théâtre National de l'Opéra, Paris, France, 1875	H	352,000 (9,960)	2,131 (+200)	158 (4.5)	1.1†
Royal Opera House, London, England, 1858	H	432,500 (12,240)	2,180 (+58)	196 (5.6)	1.1
Teatro Alla Scala, Milan, Italy, 1778	H	397,000 (11,245)	2,289 (+400)	160 (4.5)	1.2
Teatro Colon, Buenos Aires, Argentina, 1908	H	726,300 (20,550)	2,487 (+600)	261 (7.4)	1.7†
War Memorial Opera House, San Francisco, Calif., 1932	F	738,600 (20,900)	3,252 (+300)	217 (6.1)	1.6†
New Metropolitan Opera House, New York, N.Y., 1966	F	950,000† (27,000)	3,788	250† (7.1)	1.6†

°R = rectangular, F = fan-shaped, H = horseshoe-shaped.
†Estimated.

Fig. 8.14 View of the 3,800-seat auditorium of the Metropolitan Opera House, Lincoln Center, New York City (1966). (W. K. Harrison, architect; C. M. Harris and V. L. Jordan, acoustical consultants. Photograph by B. Serating.)

RT should be adjustable to satisfy particular requirements of the sound program. Acoustical conditions in rehearsal halls should simulate those of the auditorium (with capacity audience) with which they are functionally connected.

School music departments often include a band rehearsal room, a choral rehearsal room, instructional spaces (music lecture rooms), instrument practice booths, recording and listening rooms, teachers' offices, music library, and instrument storage space. Listening booths are used for monitoring and editing disks, magnetic tapes, and other sound programs. Acoustical conditions in practice booths and listening booths should resemble those of an average domestic living room, with an RT of about 0.4 to 0.5 sec.

In the acoustical design of rooms used for teaching, rehearsing, or practicing music (1) adequate floor area, room height, room shape, and volume must be established to achieve proper reverberation, diffusion, balance, and blend; (2) generous amounts of sound-absorbing materials should be applied to render these rooms sufficiently dead so that the excessive acoustical power generated by school bands or individual instruments can be soaked up; (3) transmission of undesirable sounds

Fig. 8.15 Diffusion-producing elements in the Opera Hall, National Arts Center, Ottawa. (Photograph by R. Jowett.)

between spaces used simultaneously must be reduced to an absolute minimum. Parallelism between opposite surfaces must be avoided in these rooms. At least two adjacent entire wall surfaces, down to their bases, and most or possibly all the ceiling area should be treated with sound-absorbing materials. Since the available room height in these spaces is always less than adequate, it is recommended that the use of suspended ceilings be avoided and that the underside of the floor construction above be exposed and treated acoustically to provide adequate sound insulation against noises from above without a suspended ceiling.

The importance of a high degree of sound insulation between acoustically sensitive spaces of the music department must be stressed. Sensible spatial separation not only will permit satisfactory circulation but will contribute to satisfactory sound insulation as well, at the lowest cost. Noise control of practice booths and listening rooms accessible directly from the band or choral rehearsal rooms is very expensive; they should be adequately separated from rooms in which a high level of sound is generated by buffer rooms (storage spaces) and be accessible from corridors and sound locks, constructed with appropriate sound-insulating walls, floors, and doors (Chap. 14). Ventilating and air-conditioning ducts should not transmit undesirable sounds of music from one space to another, horizontally or vertically (Chap. 16).

Figure 8.16 shows various rooms of a high-school music department.

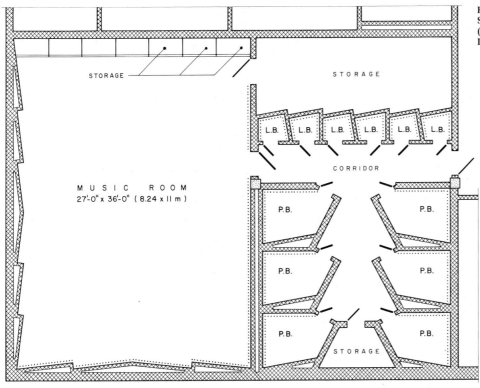

Fig. 8.16 Rooms of the music department, École Secondaire Polyvalente, Cabano, Quebec (1968). (Labelle, Labelle, and Marchand, architects; L. L. Doelle, acoustical consultant.)

PLAN

P.B. = PRACTICE BOOTHS
L.B. = LISTENING BOOTHS

.... SOUND-ABSORPTIVE

BIBLIOGRAPHY

Books

Olson, H. F.: *Musical Engineering*, McGraw-Hill Book Company, New York, 1952, 369 pp.

Culver, C. A.: *Musical Acoustics*, McGraw-Hill Book Company, New York, 1956, 305 pp.

Parkin, P. H., and H. R. Humphreys: *Acoustics, Noise and Buildings*, Frederick A. Praeger, Inc., New York, 1958, chap. 4.

Beranek, L. L.: *Music Acoustics and Architecture*, John Wiley & Sons, Inc., New York, 1962, 586 pp.

Periodicals

Bagenal, H.: "Concert Halls," *J. RIBA*, January 1950, pp. 83–93.

"Royal Festival Hall," *Architectural Review*, June 1951, pp. 337–394.

Shoesmith, D., and M. Santiago: "Reverberators: Post-war German Concert Halls and Opera Houses," *Architectural Review*, August–September 1959, pp. 86–99.

Johnson, R.: "Auditorium Acoustics for Music Performance," *Architectural Record*, December 1960, pp. 158–182.

Beranek, L. L.: "Musical-acoustics Vocabulary," *Sound*, July–August 1962, pp. 22–26.

Goodfriend, L. S.: "Acoustics for School Music Departments," *Sound*, January–February 1963, pp. 28–32.

Lanier, R. S.: "Acoustics in-the-round at the Berlin Philharmonic," *Architectural Forum*, May 1964, pp. 98–105.

"A 'Pure Hall' for Music: Warner Concert Hall, Oberlin College," *Architectural Record*, December 1964, pp. 128–129.

Allen, W.: "Acoustics Twenty Years after the Festival Hall," *J. RIBA*, February 1969, pp. 62–67.

Johnson, R.: "Opera Hall Acoustics," *Architecture Canada*, May 1969, pp. 46–47.

"National Arts Center, Ottawa," *The Canadian Architect*, July 1969, pp. 30–65.

CHAPTER NINE

Many of the auditoriums discussed in preceding chapters are used for multiple purposes, but in their acoustical design priority must be given either to speech (Chap. 7) or to music (Chap. 8). The present chapter deals with places of assembly in which more or less equally favorable conditions must be secured for both speech and music.

Places of Assembly with Mixed Acoustical Requirements

9.1 Churches and Synagogues

Excessive reverberation and lack of speech intelligibility are the main acoustical features, or rather defects, of medieval churches, particularly large ones. These acoustical characteristics have not only influenced the style of organ music composed for the church but also have left their mark on the liturgical pattern. Furthermore, the adoption of polyphonic choral music, the chanting of words, and perhaps even the use of an archaic tongue may have been associated with the highly reverberant conditions prevailing in medieval churches.

The continuing revolution in church architecture and the changes in liturgy seem to attach a growing importance to improved environmental conditions in churches. According to the new concept of liturgy, the congregation must be increasingly engaged in a dialogue between the celebrant and his attendants. Since the congregation participates in the musical portion of the service as well, churches should be designed, both architecturally and acoustically, to facilitate and encourage this verbal and musical dialogue.

Church auditoriums usually consist of several coupled spaces (nave, chancel, chapel, baptistry, confessionals, organ, choir loft, etc.). In their acoustical design, therefore, consideration must be given to the acoustical requirements of these individual spaces.

1. The chancel area and the pulpit should be well elevated and surrounded by reflective enclosures in order to provide favorable conditions for the projection of speech sound toward the congregation.

2. The organ and choir should be in an area that provides a favorable acoustical environment for music, and they should be surrounded by reflective surfaces without creating echoes, flutter echoes, or sound concentrations. The spatial relationships between organist, organ, choirmaster, and choir must be carefully considered.

3. Every sector of the congregation should enjoy good listening conditions during every part of the service. Since the space in a church auditorium is always more than acoustically necessary, the control of RT will require a certain amount of acoustical treatment.

4. Coupled spaces need individual reverberation control so that reverberation conditions in them will not conflict with those prevailing in the main body of the church auditorium.

5. Extraordinary care should be exercised to eliminate noise as a prerequisite for meditation and prayer.

Acoustical problems become more complicated and more involved as the volume of the church auditorium increases, particularly if the floor is curvilinear. Circular or curvilinear floor shapes are usually dome-roofed, thereby creating such serious acoustical defects as echoes, sound concentrations, long-delayed reflections, and uneven distribution of sound. These defects can be eliminated by applying highly absorptive finishes over the critical surfaces or by shielding the curved enclosures from incident sound by large suspended reflectors or diffusers.

In the acoustical design of churches it is essential to consider the nature of the religious service in different denominations because the optimum RT will depend on whether speech or music is regarded as the more important portion of the service. Preference must be given to the more important element since it is seldom possible to provide excellent hearing conditions for both speech and music at the same time. Recommended reverberation times for church auditoriums of various denominations were shown in Fig. 6.14. Depending on the relative importance of speech or music, the pertinent recommendations discussed in Chaps. 5 to 7 should be observed.

It is obvious that a wide gap exists between the optimum RT for speech and for organ music. It will be therefore difficult to decide on the most acceptable compromise between these two types of sound, particularly in churches where special emphasis has been placed on the full effectiveness of the organ. This situation might become serious when room-acoustical measures to be taken are in the exclusive hands of the organ builder. In the interest of a soaring organ tone, he will seldom, if ever, hesitate to recommend an RT that favors organ music only, totally disregarding the requirements of speech intelligibility. The serious consequence, that is, absence of speech intelligibility resulting in loss of interest in the sermon, is well known. It appears that the serious problem of providing a proper RT in churches may come closer to solution in the future by the use of electronic reverberators, well known in recent decades in the broadcasting and recording industry. A church auditorium can be designed with a short RT for high speech intelligibility, while the sound of the chorus and organ can be picked up by special microphones and fed through an electronic reverberator into the loudspeakers, extending the RT of the musical portion of the service as required.

Average volume-per-seat values for church auditoriums were given in Table 6.1.

Because of the ever-increasing number and intensity of noise sources inside and outside church buildings, a speech-amplification system is gradually becoming a necessity even in relatively small churches. Such a system should be designed, laid out, and operated in such a way that the congregation is unaware of its existence.

Figure 9.1 shows plans of a curvilinear church with a dome. Sound waves originating from the pulpit and reflected from a curvilinear perimeter and dome have the tendency to create echoes and sound concentrations at a certain area of the floor, which can result in highly undesirable hot spots there. These acoustical defects have been avoided by (1) the use of sound-absorptive pierced brick walls along the periphery of the auditorium (Figs. 9.2 and 9.3); (2) the application of moderately absorbent sprayed limpet-asbestos treatment along the interior surface of the dome; (3) the incorporation of large-scale diffusive surface irregularities in the form of prefabricated concrete shells for the dome structure; and (4) the installation of a high-quality, directional speech-reinforcement system. The sound-absorptive treatments used in this church auditorium have also contributed to reverberation control.

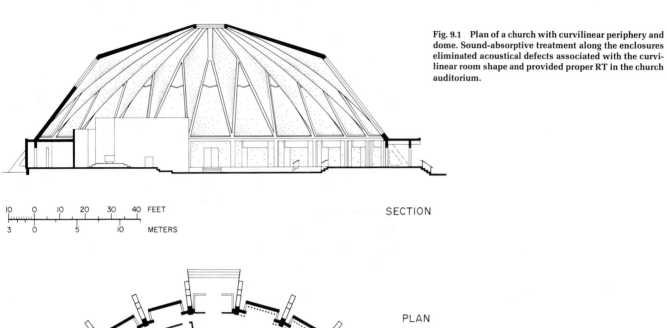

Fig. 9.1 Plan of a church with curvilinear periphery and dome. Sound-absorptive treatment along the enclosures eliminated acoustical defects associated with the curvilinear room shape and provided proper RT in the church auditorium.

SECTION

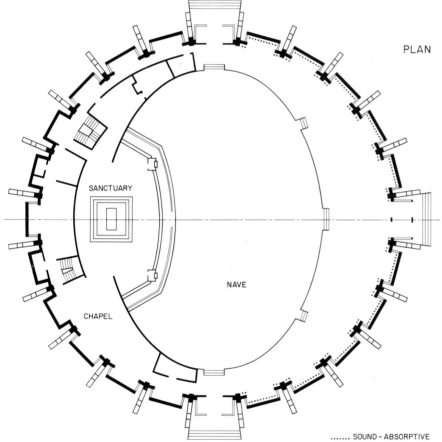

PLAN

.... SOUND – ABSORPTIVE

ST. JOHN BREBEUF'S CHURCH , LASALLE , QUE. (1965)   CAPACITY : 875
J.BIRD ARCHITECT , L.L.DOELLE ACOUSTICAL CONSULTANT

Fig. 9.2 Interior of the 875-seat church of St. John Brebeuf, La Salle, Quebec. (Photograph by Bowe Studio.)

Fig. 9.3 Sound-absorptive pierced brick walls along the periphery of the church of St. John Brebeuf. (Photograph by Bowe Studio.)

9.2 Multipurpose Auditoriums and Community Halls

Since multipurpose auditoriums must serve equally well for a great variety of programs, in their acoustical design the general principles outlined in Chap. 6, with additional recommendations for speech and music described in Chaps. 7 and 8, respectively, should be followed. Municipal, or civic, auditoriums are typical examples of this group. They best serve their diverse users if the most reasonable compromise between optimum acoustics for speech and music is achieved.

A special acoustical problem is often created in municipal auditoriums by the unraked floor required for exhibitions, bazaars, dances, social gatherings, and dinners. A level floor introduces the following acoustical problems: (1) it makes it difficult to supply the audience with the required amount of direct sound; (2) if the ceiling is reflective and horizontal, interreflections (flutter echoes) may originate between floor and ceiling when the audience area is cleared of chairs; (3) portable chairs usually have a negligible amount of upholstering (if any), thus providing much less absorption than fully upholstered seats.

The following points should be noted in the acoustical design of these often very large auditoriums.

1. The sending end should be elevated as high as sight lines will allow.

2. A large amount of reflective surface (panels) should be placed near the sound source and, if necessary, suspended from the ceiling to provide short-delayed, reflected sound energy. These reflective surfaces must be oriented so as to secure evenly distributed sound reinforcement throughout the entire auditorium.

3. The stage floor should protrude as far as possible into the audience area.

4. An attempt should be made to accommodate a raked or raised portion of the audience floor, at least at the sides or at the rear of the main audience area.

5. Optimum RT should be secured for one-half of capacity audience because a considerable fluctuation in attendance must be expected.

6. In an auditorium with a flat floor, the loudspeaker, if used, should be placed somewhat higher than it would be in an auditorium with a raked floor.

Social halls in church buildings (Fig. 9.4) constitute a particular type of multipurpose auditorium. In the construction of church buildings,

Fig. 9.4 Interior of the social hall of the Shaar-Hashomayim Congregation, Montreal (1968). (Eliasoph and Berkowitz, architects; L. L. Doelle, acoustical consultant. Photograph by Bowe Studio.)

it often happens that very little money (if any) is set aside for the finishing touches of these halls, which are usually located in the basement. In most cases they have concrete floors and an exposed concrete slab above, and consequently they can be described as large echo chambers, frequently with an RT of 5 to 8 sec. Despite their poor acoustics, they are used for the widest range of religious, educational, cultural, social, and political functions, without being acoustically qualified for any of them. Acoustical correction (briefly described in Chap. 12), at least by simple means, would be the most important contribution to the successful use of the space.

Figures 9.5 to 9.7 illustrate and Table 9.1 lists examples of multipurpose auditoriums.

9.3 Motion-picture Theaters

The motion-picture theater represents an exclusively single-purpose auditorium. If it is properly designed acoustically, it will be difficult to use for purposes other than film projection.

In the various types of auditoriums discussed so far both the sound source and the audience are present, and both are live. In such auditoriums, assuming any normal sound source, hearing conditions depend solely upon the acoustical qualities of the room. In a motion-picture theater the original sound source is not present but reproduced from the sound track of the film by a loudspeaker. The reproduced sound which is heard in the auditorium reflects the acoustical characteristics of the motion-picture studio in which the scene was shot, for example, the acoustical features of a cathedral (with an RT of 8 sec) or of a snow field (an acoustically dead space). This means that the sound track on the film has a built-in RT independent of the RT of the theater in which the film is shown.

An important goal in the acoustical design of motion-picture theaters is to reduce the room-acoustical effect of the cinema auditorium to a minimum in order to preserve the genuine acoustical environment of the film as recorded on the sound track and as reproduced by the loudspeakers behind the screen. This goal is achieved by providing a relatively short RT in the cinema auditorium, as recommended in Fig. 6.14. The considerable improvement in the quality of a film and in the reproductive fidelity of the sound equipment will not be of any value unless they are matched by proper reverberation conditions in the cinema auditorium. The RT, however, should not be too short, because this would render the auditorium dead and necessitate excessive acoustical power from the loudspeaker, leading to annoying loudness in the front and central seats.

Favorable hearing conditions are achieved in motion-picture theaters by the following room-acoustical measures, in addition to the recommendations outlined in Chaps. 6 and 7.

1. Rectangular floor shape with horizontal floor should be avoided. An appropriate fan-shaped floor plan adequately raked will best suit both viewing and acoustical requirements.

2. The RT for monophonic sound reproduction should be as close

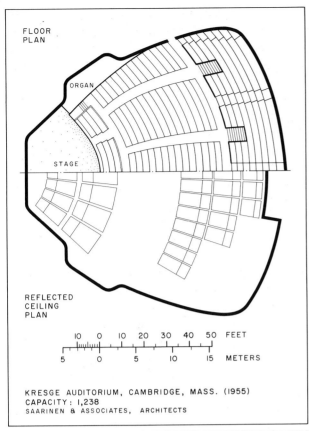

FLOOR
PLAN

ORGAN

STAGE

REFLECTED
CEILING
PLAN

```
10   0   10  20  30  40  50  FEET
|||ıılıılı|    |    |    |    |
5    0    5       10      15  METERS
```

KRESGE AUDITORIUM, CAMBRIDGE, MASS. (1955)
CAPACITY: 1,238
SAARINEN & ASSOCIATES, ARCHITECTS

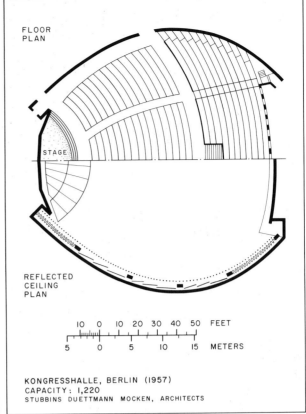

FLOOR
PLAN

STAGE

REFLECTED
CEILING
PLAN

```
10   0   10  20  30  40  50  FEET
|||ıılıılı|    |    |    |    |
5    0    5       10      15  METERS
```

KONGRESSHALLE, BERLIN (1957)
CAPACITY: 1,220
STUBBINS DUETTMANN MOCKEN, ARCHITECTS

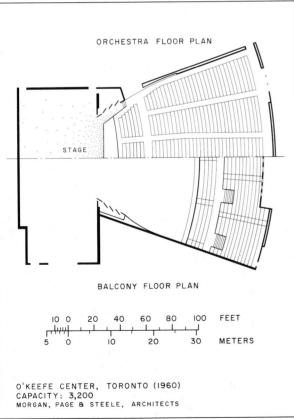

ORCHESTRA FLOOR PLAN

STAGE

BALCONY FLOOR PLAN

```
10 0    20    40    60    80   100  FEET
|ıılı|   |     |     |     |
5  0      10      20      30  METERS
```

O'KEEFE CENTER, TORONTO (1960)
CAPACITY: 3,200
MORGAN, PAGE & STEELE, ARCHITECTS

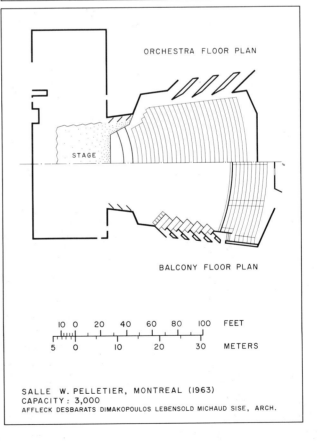

ORCHESTRA FLOOR PLAN

STAGE

BALCONY FLOOR PLAN

```
10 0    20    40    60    80   100  FEET
|ıılı|   |     |     |     |
5  0      10      20      30  METERS
```

SALLE W. PELLETIER, MONTREAL (1963)
CAPACITY: 3,000
AFFLECK DESBARATS DIMAKOPOULOS LEBENSOLD MICHAUD SISE, ARCH.

Fig. 9.5 Examples of multipurpose auditoriums.

TABLE 9.1   Multipurpose Auditoriums (Listed Chronologically)

Name	Location	Completion date	Seating capacity
Eastman Theater	Rochester, N.Y.	1923	3,347
Aula Magna	Caracas, Venezuela	1954	2,660
Grace R. Rogers Auditorium	New York, N.Y.	1954	708
Henry and Edsel Ford Auditorium	Detroit, Mich.	1956	2,926
Civic Auditorium	Bofu, Japan	1960	1,604
Arie Crown Theater	Chicago, Ill.	1961	5,081
Civic Auditorium	Nagasaki, Japan	1962	1,800
Opera House	Seattle, Wash.	1962	3,075
Civic Auditorium	Jacksonville, Ala.	1962	3,200
Civic Auditorium	Fukuoka, Japan	1963	1,800
Clowes Hall	Indianapolis, Ind.	1963	2,200
G. Gammage Auditorium	Tempe, Ariz.	1964	3,000
Memorial Auditorium	Chiba, Japan	1965	960
Civic Auditorium	Gifu, Japan	1966	1,500
Civic Auditorium	Niigata, Japan	1967	1,874
Civic Auditorium	Iizuka, Japan	1967	1,000
National Cultural Center	Manila, Phillippine Islands	1968	2,000
Grand Théâtre	Quebec, Que.	1971	1,780

as possible to the optimum values indicated in Fig. 6.14. For stereophonic sound the RT should be somewhat less.

3. The volume-per-seat value should be kept within 100 to 150 cu ft (2.8 to 4.3 cu m), preferably closer to the lower figure.

4. Overhead sound reflectors should be used above the screen; the entire ceiling or at least its major central portion should be made reflective.

5. The initial time-delay gap (Chap. 6) between direct sound from the loudspeaker (behind the screen) and first reflected sound from any reflective surface should not exceed 40 msec at any part of the seating area, corresponding to a path difference of 45 ft (13.7 m) between direct and reflected sounds.

6. The audience floor should be steeply ramped toward the rear to provide clear sight lines for the entire audience, thereby providing an ample supply of direct sound.

7. The projection screen and the loudspeaker behind it should be high enough for the entire audience to be well covered by the sound beam.

8. Vertical boundary surfaces, except those close to the screen, should be generously treated with sound-absorbing finishes in order to achieve a short RT and to avoid acoustical defects particularly noticeable in an acoustically dead room such as a motion-picture theater. In cinema auditoriums with wide-screen projection, where the loudspeakers are installed behind the screen, from one end to the other, acoustical treatment along the side walls should prevent long-delayed reflections (from side walls); these reflections are especially to be avoided because they make the sound appear to come from the wrong place, thus spoiling the illusion.

9. Parallelism between reflective surfaces close to the screen should be avoided. The wall behind the projection screen should be made

Fig. 9.6 (opposite, above) Interior of the 3,000-seat Salle Wilfrid Pelletier, a multipurpose auditorium in Montreal (1963). (Affleck, Desbarats, Dimakopoulos, Lebensold, Michaud, and Sise, architects; Bolt, Beranek, Newman, and N. Pappas and Associates, acoustical consultants. Photograph by Panda Associates.)

Fig. 9.7 (opposite, below) Interior of a 1,000-seat multipurpose auditorium in Quebec (1963). (Amyot and Vagi, architects; L. L. Doelle, acoustical consultant. Photograph by Legare & Kedl.)

absorptive if too long delayed reflections are expected from this surface. In this case the acoustical treatment behind the screen should be finished in black to prevent light reflections from penetrating the perforated screen.

10. Excessive room length, above about 150 ft (46 m), should be avoided, partly to obviate the need for excessive acoustical power of the loudspeakers and partly to prevent lack of synchronism between sight and sound at the remote seats.

11. Balconies should not be too deep.

12. The correct distance between the screen and the first row of seats should be determined from the *aspect ratio* (height-to-width ratio) and the dimensions of the projection screen.

13. Heavily upholstered seats should be used to counteract detrimental room-acoustical effects of widely fluctuating attendance.

14. The floor between the screen and the first row of seats should be carpeted in order to prevent psychologically disillusioning reflections at the front of the auditorium, coming from directions other than the loudspeaker.

Stereophonic sound reproduction in motion-picture theaters, which can be expected in the foreseeable future, will require a meticulous approach to acoustical design, affecting room shape, RT, distribution of acoustical treatments, and layout of the sound system.

A somewhat higher background-noise level can be tolerated in motion-picture theaters than elsewhere because of the higher sound level produced by the loudspeaker.

The noise originating from the projection booth is often a nuisance, particularly for those seated close to the booth. Penetration of this noise into the audience area should be prevented by treating interior surfaces of the projection booth with efficient sound-absorbing (and also fireproof) materials; using double glazing in the projection and observation portholes (optical glass should be used in the projection ports, and plate glass in the observation ports; the glass panes should be of different thickness and hermetically sealed in their frames); and using a partition wall with adequate sound insulation between the auditorium and the projection room.

9.4 Open-air Theaters and Concert Platforms

Contemporary architecture cannot boast of any remarkable progress in the design of open-air theaters since this type of auditorium was first built by the Greeks and Romans. The masks they wore are being replaced by electronic sound systems.

Open-air theaters are used equally for spoken programs (live stage presentations) and for musical performances (concerts and musicals). When no sound-amplification system is used, a musical performance, thanks to the higher inherent acoustical power of the instruments, can reach a much larger audience than a spoken program.

Since the natural reinforcement of direct sound from nearby reflective surfaces is very limited, a reduction of about 6 dB in sound intensity can be expected every time the distance from the source is doubled (Chap. 3). To counteract this excessive drop in the open air, attention should be given to the following recommendations.

1. The site should be carefully selected in view of effects of topographical and atmospherical conditions (wind, temperature, etc.) and of exterior noise sources upon the propagation and reception of sound.

2. The basic shape, size, and capacity of the seating area should be determined to ensure satisfactory speech intelligibility throughout the entire audience area. The distance of the seats from the sound source should be kept at a reasonable minimum, with strict economy in the layout of aisles and gangways.

3. An attempt should be made to accommodate the maximum amount of reflective surfaces close to the sound source. A reflective and diffusive enclosure (band shell), to direct the reflected sound waves both toward the audience and back to the performers, will be of great advantage. A paved space, an artificial brook, or other reflective surface between stage and audience will improve hearing conditions.

4. The platform should be well elevated and the seating area steeply banked, with increased rake toward the rear, to provide the maximum amount of direct sound for the entire audience.

5. Back reflections converging upon the platform from the concentric benches, particularly noticeable with partially or totally unoccupied seating area, should be eliminated.

6. Nearby reflective surfaces of existing buildings should be carefully checked for echoes or harmful reflections.

Many of the recommendations in Chaps. 6 to 8 also apply to open-air theaters.

If audience capacity exceeds about 500, a high-quality sound-amplification system should be installed. Its layout and volume should be such that the audience is unaware of its existence.

BIBLIOGRAPHY

Books

Beranek, L. L.: *Music Acoustics and Architecture*, John Wiley & Sons, Inc., New York, 1962, 586 pp.

"Pipe Organs," in J. H. Callender (ed.), *Time-saver Standards*, 4th ed., McGraw-Hill Book Company, New York, 1966, pp. 934–936.

Schlanger, B.: "Motion-picture Theaters," in J. H. Callender (ed.), *Time-saver Standards*, 4th ed., McGraw-Hill Book Company, New York, 1966, pp. 1101–1106.

Theater Planning, part 2, reprinted from *The Architects' Journal*, including information sheets 1467 to 1473 on film projection, distributed by the Association of British Theater Technicians, London, 1967.

Sharp, D.: *The Picture Palace*, Frederick A. Praeger, Inc., New York, 1969, 224 pp.

Periodicals

Bagenal, H.: "Cathedral Acoustics," *J. RIBA*, April 1954, pp. 223–226.

Berry, R., and B. Y. Kinzey: "Planning for Sound in Church Worship," *Architectural Forum*, December 1954, pp. 164–166.

Rienstra, A. R.: "Church Design for Music," *Architectural Record*, December 1955, pp. 193–194.

Lane, R. N.: "Room Shapes and Materials Determine Church Acoustics," *Architectural Record*, December 1957, pp. 190–192.

Northwood, T. D.: "Acoustics and Church Architecture," *J. RAIC*, July 1962, pp. 51–55.

Schlanger, B.: "Multi-purpose and Multi-form Places of Assembly," *J. AIA*, December 1964, pp. 66–70.

"Better Architecture for the Performing Arts," *Architectural Record*, December 1964, pp. 115–142.

"The Jesse H. Jones Hall for the Performing Arts," *Architectural Record*, February 1967, pp. 115–121.

"The Loretto Hilton Center for the Performing Arts," *Architectural Record*, February 1967, pp. 122–125.

Risser, A. C.: "Alfresco Spectaculars," *J. AIA*, August 1969, pp. 67–73.

Ramakrishna, B. S., and T. I. Smits: "Acoustics of Northrop Memorial Auditorium," *J. Acoust. Soc. Am.*, April 1970, pp. 951–960.

"Concert Shell for a Roman Ruin," *Architectural Record*, December 1970, pp. 67–74.

The design of rooms used primarily for microphone pick-up is a special subject governed by highly technical requirements. It is not the purpose of this chapter to describe the elaborate procedure that takes place in a contemporary sound-studio complex during a broadcast, telecast, or recording, as it is unlikely that the architect in charge of such a project would also assume responsibility for its acoustical design. Nevertheless, a brief review of pertinent room-acoustical principles is given below.

In addition to the general acoustical principles and recommendations discussed in preceding chapters, which are equally applicable to studio design, room-acoustical requirements have to be met with greater precision, and a particularly high degree of isolation must be provided against extraneous noise and vibration. Pertinent acoustical calculations are applied to a wider frequency range than in normal cases, that is, from 63 Hz usually up to 8000 Hz (Fig. 10.1).

This meticulous approach to studio acoustics is necessary because the human (binaural) listener in the studio is replaced by the microphone, a most sensitive electronic instrument which picks up sounds very much as a person would with monaural hearing. The microphone will indicate it clearly (1) when reverberation characteristics are not optimum over a wide frequency range, (2) when diffusion is not high enough, (3) when any acoustical defect such as echo or sound concentration is noticeable, and (4) when the faintest noise or vibration exists in the studio.

10.1 Acoustical Requirements

Since studios form an important acoustical link between sound source and microphone, particular attention must be given to the following requirements in their design.
1. An optimum size and shape for the studio must be established.
2. A high degree of diffusion must be secured.
3. Ideal reverberation characteristics must be provided.
4. Acoustical defects must be totally prevented.
5. Noises and vibrations must be completely eliminated.

The listed requirements may be condensed into the following admonition: in studio design nothing can be left to chance.

The size of a studio is determined by the physical space required for its occupants, equipment, and furniture, by the function for which the room is to be used, and by the acoustical requirements. The smallest dimension should not be less than about 8 ft (2.4 m).

In establishing the necessary floor area for a music studio, even though a single instrumentalist occupies only about 6 to 10 sq ft (0.55 to 0.95 sq m) of floor area, it will be found that a total average of about 15 to 20 sq ft (1.4 to 1.85 sq m) of floor space is required for each musician in a small music studio and about 20 to 40 sq ft (1.85 to 3.7 sq m) of floor space in a large one. The extra space is taken up by circulation, music stands, and microphone placing. An average floor area of 4 to 6 sq ft (0.37 to 0.55 sq m) is required for singers, depending on whether they are standing or seated. If audience participation is required, a separate floor area must be set aside for audience seating.

CHAPTER TEN

Acoustical Design of Studios

Fig. 10.1 In radio, television, recording, and film studios the tolerant ears of a live audience are replaced by a most sensitive electronic instrument, the microphone.

There are no room proportions that are universally or unanimously recommended as optimum. For rectangular studios the ratios for room proportions shown in Table 10.1 are generally advocated. Some authors recommend different proportions. It must be stressed that the significance of room proportions in studio acoustics diminishes when (1) the studio has a nonrectangular floor, (2) ideal reverberation characteristics have been achieved, (3) acoustical finishes, particularly those with efficient low-frequency absorption, are generously used and evenly distributed, (4) a high degree of diffusion has been provided, and (5) the volume of the studio is above 25,000 cu ft (710 cu m).

TABLE 10.1 Recommended Proportions for Rectangular Studios

Studio type	Height	Width	Length
Small	1	1.25	1.60
Medium	1	1.50	2.50
With relatively low ceiling	1	2.50	3.20
With unusual length relative to width	1	1.25	3.20

Provision for a high degree of diffusion (Chaps. 4 and 6) is of vital importance in studio acoustics. With ideal diffusion the number of positions at which noticeable sound-pressure variations occur is considerably reduced, so that the microphones can be placed safely in almost any convenient position.

Optimum RTs for studios are generally shorter than those for auditoriums in which the sound program is perceived by binaural listeners. An optimum RT for a studio (Fig. 10.2) is of vital importance to the final quality of sound, but the apparent RT in a studio, as eventually perceived by the listener, will depend also on the microphone pick-up technique (position of microphone, distance between sound source and microphone, number of microphones used simultaneously, etc.) and on the quality of the microphone, particularly its directional characteristics. The acoustical characteristics of the room in which the broadcasted or recorded sound is received or reproduced will add to the apparent RT.

It is essential that acoustical treatments, as indicated by reverberation calculations, be uniformly and proportionately distributed over the three pairs of opposite enclosures of the studio.

Wherever possible, most broadcasting organizations prefer to have acoustical treatments installed so that temporary removal of the exposed finish treatment for later adjustment is possible. The choice of suitable acoustical materials was discussed in Chap. 5.

Broadcasting and recording studios must frequently be used for programs differing widely in type, scale, or complexity. The necessary variable reverberation conditions can be achieved by the following means:

1. Variable absorbers on wall or ceiling surfaces, such as, hinged or sliding panels, rotatable cylinders, adjustable drapery, etc. (Sec. 5.5)

2. Portable acoustic screens (*flats*)

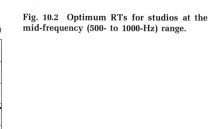

Fig. 10.2 Optimum RTs for studios at the mid-frequency (500- to 1000-Hz) range.

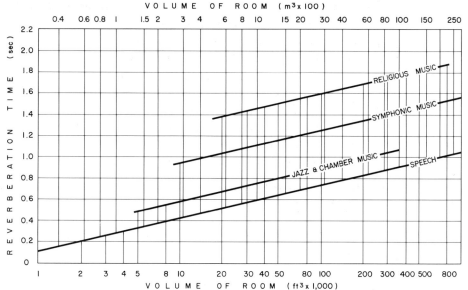

3. A reverberation chamber

4. A special mechanism to control the RT electronically, which is operated from the control room

Boundary surfaces must be carefully checked for echoes, flutter echoes, and sound concentrations. Parallel surfaces must be eliminated (particularly in medium and large studios) or treated with acoustical materials highly absorptive throughout the frequency range between 63 and 8000 Hz.

The important requirement of noise and vibration control in studios is covered in Chap. 17.

10.2 Radio Studios

Studios used for broadcasting purposes can be divided, quite arbitrarily, into several types.

1. *Announcer's booth.* This is the smallest studio, normally associated with a larger one. It is used for newscasts, narrations, commentaries, etc., and has a floor area of up to about 150 sq ft (14 sq m). It is visually linked with the associated studio by a large sound-insulating observation window.

2. *Talk studio* (Fig. 10.3). Used for newscasts, panel discussions, addresses, talks, and sometimes recitals, it has a floor area of up to about 500 sq ft (47 sq m).

3. *Drama studio.* The floor area is usually from about 600 to 1,500 sq ft (56 to 140 sq m).

4. *Versatile studio.* The floor area varies between about 1,500 and 4,000 sq ft (140 and 370 sq m). It is used equally for spoken and muscial presentations.

5. *Audience studio.* Used for broadcasting orchestral and choral programs, this large studio is, in fact, a regular concert hall; therefore the acoustical requirements and design principles discussed in Chap. 8 should be strictly adhered to. Besides other technical rooms, a control

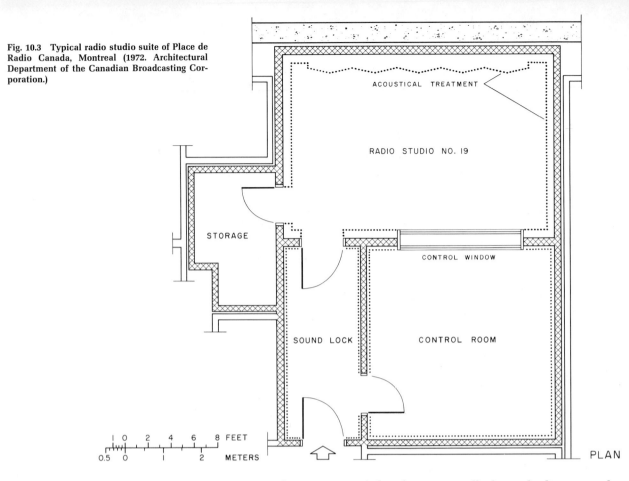

Fig. 10.3 Typical radio studio suite of Place de Radio Canada, Montreal (1972. Architectural Department of the Canadian Broadcasting Corporation.)

ACOUSTICAL TREATMENT

RADIO STUDIO NO. 19

STORAGE

CONTROL WINDOW

SOUND LOCK

CONTROL ROOM

1 0 2 4 6 8 FEET
0.5 0 1 2 METERS

PLAN

room and an announcer's booth are normally located adjacent to the audience studio, linked to one another by large sound-insulating windows. A sound-amplification system is usually required to provide adequate sound coverage for the audience.

Figure 10.4 illustrates examples of radio audience studios.

Fig. 10.4 Examples of radio audience studios.

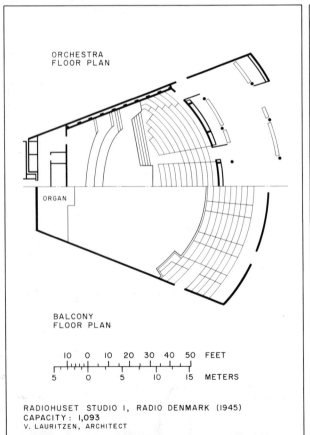

ORCHESTRA
FLOOR PLAN

ORGAN

BALCONY
FLOOR PLAN

10 0 10 20 30 40 50 FEET
5 0 5 10 15 METERS

RADIOHUSET STUDIO I, RADIO DENMARK (1945)
CAPACITY: 1,093
V. LAURITZEN, ARCHITECT

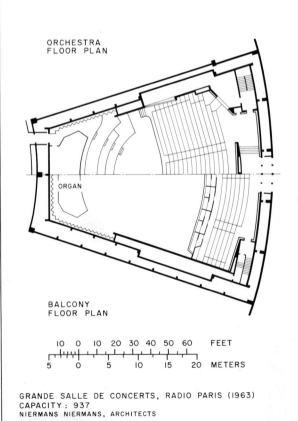

ORCHESTRA
FLOOR PLAN

ORGAN

BALCONY
FLOOR PLAN

10 0 10 20 30 40 50 60 FEET
5 0 5 10 15 20 METERS

GRANDE SALLE DE CONCERTS, RADIO PARIS (1963)
CAPACITY: 937
NIERMANS NIERMANS, ARCHITECTS

Acoustical conditions in television studios are not as critical as those in radio studios because the settings, scenery, and properties installed for a program will change the original acoustical environment of the studio anyway.

Acoustical conditions are basically dead in a television studio. Reverberation, if necessary, can be increased by using appropriate settings and properties, movable (portable) acoustical screens, and artificial reverberation. If more reverberant conditions are required for the sake of the performers themselves, the portion of the program requiring a longer RT can be produced in an adequately reverberant radio studio, called a *satellite audio studio*.

Television studios are constructed in different sizes, according to the required floor area and height. There are four main types:

1. *Audience studios* with permanent audience seating. Their area may be as large as 15,000 sq ft (1,400 sq m) and their volume about 500,000 cu ft (14,200 cu m).

2. *General-purpose studios*, for all types of programs.

3. Small *interview* and *announce studios*.

4. *Dubbing suites*.

A considerable clear height is usually required over the working area of the larger studios to accommodate the lighting grid, with its system of catwalks, and for flying the scenery.

Television studios normally have most of the following auxiliary rooms: production (video) control room, with a required RT of about 0.25 sec; sound (audio) control room; lighting control room; sound-effects room; announcer's booth, with a required RT of about 0.25 to 0.30 sec; and a number of storage rooms. The control rooms, usually grouped in a suite, are often located one story higher than the studio floor (Fig. 10.5). Occasionally sound control can take place in the studio

Fig. 10.5   Television audience studio of Place de Radio Canada, Montreal (1972). (Architectural Department of the Canadian Broadcasting Corporation.)

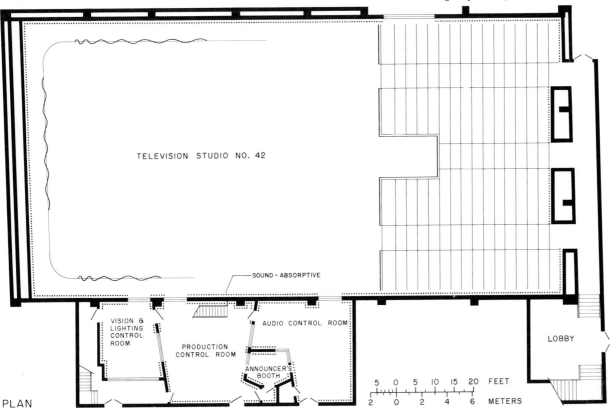

TELEVISION STUDIO NO. 42

SOUND - ABSORPTIVE

VISION & LIGHTING CONTROL ROOM

PRODUCTION CONTROL ROOM

AUDIO CONTROL ROOM

ANNOUNCER'S BOOTH

LOBBY

5   0   5   10   15   20   FEET

2   0   2   4   6   METERS

PLAN

on a portable sound-control console at a mixer carrying earphones.

In television audience studios a sound-amplification system is essential if the audience is to receive adequate coverage.

Simple and inexpensive acoustical treatments are usually applied in television studios, such as mineral-wool blankets (covered with metal lath, wire screen, glass cloth, chicken-wire mesh, or perforated board), wood-wool slabs, etc. The required low-frequency absorption can be obtained by using plywood, hardboard, or plasterboard panels, which simultaneously form a suitable treatment for the lower portion of the wall up to a height of 6 to 8 ft (1.8 to 2.4 m). Most of the wall treatment is eventually shielded by a cyclorama curtain spaced some 3 to 6 ft (0.9 to 1.8 m) away from the wall, thereby providing adequate space for unobtrusive circulation along the periphery of the studio.

10.4 Recording Studios

Recording studios (or recording rooms), which are similar to radio studios, with a dead acoustical environment, are usually connected with a control room and other auxiliary rooms. The floor area and shape depend on the furniture and technical equipment to be accommodated. Since, as a rule, the public is not admitted into recording studios, priority can be given to acoustical rather than aesthetic requirements. Temporary changes can be made in the acoustical treatment without regard to appearance and broad experimentation is possible.

10.5 Control Rooms

Every radio, television, or recording studio is linked with one or more control rooms, where the control desk, that is, the nerve center of the broadcast or recording session, is located. All the sound sources are controlled and mixed here, before the signal finally leaves the transmitter. Visual contact between the studio and control room is provided by a wide control window (Fig. 14.33) with an unobstructed view of the studio floor. As long as the studio floor area does not exceed about 800 to 1,200 sq ft (75 to 110 sq m), both control room and studio can be on the same floor level. Control rooms linked with studios of larger size must be elevated.

The size and shape of the control room depend on how many people and how much equipment it must accommodate, for example, audio console, monitoring and talk-back facilities, tape and disk reproducers, tape recorder, clock, reverberation control unit, video monitor, intercom key panel, and seats for the control personnel.

In control rooms an RT of about 0.4 sec is recommended at the mid-frequency range.

10.6 Motion-picture Studios

The site for a motion-picture studio is chosen generally as a compromise between quiet surroundings and reasonable accessibility.

Motion-picture studios are usually built as large halls with highly absorbent enclosures so that the sets can contribute their own acoustical characteristics as required. Economy in construction and efficiency of operation suggest that several large-size motion-picture studios be grouped together. This allows set construction and preparation to be carried out in one or more studios while normal production continues in the adjacent ones. Provision for the required short RT and for a high degree of noise and vibration isolation within these studios is the main acoustical objective.

BIBLIOGRAPHY

Books

Duschinsky, W. J.: *Television Stations*, Reinhold Publishing Corporation, New York, 1954, 136 pp.

Parkin, P. H., and H. R. Humphreys: *Acoustics, Noise and Buildings*, Frederick A. Praeger, Inc., New York, 1958, chap. 5.

Nisbett, A.: *The Technique of the Sound Studio*, Hastings House, Publishers, Inc., New York, 1962, 288 pp.

Periodicals

"Radiohus, Oslo, Norway," *Progressive Architecture*, September 1947, pp. 67–70.

"Radio and Television Buildings," *Architectural Record*, June 1949, pp. 120–141.

Beranek, L. L.: "Broadcast Studio Redesign," *J. SMPTE*, October 1955, pp. 550–559.

Gilford, C. L. S.: "The Acoustical Design of Talk Studios and Listening Rooms," *Proc. IEE*, May 1959, pp. 245–258.

Rettinger, M.: "Acoustic Considerations in the Design of Recording Studios," *J. Audio Eng. Soc.*, vol. 9, no. 3, pp. 178–183, 1961.

Schaudinischky, L., and A. Schwartz: "The Acoustical Design of Multi-purpose Recording Studios in Existing Buildings," *Applied Acoustics*, October 1970, pp. 283–298.

CHAPTER ELEVEN

Sound-amplification Systems

It has been mentioned in preceding chapters that the sound level can be increased at the back of an auditorium if the shape and volume of the room are acoustically favorable, suitable reflective surfaces have been provided, RT is optimum, acoustical defects have been successfully avoided, and disturbing noise has been eliminated from the auditorium.

In large halls, however, no matter how much attention has been given to these points, speech level is often too low for satisfactory hearing conditions. Therefore, in large auditoriums and outdoors a *sound-amplification system* is nearly always necessary for adequate loudness and good sound distribution.

It is difficult to specify the exact size and volume of a small or medium-sized auditorium above which a sound-amplification system is needed. For example, in the ancient arena of Verona, Italy, still used today, 20,000 spectators enjoy opera without the aid of any sound system.

A professional performer can make himself understood in front of 1,500 to 2,000 listeners without a speech-reinforcement system as long as the audience is quiet and attentive and the background noise in the room is properly controlled (Chap. 15). However, this is strenuous for both performer and audience: the performer must exert a special effort to communicate to such a large audience, and the attention span of the listeners who have to make a similar effort to hear lasts for a limited time.

In an acoustically well-designed auditorium a sound system will normally be needed if the room volume exceeds 60,000 cu ft (1,700 cu m) and if the voice must travel more than 60 ft (18 m) to a listener (Fig. 11.1), but in certain cases, a sound system may be required in rooms having a volume greater than about 15,000 cu ft (425 cu m) if the room is filled to capacity (120 to 150 people), if it is heavily treated with sound-absorbing finishes, and if the distance between sound source and listener exceeds 40 ft (12 m). A sound system may be needed in small rooms if they are too noisy or if the room is extremely reverberant. Whether or not a sound-amplification system is needed depends on the acoustical conditions in the room, the intensity of the voice of the performer, whether he is talking or singing, the distance between sound source and listener, and the prevailing background-noise level.

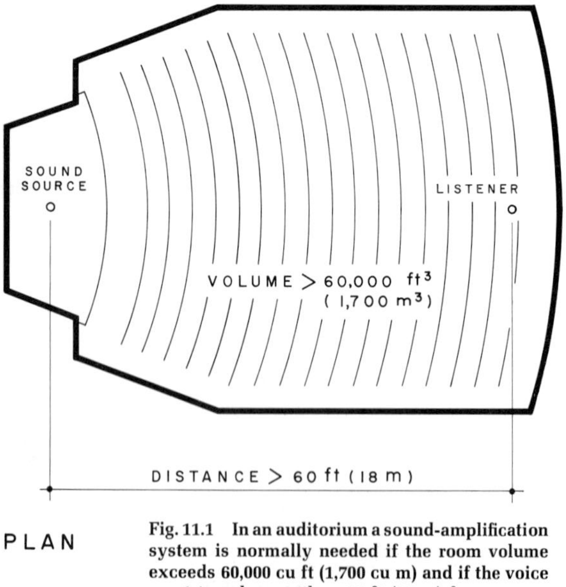

11.1 Principal Uses of Sound Amplification

Sound amplification systems are used for the following purposes:

1. To reinforce the sound level in an auditorium or in outdoor locations when the sound source is too weak to be heard
2. To provide amplified sound for overflow audiences
3. To increase the sound level on the stage of an auditorium for the benefit of performers or listeners seated on the stage
4. To provide the sound in motion-picture theaters
5. To minimize room reverberation

Fig. 11.1 In an auditorium a sound-amplification system is normally needed if the room volume exceeds 60,000 cu ft (1,700 cu m) and if the voice must travel more than 60 ft (18 m) from source to listener.

6. To provide artificial reverberation in rooms which are too dead for satisfactory listening, for example, *assisted resonance* in the Royal Festival Hall, London

7. To provide a multitude of electroacoustical facilities in theaters, opera houses, and the like for the convenience of the audience, performers, and staff, and also to produce sound effects

8. To operate electronic organs, chimes, carillons, etc.

9. To reduce the masking effect of an excessive background-noise level in an auditorium or in the open air

10. To distribute radio or recorded programs in factories, schools, hospitals, hotels, restaurants, recreational buildings, etc., for entertainment, audio instruction, or therapeutic purposes, and to enhance morale, thus increasing productivity and the quality of the product

11. To provide paging and announcing facilities in offices, stores, industrial buildings, schools, hotels, hospitals, transportation buildings, or in any other building for the purpose of transmitting spoken or recorded announcements or for locating individuals

12. To provide personal communicating facilities between individuals at separated locations in the same or different buildings

13. For signaling, that is, relaying instructions for emergency action or for indicating the beginning and end of work periods

14. To provide individual hearing aids in auditoriums

15. To provide simultaneous translation for certain types of conferences

Some of these functions, namely 10 to 15, also fall under the classification of a *public-address system* rather than a sound-amplification system. While a public-address system produces artificial (not necessarily amplified) sound in remote locations which could not be supplied with direct or amplified sound, the purpose of a sound-amplification system is to reinforce the sound of a visible source in large rooms.

The remainder of this chapter is devoted mainly to sound-amplification systems used to reinforce the sound level in auditoriums. Generally a sound system is expected to meet the following criteria:

1. It should properly transmit a wide range of frequencies (from about 30 Hz to about 12,000 Hz) in order to maintain a correct balance between fundamentals and harmonics, to achieve perfect tone color for each musical instrument, and to provide clear, undistorted sound, that is, high intelligibility for the spoken word.

2. It should provide a wide dynamic range; that is, a pianissimo sound must be clearly audible, and a fortissimo must be reproduced without distortion.

3. It should be free from disturbing echoes or feedback.

4. It should create a sufficiently low room reverberation.

5. It should remain undetected. The illusion should be preserved that the amplified sound comes from the natural sound source. The audience should be unaware of the existence of a sound-amplification system, and the acoustical excellence of any performance should be attributed to the performers and to the acoustics of the auditorium.

In a relatively small auditorium a sound-amplification system will remain undetected if the loudspeaker is placed right beside the person who is speaking or directly above him. The time delay between the arrival of the direct and amplified sound should not exceed $\frac{1}{50}$ sec; this means a maximum separation of 23 to 25 ft (7 to 8 m) between the speaker and the loudspeaker.

A sound-amplification system should be used with moderation and restraint. It should serve the needs of talkers, singers, actors, and musicians and should be subordinate to them. In the layout and use of a sound system the human scale should be observed.

11.2 System Components

A detailed discussion of the system components is beyond the scope of this book, but it can be noted that every single-channel sound-amplification system is a hookup of three essential components: *microphone, amplifier,* and *loudspeaker* (Fig. 11.2).

Fig. 11.2 Basic components of a single-channel sound-amplification system.

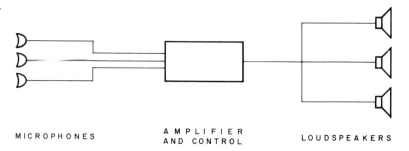

MICROPHONES   AMPLIFIER
                     AND CONTROL   LOUDSPEAKERS

The microphone, placed near the actual sound source, picks up the sound energy radiated by the source, converts it into electric energy, and feeds it into the amplifier. The amplifier increases the magnitude of the electric signal and delivers it to the loudspeaker, which converts the electric signal into air-borne sound waves for distribution to the listeners at a required level. A sound system will give satisfactory results only if all components are of the highest quality, if its design is carefully integrated with the architectural and acoustical characteristics of the auditorium, and if it is operated by a competent person who understands the sound program and can adapt to different performers.

11.3 Loudspeaker Systems

If the microphones are to be located at the sending end of an auditorium, three principal types of loudspeaker systems are available:

1. The centrally located system with a single cluster of loudspeakers over the sound source

2. The distributed system, using a number of overhead loudspeakers located throughout the auditorium

3. The stereophonic system, with two or more clusters of loudspeakers around the proscenium opening or the sound source

The *central* (or *front-of-the-room*) *system* (Fig. 11.3), the preferred one, gives maximum realism because the amplified sound comes from the same direction as the original sound. This creates the impression

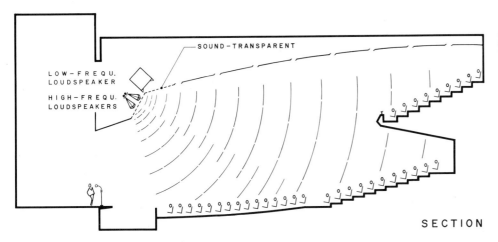

Fig. 11.3 Central, or front-of-the-room, loudspeaker system.

SECTION

of increased loudness and clarity, but the audience identifies the sound with the performer, not with the loudspeaker.

Although as a rule it is preferable to use a central loudspeaker system, there are many situations in which a *distributed system* (Fig. 11.4) must be used, for example:

1. In auditoriums with a ceiling height too low for installation of a central system

2. Where a majority of the listeners would not have an adequate sight line to a central loudspeaker

3. When sound has to be provided for overflow audiences

4. In large halls (convention halls, ballrooms, terminal buildings, etc.) where maximum flexibility is required to amplify sound sources in any part of the hall and where the amplified sound has to override the prevailing high background-noise level

5. In halls where the possibility exists of dividing the space into several smaller areas

Fig. 11.4 Distributed loudspeaker system.

SECTION

While realism cannot be expected from a distributed loudspeaker system, it does provide high intelligibility if the room is not too reverberant.

In the distributed system several loudspeakers are placed in the ceiling, facing down toward the audience and operated at a relatively low but comfortable sound level. Each loudspeaker is placed to cover only a specified area. The loudspeakers of a distributed system should be about 20 to 45 ft (6 to 13.5 m) above the floor level.

If amplified sound is supplied through a distributed system to a listener seated at the rear of a very long room, he will receive the amplified sound from a loudspeaker overhead before the direct sound from the speaker reaches him, because direct sound travels in air at the rate of 1,130 ft per sec (344 m per sec) while the electronically amplified signals between microphone and loudspeakers travel with the speed of light. If this delay in the arrival of the natural sound is excessive (65 msec or more), the sound will appear to come from the loudspeaker; the result is an artificial echo, loss of intelligibility, and a loss of the illusion of reality on the part of the listener. This can be overcome if an appropriate time-delay mechanism is introduced in the electric circuit of the amplification system. Such a system delays the amplified sound in the loudspeakers so that the amplified sound reaches the listeners at the same time as the direct (natural) sound.

The simultaneous use of both central and distributed loudspeaker systems is feasible in certain auditoriums and sometimes necessary.

A *stereophonic sound system* employs two or more microphones adequately spaced in front of the performing area and connected through separate amplifying channels to two or more corresponding loudspeakers, which must be spaced in front of the listening area in the same pattern as their corresponding microphones. Such a system preserves the illusion that the sound is coming from the original, unamplified source, because the sound will, in fact, approach from loudspeakers above (or below) the original source at intensities proportional to the distance from the source to the microphone and because the ear is unable to locate sound sources in the vertical plane; it can locate them only in the horizontal plane.

A stereophonic sound system, used mostly on large stages where the sound originates from moving sources or grouped voices and instruments, preserves the audio illusion in the spatial distribution of sound sources. It increases the realism of sound and listening pleasure remarkably. It must be emphasized, however, that in stereophonic reproduction sounds should be separated only where musically required, without destroying the necessary coherence between them. Using a stereophonic sound system in auditoriums demands particular attention to achieving the optimum layout of equipment and including an increased number of system components in the overall design.

If the microphones are distributed in an auditorium (parliamentary halls, conference halls, etc.), the loudspeaker layout requires an individual solution on every occasion.

In placing the loudspeakers, it must be remembered that (1) every listener in the room must have a sight line on the particular loudspeaker planned to supply him with amplified sound; (2) a loudspeaker cluster (particularly the central type) requires a great deal of space; and (3) concealed loudspeakers must be hidden behind a sound-transparent grille which should not contain large-scale elements. The loudspeaker should not be placed behind a sound-reflective panel.

Loudspeakers should always radiate their sound energy on the sound-absorbing audience with no (or minimum) sound energy radiated on sound-reflective surfaces. This is particularly important in auditoriums with excessive RT.

Various types of loudspeakers can be used for both the central and distributed system. In certain cases *line*, or *column*, loudspeakers are preferred to the conventional radial or multicellular horns. Column loudspeakers concentrate most of the sound into a beam which has a wide angular spread in the horizontal plane and a narrow spread in the vertical plane, as shown in Fig. 11.5.

Even though the selection of the central loudspeaker cluster is in the hands of the electrical engineer, integrating the space-consuming central loudspeaker system into the architectural layout is always a serious problem unless the architect is consulted at the outset.

Particular attention must be paid to the locations of microphones relative to the loudspeakers in both central and distributed systems, in order to avoid the familiar feedback, that is, squealing or howling. This phenomenon, typical of a poorly designed sound system, usually occurs (1) if the sound radiated from the loudspeaker is picked up by the microphone, (2) whenever reflective surfaces of the room are so located that reflected sound is concentrated on the microphone, (3) in highly reverberant rooms. The feedback is often noticeable in the frequency range of maximum reverberation, which can be eliminated by the method called *critical band equalization* in electroacoustics. This method, for example, makes it possible to maintain a relatively long RT in a church without danger of feedback.

The control of a sound-amplification system during use in auditoriums of particular acoustical importance (such as theaters, opera houses, concert halls, and multipurpose auditoriums) takes place from a properly sound-insulated control room, usually located behind the audience in the rear of the room. In addition to the sound-control console, a sound-control room normally also houses such other equipment as amplifier racks, communication switches, tape recorder, record player, mixer controls, and monitor loudspeakers. The sound-control room should have a window facing the audience area that can be opened, so that the operator can see and hear the performance under the same conditions as the audience; it should have a view over a considerable portion of the audience area; and it should be accessible during the performance but not through the audience area.

In special cases the sound system is controlled from within the audience area. Although this arrangement sacrifices a few seats to accommodate the sound-control console, it normally results in increased quality of control.

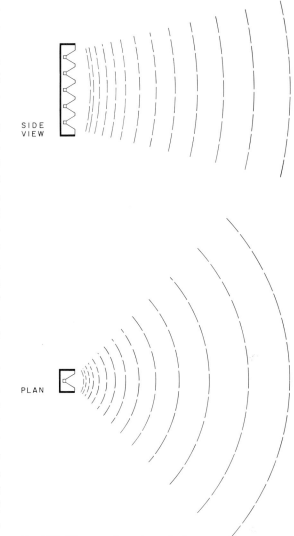

Fig. 11.5 Diagram of a column loudspeaker, showing its wide angular spread in the horizontal plane and its narrow angular spread in the vertical plane.

BIBLIOGRAPHY

Books

Rettinger, M.: *Practical Electroacoustics*, Chemical Publishing Company, Inc., New York, 1955, 271 pp.
Parkin, P. H., and H. R. Humphreys: *Acoustics, Noise and Buildings*, Frederick A. Praeger, Inc., New York, 1958, chap. 6.
Burris-Meyer, H., and V. Mallory: *Sound in the Theater*, Radio Magazines, Inc., Mineola, N.Y., 1959, 95 pp.
McPartland, J. F.: "Sound Systems," in J. H. Callender (ed.), *Time-saver Standards*, 4th ed., McGraw-Hill Book Company, New York, 1966, pp. 930–933.

Periodicals

Muncey, R. W., and A. F. B. Nickson: "Improving Church Acoustics with Sound Reinforcement," *J. RAIC*, August 1956, pp. 306–308.

Klepper, D. L.: "Sound Systems," *Progressive Architecture*, August 1961, pp. 140–148.

Newman, R. B., and W. J. Cavanaugh: "Sound Systems," *Architectural Record*, December 1961, pp. 161–162; January 1962, p. 158.

Klepper, D. L.: "Designing Sound-amplification Systems," *Architectural and Engineering News*, March 1964, pp. 26–35.

Boner, C. P., and C. R. Boner: "Sound-reinforcing System Design," *Applied Acoustics*, April 1968, pp. 115–119.

Davis, D.: "Sound Systems Equalization," *Progressive Architecture*, September 1969, pp. 121–123.

Caddy, R. S.: "Elements of Voice-reinforcement Systems in Halls," *Applied Acoustics*, October 1969, pp. 259–268.

Parkin, P. H., and K. Morgan: "Assisted Resonance in the Royal Festival Hall, London: 1965–1969," *J. Acoust. Soc. Am.*, November 1970, pp. 1025–1035.

Unfortunately a large number of existing auditoriums, practically all over the world, suffer from acoustics ranging from poor to disastrous. Some were built when the science of acoustics was in a comparatively undeveloped state and architects had no reliable acoustical basis on which to proceed in auditorium design; achieving acoustical success was often a question of sheer luck. Some auditoriums specifically built for selected purposes were subsequently used for a much wider range of functions, which revealed acoustical defects.

12.1 Room-acoustical Features in Auditoriums of Poor Acoustical Design

In auditoriums of poor acoustical design, one or more of the following features are usually noticeable:

1. Reverberation is excessive.
2. Loudness is inadequate.
3. Such acoustical defects as echo, long-delayed reflections, sound concentrations, and dead spots are obvious.
4. The sound-amplification system is inadequate.
5. Disturbing noises interfere with the sound program.

Chapters 4 and 6 showed that the RT depends on the volume of the auditorium and the amount of sound-absorbing elements (acoustical treatment, audience, carpet, etc.) in the room. The RT can vary between 0.5 sec (in a normal living room) and 8 to 12 sec or more (in a large church). If the RT is short (about 1 sec or less), the reverberation of the room will generally be considered pleasant and acceptable because it does not interfere with the sound program. On the other hand, if it is longer than 1 sec, it will interfere with speech, and if it is much longer than 2 sec, it will spoil the enjoyment of most types of music.

Excessive RT in auditoriums occurs either because the auditorium is too large (normally the height of the room is excessive) or because sound-absorbing surface treatment is missing. As is well known, lack of acoustical treatment will not cause excessive reverberation as long as the auditorium is filled to capacity; the absorption provided by the audience will satisfactorily reduce the RT (sometimes even to excess). Only when the auditorium is partially occupied does the room become too reverberant. Recommended RTs for auditoriums were given in Fig. 6.14.

Inadequate loudness is due to the lack of sound-reflective surface treatment around the sound source and along the ceiling and also to a level floor in the audience area. Poor acoustical design in several auditoriums is compounded by the incorrect use of acoustical tiles over the entire ceiling area, which also contributes to inadequate loudness. Loudness is usually considered adequate as long as listeners are reasonably close to the sound source, but at a distance of 20 ft (6 m) or more, loudness drops and the effect of excessive room reverberation becomes disturbingly apparent.

Such acoustical defects as echo, long-delayed reflection, flutter echo, and sound concentration are due to the lack of sound-absorptive treatment along the defect-producing areas or undesirable parallelism between opposite reflective surfaces close to the sound source.

CHAPTER TWELVE

Acoustical Correction of Existing Auditoriums

Since the science of electroacoustics was embryonic when many of these acoustically poor auditoriums were built, it is no surprise that their sound-amplification systems usually emphasized acoustical defects, increased excessive reverberation, and did little to enhance intelligibility. In addition, they were inappropriately operated, often resulting in annoying feedback.

About 20 years ago the concept of sound insulation, so prominent today, was virtually nonexistent; information on the sound insulation of enclosures was fragmentary, sometimes even misleading. In the last decades noise sources and their intensity levels have multiplied to a destructive extent. For all these reasons, exposure to uncontrolled interior (mechanical) and exterior noises and vibrations is probably the most serious acoustical deficiency of existing auditoriums. Figure 12.1 shows several features in an auditorium of poor acoustical design.

12.2 Recommended Measures to Improve Acoustics

Existing environmental and financial considerations usually limit the measures available for acoustical improvement of an existing auditorium.

Reduction of the RT can be accomplished by reducing the room

Fig. 12.1 Common faults in an auditorium of poor acoustical design: (1) excessive room height with respect to length; (2) lack of acoustical treatment along the walls opposite the sound source; (3) lack of sound reflectors at the sound source; (4) parallelism between opposite surfaces at the sound source; (5) level audience floor; (6) curved rear wall; (7) aisle along the longitudinal axis of the audience area; (8) excessive balcony depth.

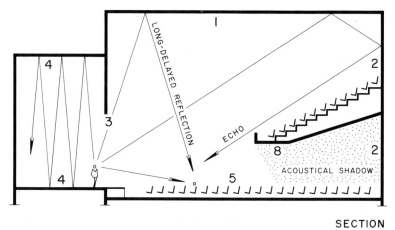

SECTION

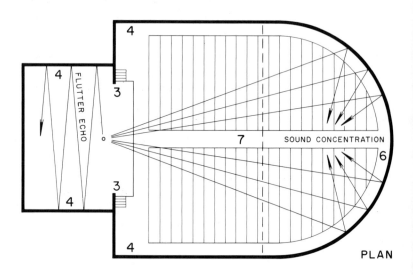

PLAN

volume or by introducing sound-absorptive surface treatment along the enclosing members (walls, doors, etc.). Reduction of the room volume is uneconomical because it would seriously interfere with existing structural, mechanical, and lighting conditions; acoustical treatment is a more realistic means of improvement. The echo-producing wall surfaces opposite the sound source should be treated first, then furthermost portions of the side walls, and perhaps the perimeter of the ceiling. If the existing ceiling is so high that it creates harmful long-delayed reflections, the entire ceiling should be treated acoustically. For the selection of suitable sound-absorptive surface treatment, pertinent recommendations described in Chaps. 5 and 6 should be followed. The use of carpet along floor and walls, upholstered seats, and draperies along fenestrated or sound-reflective walls should be also considered.

To improve loudness in an existing room, the sound source should be raised as much as possible, to provide an ample supply of direct sound to the listeners. Large sound-reflective surfaces should be suspended around the sound source and along the ceiling. By creating short-delayed reflections, they ensure that the time delay between direct and reflected sound does not exceed 30 to 35 msec, corresponding to a maximum path difference of 35 to 40 ft (11 to 12 m) between them. Raking a level audience floor is an unrealistic solution because in addition to the high cost it would require stairs or steps at entrace doors, difficult to incorporate into any layout. Efficient and ample sound reflectors will counterbalance the harmful effect of a level audience floor because sound reflections will not reach the listeners at a grazing incidence, thus carrying powerful additional sound energy to the remote seats. For sound reflectors, plastered walls, brick, concrete, plywood at least $\frac{3}{4}$ in. (19 mm) thick, or gypsum board panels at least $\frac{5}{8}$ in. (16 mm) thick weighing at least about 2.5 lb per sq ft (12 kg per sq m) should be used.

Echo, flutter echo, etc., can be eliminated by using acoustical finishes along the defect-producing surfaces.

The necessity for replacing an existing poor speech-reinforcement system with a new, high-quality sound-amplification system (Chap. 11) is obvious. A properly designed, installed, and operated sound system will contribute to the desirable reduction of room reverberation; adequate loudness, particularly when for any of the reasons described above the entire ceiling of the auditorium is acoustically treated; the elimination of acoustical defects; and the reduction of the harmful interference of excessive interior and exterior noises. Elimination of undesirable noises and vibrations is dealt with in subsequent chapters.

Figure 12.2 illustrates a practical example of an acoustical correction in an existing auditorium, originally built with excessive height and a ceiling lined with acoustical tiles. The acoustical correction included (1) installation of properly splayed and tilted sound reflectors around the podium and suspended from the ceiling (Fig. 12.3), (2) floor and desk-wall carpeting and sound-absorptive treatment along the echo-producing rear wall (Fig. 12.4), (3) hanging a Fiberglas drapery along one of the side walls, and (4) installation of a high-quality speech-reinforcement system. Figure 12.5 shows the interior of the hall after acoustical correction.

BIBLIOGRAPHY

Digest

Improving Room Acoustics, Building Research Station Digest 82, Garston, Herts, May 1967, 8 pp.

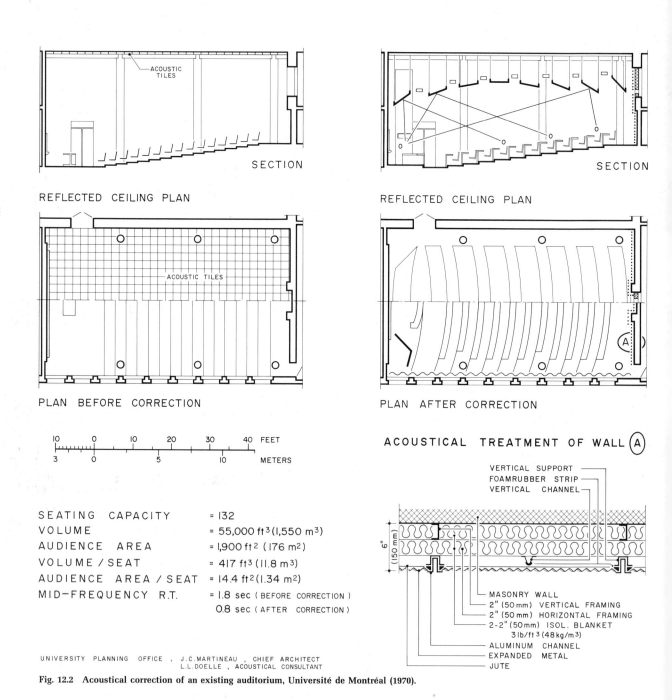

SEATING CAPACITY = 132
VOLUME = 55,000 ft³ (1,550 m³)
AUDIENCE AREA = 1,900 ft² (176 m²)
VOLUME / SEAT = 417 ft³ (11.8 m³)
AUDIENCE AREA / SEAT = 14.4 ft² (1.34 m²)
MID-FREQUENCY R.T. = 1.8 sec (BEFORE CORRECTION)
0.8 sec (AFTER CORRECTION)

UNIVERSITY PLANNING OFFICE , J.C.MARTINEAU , CHIEF ARCHITECT
L.L.DOELLE , ACOUSTICAL CONSULTANT

Fig. 12.2 Acoustical correction of an existing auditorium, Université de Montréal (1970).

Fig. 12.3 Suspended sound reflectors in the auditorium illustrated in Fig. 12.2. (Photograph by Bowe Studio.)

Fig. 12.4 Close-up of wall A in the auditorium shown in Fig. 12.2. (Photograph by Bowe Studio.)

Fig. 12.5 Interior of the 132-seat auditorium shown in Fig. 12.2 after acoustical correction. (Photograph by Bowe Studio.)

PART THREE

Environmental Noise Control

W ith the growing urbanization related to the enormous growth in transportation and the increased use of new, larger, and more powerful machines everywhere, noise has become an unavoidable by-product of our mechanized life and a serious hazard to our health. In the past few decades the overall noise level in the average North American home has more than doubled.

The fundamental objective of noise control is to provide an acceptable acoustical environment indoors and outdoors, so that the intensity and character of all sounds within or around a given building will be compatible with the intended use of the space. The provision of an acceptable acoustical environment, that is, the elimination or reasonable reduction of interior and exterior noises, is the subject of subsequent chapters. Freedom from noise is one of the most valuable environmental qualities a building or exterior space can possess today.

13.1 Effects of Noise

All sounds that are distracting, annoying, or harmful to everyday activities (work, rest, entertainment, or study) are regarded as *noise*. As a standard definition, any sound judged as undesirable by the recipient is considered to be noise. Thus, even speech or music will be regarded as noise when they are unwanted. Whether or not a sound is undesired by a person will depend not only on the loudness of the sound but also on its frequency, continuity, time of occurrence, and information content, and also on such subjective aspects as the origin of the sound and the recipient's state of mind and temperament. A child practicing on the piano may be a musical treat to his father while the neighbors contemplate calling the police. Aircraft noise may be acceptable during the day in a downtown office but will certainly be an undesirable intrusion upon rest or sleep in the late evening or night at home. In general, noise creates a far greater disturbance at night than it does during the day. An incessantly dripping tap is not a loud noise, but it can be irritating; on the other hand, a high level of sound, like that of a full orchestra playing fortissimo, can be an intense pleasure.

An individual tends to ignore the noise he creates himself if it constitutes a natural accompaniment to work, such as the noise of a typewriter or a working machine. As a rule, noises of mechanical or electrical origin, caused by fans, transformers, motors, pumps, vacuum cleaners, or washing machines, are always more annoying than noises of natural origin (wind, rain, waterfall, etc.). High-frequency noises are more disturbing than low-frequency noises.

The effects of noise ranging from distracting to severely disturbing are well known. Even a faint noise can interfere with listening to speech or music, causing a masking effect and raising the threshold of audibility. It can interfere with rest and sleep and may even disrupt or prevent dreams. However, the human body's power of adaptation to a noisy environment is amazingly effective, particularly if the noise is continuous, not too loud, and carries no meaningful information, that is, intelligible speech or identifiable music.

Moderately loud noise, above about 70 dB, may produce nervousness,

CHAPTER THIRTEEN

Introduction to Environmental Noise Control

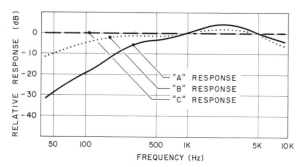

Fig. 13.1 A, B, and C responses of standard sound-level meters.

indisposition, auditory fatigue, indigestion, and circulatory troubles. Very loud noise, above about 85 dB, may induce a serious deterioration in a person's general state of health; and if long endured, temporary or permanent loss of hearing can result. Excessive and lasting noises are implicated in such troubles as heart disease, hypertension, and stomach ulcer.

The detrimental effect of noise on working efficiency and production has been statistically proved in several fields of industry. Production drops and workers make more errors when exposed for a sustained period to a high noise level, above about 80 dB, but this does not mean that people work most efficiently in soundproof rooms. On the contrary, it has also been observed that when the acoustical environment of a work room is too quiet, production drops and workers make more mistakes. This proves that a certain amount of noise is easily tolerated, and indeed a certain amount of noise is needed to maintain sanity. Anyone who has had an opportunity of spending time in a soundproof chamber (such as an *anechoic room*) into which not the faintest sound can penetrate, knows that human beings simply cannot tolerate a perfectly soundproof environment for any length of time. It is not silence which is needed but quiet: the absence of distraction, not the utter lack of sound. This recognition is taken into account by the suppliers of background music, which, properly selected and timed, can create a pleasant and profitable environment in a department store, office, supermarket, hotel, or workshop.

13.2 Measurement of Noise

Noise can be measured by means of a sound-level meter (Chap. 3) in terms of decibels. To measure sound or noise physically and also to relate the measurements to subjective human reactions, the sound-level meter provides alternate frequency-response characteristics by including *weighting networks* designated A, B, and C, as shown in Fig. 13.1. These networks selectively discriminate against low and high frequencies according to the equal-loudness-level curves in Fig. 3.7 and approximate the frequency response of the human ear by following the 40-, 70-, and 100-phon equal-loudness curves, respectively. If, for example, A weighting is used, for measuring noise levels below 55 dB, it will indicate the *A-weighted sound level*, and the measurements should be labeled dB-A. B weighting is used for noise between 55 and 85 dB, and C weighting for noise above 85 dB. When noise is measured on a sound-level meter with the frequency-response weighting selected according to the level of the measured noise, the reading obtained is the sound level. Readings obtained with the C (or *flat*) frequency response are sound pressure levels. The A network is sometimes used as a measure of the extent of irritation caused by noise. It is essential to record the weighting position with the observed level.

Figure 13.1 shows, for example, that on the A scale a noise of 50 Hz would be shown at a level 30 dB less than a noise of 1000 Hz, without any change in their sound pressure levels.

When the frequency characteristic of a noise is to be investigated, the sound-level meter is used with a frequency analyzer. The analyzer has a set of filters which allow only certain bands of frequencies, one band at a time, to pass through. Only those frequencies which are allowed through will be measured by the sound-level meter. The usual type of analyzer, called an *octave-band analyzer*, is divided into several bands of one octave each.

Sound levels for typical noise sources, measured with a sound-level meter, are listed in Table 13.1.

TABLE 13.1 Typical Average Noise Levels (Some Measured at a Given Distance from the Source)

Noise source	Noise level, dB
Watch ticking	20
Quiet garden	30
Average quiet home	42
Quiet residential street	48
Private business office	50
Landscaped office	53
Large conventional office	60
Normal conversation, 3 ft (90 cm)	62
Passenger car in city traffic, 20 ft (6 m)	70
Quiet factory	70
Passenger car on highway, 20 ft (6 m)	76
Loud conversation, 3 ft (90 cm)	78
Noisy factory	80
Business machines, 3 ft (90 cm)	80
Teletype room of a newspaper	80
10-hp outboard motor, 50 ft (15 m)	88
Rush-hour city traffic, 10 ft (3 m)	90
Large jet taking off, 3,300 ft (1,000 m)	90
Sports car or truck, 30 ft (9 m)	94
Riveting gun, 3 ft (90 cm)	100
Power mower, 10 ft (3 m)	105
Rock music band	113
Large jet taking off, 500 ft (150 m)	115
50-hp siren, 100 ft (30 m)	138
Space rocket	175

The combined noise level of two or more noise sources is not the sum of the individual levels. The diagram in Fig. 13.2 can be used as a reasonable approximation of the combination of two noise levels, but it can also be used to combine any number of noise levels. If the sound pressure levels S_1 and S_2 of two noise sources are to be added, and if S_2 is greater than S_1, the total noise level in decibels is equal to $S_2 + N$, where N is the increment to be determined from Fig. 13.2, corresponding to the difference between the two sound pressure levels being added. It will be seen that when the sound pressure levels of two noise

DIFFERENCE (IN dB) BETWEEN TWO LEVELS BEING ADDED

INCREMENT (IN dB) TO BE ADDED TO HIGHER LEVEL

Fig. 13.2 Scale for combining noise levels.

sources are equal, the difference between them equals zero, and the resultant noise level is 3 dB higher than the level of either sound source. If several noise sources all having the same sound pressure levels are added, they will have a total sound pressure level which is 10 log q dB above the common sound pressure level, where q is the total number of noise sources.

Various methods are known and a variety of instruments used to measure vibration. Their description, however, is beyond the scope of this book.

13.3 Noise Sources

The main sources of noise in environmental noise control can be classified in two groups: (1) *Interior noises*, originating from people, household equipment, or machinery within a building. Partition walls, floors, doors, and windows must provide adequate protection against these noises inside the buildings. (2) *Outdoor noises*, originating from traffic, transportation, industry, exposed mechanical equipment in buildings, construction sites, road repairs, sports and other outdoor activities, and advertising.

If the noise originates in one room and the recipient is in another room, they are called the *source room* and the *receiving room*, respectively.

13.3.1 Interior Noises   The most common noise sources for which people are responsible are those produced by radio and television, musical instruments, door banging, loud conversation, and traffic on a staircase. To this can be added the sound of people moving, children playing, babies crying, etc.

Building noises are produced by machines and household equipment, such as fans, motors, compressors, refrigerators, dishwashers, garbage-disposal units, washing machines, dryers, vacuum cleaners, air conditioners, food blenders, can openers, floor polishers, electric shavers, hair dryers, etc. They represent serious sources of interference since they are increasingly replaced by more up-to-date units of greater output, higher speed, and consequently increased noise.

Extremely high noise levels are produced in certain industrial buildings by manufacturing or production processes.

Measured noise levels like those listed in Table 13.1 provide us with important clues whenever noises have to be reduced in the receiving room by the use of appropriate sound-insulating constructions, discussed in Chap. 14.

The noise level at any position in a room is made up of two parts: (1) sound received *directly* from the source, and (2) the *reverberant* (or *reflected*) sound reaching a particular position after repeated reflections from the boundary surfaces of the room. This is illustrated in Fig. 13.3. Around the noise source the direct sound predominates, gradually falling off with increasing distance. Further away from the noise source the reverberant sound prevails throughout the room (provided that the noise source is nondirectional).

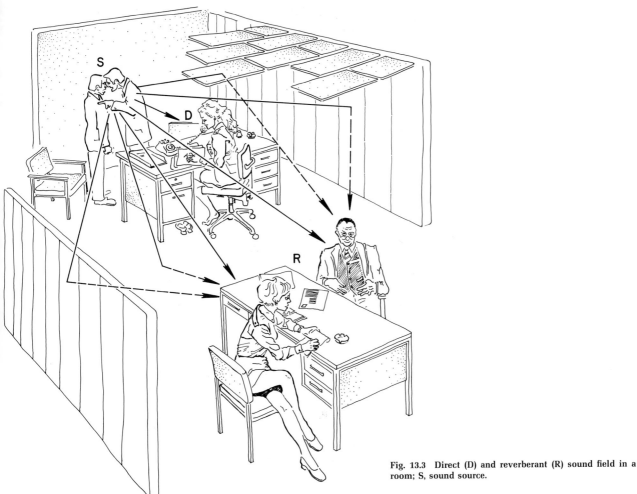

Fig. 13.3 Direct (D) and reverberant (R) sound field in a room; S, sound source.

13.3.2 Outdoor Noise   The most annoying noises of this category are produced by vehicular, rail, water, and air transportation, including trucks, buses, sports cars, motorcycles, railroad cars, diesel engines, motorboats, tugboats, and commercial and military aircraft. Additional sources of outdoor noise are to be found in exposed mechanical equipment in buildings (cooling towers, air conditioners, compressors) and earth-moving and construction equipment (air hammers, shovels, etc.). A preliminary noise survey should always be made at sites chosen for buildings in which quietness is essential (churches; recording, radio, and television studios; hospitals; schools; research laboratories, etc.) in order to make an allowance for the noise-control measures necessitated by outdoor noises.

Because of its particular significance and the extraordinary threat it poses to society, aircraft noise, is discussed separately in the following section. The problem of vehicular noise, because of its relationship to town planning, is included in Sec. 13.6.2.

The reduction of outdoor noise with distance is governed by the inverse-square law. A drop of 6 dB will be noticeable every time the distance between the source and recipient is doubled (Chap. 3), provided that there are no sound-reflective surfaces near the noise source. There is also an additional attenuation of outdoor noise due to molecular absorption, mainly at frequencies above 1000 Hz.

13.3.3 Aircraft Noise

Aircraft noise poses an unprecedented threat to our environment because it affects a rapidly increasing number of people. Air travel and transportation will continue to expand: by 1975 the John F. Kennedy Airport in New York will handle about 50 million people, and London (Heathrow) Airport will be used annually by about 31 million people. While aircraft noise (the greatest noise pollutant of our times) is being increasingly protested, it appears that the widespread dissatisfaction in many countries was not channeled quickly enough into effective protest. By the time the enormous sonic threat of the supersonic transport (SST) was realized, it became evident that the intensity of protests might not be able to overcome the fact that billions of dollars had been spent by England, France, and the United States to develop the supersonic aircraft. It is reasonable to predict that a heavy toll in terms of environmental destruction will have to be paid for the marginal increase (if any) in efficiency, economy, or convenience offered by the SST. At the time of writing, the issue in the United States remained in doubt.

In spite of the enormous effort to reduce aircraft noise, no technical breakthrough is in sight. By the time that some measures have been taken to alleviate, at least partially, the noise caused by aircraft, man's urge to fly faster or to increase profit will produce larger and more powerful aircraft, certainly with increased noise levels. And the takeoff and landing effort of these flying monsters with their high-powered machinery and enormous weight is certainly bound to create an increasingly high noise level. More and more people in urban areas will have to put up with aircraft noise or move to country over which aircraft do not normally fly. The need is ever more urgent, therefore, that architects and town planners take a serious look at this dangerous threat to our environment and make a determined effort to control aircraft noise by any means that environmental acoustics can offer.

Noises created by jet aircraft are different from those generated by propeller aircraft with piston engines. The noise characteristics of the different aircraft also vary with different power conditions. Jet noise originates from different parts of the engine, such as the jet, the compressor, and the turbine. The typical roar of a flying jet is generated by the violent mixing of the hot exhaust gases with the surrounding air, particularly noticeable during takeoff and climb, when maximum power is needed.

Airport authorities normally stipulate that after takeoff the noise level on the ground at the first built-up area reached by the aircraft should not exceed certain maximum values, for each direction of each runway. These maximum permissible noise levels are higher during the day than at night. The aircraft is free to achieve this limit in any preferred way, considerably affected by safety requirements. For landing, a descent slope of 3° to the horizontal has been adopted because for safety's sake the aircraft must come in at a low glide angle. This means that a very long corridor has to be left free of buildings for descending aircraft before they reach the runway threshold. Clearly, airports with runways which continue over water (lake or sea) can observe the noise-control requirements much more easily and with added safety.

In order to evaluate reactions of people to the noise and disturbance of aircraft, various scales and diagrams have been developed as a result of extensive studies to reflect subjective human response, such as the *noise and number index* (NNI), the *perceived noise level* (PNdB), *equal listener response* (ELR), and others. In establishing these scales an attempt has been made to take into account the objective and subjective influences which affect reactions, for example, intensity and frequency of the noise, duration and number of overflights heard, time characteristics (day or night), unexpectedness, unwantedness, connotation of danger, momentary interference with activity, etc. The interested reader is referred to the bibliography at the end of this chapter.

The most serious type of aircraft noise, basically a shock wave called *sonic boom*, is the well-known by-product of an aircraft flying at supersonic speed, that is, above about 770 mph (about 1,230 km per hr). A sonic boom is created continuously when an aircraft is flying at supersonic speed, and not only when it accelerates from subsonic to supersonic speed. The sonic boom will be heard, without warning, on the ground below and along both sides of the projected flight path. The affected area, that is, the width of this *belt* or *sonic carpet*, may extend over 50 to 80 miles (80 to 130 km), depending on the speed and altitude of the flying aircraft and on the prevailing atmospheric conditions. Although there is serious concern about the extent to which individuals and buildings can tolerate the sonic boom, it is also clear that a much larger segment of the population will be affected by it than by the noise of conventional aircraft. It is fair to hope that SST will be limited to operations over water until there is sufficient evidence that the physical and physiological consequences can be understood by the majority of the population. Some countries, for example, Switzerland, have banned the SST.

Another flying machine that is bound to cause objectionable noises in heavily populated urban areas is the vertical takeoff and landing aircraft (VTOL), for example, the helicopter. Thanks to its vertical takeoff capacity, it will continue to be used for a wide range of purposes. It is particularly helpful in providing convenient shuttle service between downtown areas and airports. The noise of a turbocopter flying at an altitude of 200 ft (60 m) is comparable to that of a heavy diesel truck 10 ft (3 m) away. The noise of a helicopter in level flight at about 1,000 ft (300 m) will probably cause the same disturbance as heavy traffic noise in a busy downtown area during rush hours. In areas close to helicopter stations (heliports) noise would be obviously much greater. However, if heliports were located on top of high-rise buildings, their noise could be accepted, for a short time at least, as part of the cacophony of the downtown area.

13.4 Airborne and Structure-borne Sound

Sound can be produced (1) in the air, for example, the human voice or a musical sound; (2) by impact, such as walking, dropping an object on the floor, or slamming a door; and (3) by machinery vibration. The sound thus generated travels from the source through various paths in a building.

If a sound is transmitted through the air only, it is called *airborne sound.* Someone talking, a singer, a violin, a trumpet—all generate airborne sounds (Fig. 13.4).

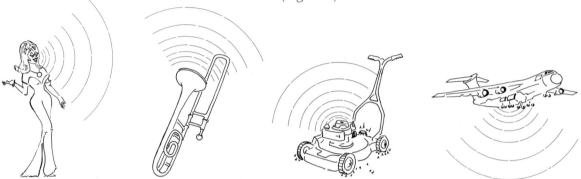

Fig. 13.4 Sources of airborne sounds.

When a sound source not only radiates its energy through the air but also simultaneously sets into vibration solid parts of the building structure, it is termed *structure-borne sound* or *impact sound.* The sounds of a cello or double bass, footstep noises, and much of the noise generated by motors, fans, and the like represent typical structure-borne sounds (Fig. 13.5).

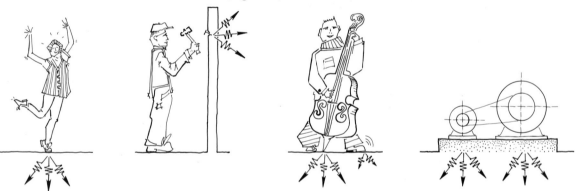

Fig. 13.5 Sources of structure-borne (or impact) sounds.

From the point of view of the recipient, structure-borne sounds cannot be distinguished from airborne sounds. Structure-borne sounds transmitted directly through the structure are reradiated from certain building elements, such as walls, slabs, panels, suspended ceilings, furred-out plaster, and building boards, and eventually reach the recipient as an airborne sound.

13.5 Transmission of Noise in Buildings

The transmission of airborne noise differs considerably from that of structure-borne noise. Air-borne noise is attenuated by air absorption and also by intervening enclosures (walls, floors, etc.), so that its effect is mostly confined to areas near its origin.

Structure-borne noise, by setting solid parts of the building structure into vibration, virtually multiplies the area of the sound-radiating surface, thereby increasing the radiated sound pressure. Sometimes this extension of the area of the sound-radiating surface is useful, even desirable, as for such musical instruments as the cello, double bass, and piano. In most cases, however, this phenomenon is very harmful. A vibrating heating pipe or water pipe alone can radiate only a small amount of airborne noise, due to its limited surface, but if, as is usual, these pipes are rigidly anchored to a wall or to a floor slab, additional large surfaces will be set into vibration, greatly increasing the radiated noise and transmitting the vibration over surprisingly wide areas.

The methods of suppressing airborne noise (airborne sound insulation) are different from those used to insulate structure-borne noise (structure-borne sound insulation). A boundary that provides good protection against the one may be a poor insulator against the other. It is therefore important to determine whether the noise to be controlled originates from an airborne sound, from a structure-borne sound, or from a mixture of both.

13.5.1 Airborne Noise Airborne noise originating in the source room can be transmitted to the receiving room in the following ways (Fig. 13.6): (1) along continuous air paths through openings, such as open doors and windows, ventilating ducts and grilles, shafts, crawl spaces,

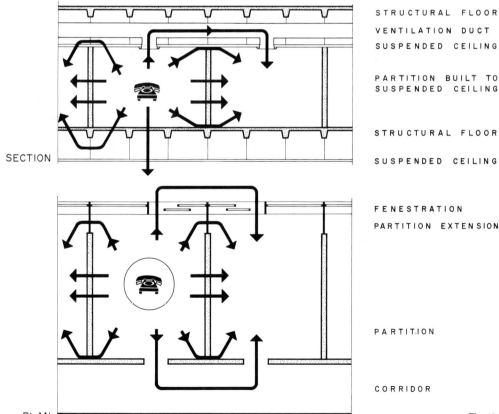

SECTION

STRUCTURAL FLOOR
VENTILATION DUCT
SUSPENDED CEILING

PARTITION BUILT TO
SUSPENDED CEILING

STRUCTURAL FLOOR
SUSPENDED CEILING

FENESTRATION
PARTITION EXTENSION

PARTITION

CORRIDOR

PLAN

Fig. 13.6 Transmission of airborne noises in a building.

gaps and cracks around doors, pipes, conduits, electrical fixtures, and built-in elements, and (2) by means of forced vibration set up in the boundaries (walls, floor, ceiling) of the source room and transmitted to the boundaries of the receiving room. This forced vibration is then reradiated in the receiving room. Actually what the listener hears in the receiving room is not a fraction of the original sound but a reproduction of it. If the source room and receiving room have a common boundary (partition wall or floor), the reradiated sound can be particularly noticeable unless the boundary in question offers sufficient resistance to vibrations, that is, its mass is adequate.

13.5.2 Structure-borne Noise and Vibration   Since they are readily transmitted with little attenuation and over great distances in a building, structure-borne noise and vibration should be suppressed at the source or as close to it as possible. This can be accomplished (1) by the use of adequately resilient flooring (carpeting, rubber tile, cork tile, etc.) to reduce impact transmission into the floor and (2) by the use of flexible mountings, antivibration pads, floating floors (Chap. 14), etc., to prevent the transmission of vibration and shock from various machines or exterior sources into the building.

**13.6   Methods of Environmental
     Noise Control**

Various methods can be followed to achieve an effective and economical elimination or reduction of noise inside and outside buildings. It is becoming strikingly obvious that the fight against an increasing number of harmful noises will lead to satisfactory results only if all people associated with the design and use of both the interior and exterior environment work to achieve the common goal.

Noise control can also be accomplished by means other than design, for example, through certain modifications of the source or transmission paths or by adequate reorganization of the entire noisy area. These measures are in the hands of the manufacturers, office management, etc.

13.6.1   Suppression of Noise at the Source   The most economical noise-control measure is to suppress the noise right at the source by choosing relatively quiet machines and equipment and by adopting manufacturing processes or working methods which do not cause disturbing noise levels. For example, the noise from doors slamming can be avoided by using sponge-rubber door stops. A change from riveting to welding or from hammering to hydraulic presses will eliminate some of the most intense noises in industry. The subway trains of Montreal and Paris run on rubber wheels; this eliminates at the source much of the noise normally associated with subways.

Proper maintenance of machinery is always a good noise-control practice because defective, loose, and vibrating components are always noise sources. Sometimes very noisy machines can be enclosed in specially designed housings if they cannot be made to operate quietly themselves. An enclosure around the offending unit should (1) have weight, (2) be impermeable to air, and (3) be lined with sound-absorbing material.

In the design and manufacture of typewriters, vacuum cleaners, motors, fans, compressors, boilers, etc., achieving a relatively noiseless operation is one of the competitive objectives. Electrically operated vehicles eliminate most of the noise normally generated by combustion engines.

Footstep noise can easily be reduced at the source by installing soft floor finishes such as carpet, cork, rubber tile, or vinyl tile.

Undesirable sounds can be also eliminated at the source by nontechnical means, for example by courtesy and consideration for others. The programs issued for the concerts in the Royal Festival Hall, London, carry the following introductory paragraph: "During a recent test in the Hall, a note played mezzoforte on the horn measured approximately 65 decibels of sound. A single 'uncovered' cough gave the same reading. We would respectfully ask that when you need to cough you muffle the sound by placing a handkerchief over your mouth." This method seems to be working: scarcely any coughs have been heard during recent concerts.

13.6.2 Town Planning

In view of the rapid growth of surface and air transportation, noise has become an environmental factor of great importance in cities, and it is not unrealistic to predict that rural areas, too, will be similarly affected in the foreseeable future. Unless legislated or voluntary noise-control measures are introduced, there is a regrettable probability that in about a decade in urban areas, for a considerable part of the population, the noise level will reach a limit which is close to unbearable.

The following are the principal types of urban noises:

1. Traffic and transportation noise (automobiles, trucks, motorcycles, streetcars, trains, diesel engines, subways, watercraft, aircraft, etc.)

2. Industrial noise (factories, workshops, plants, cooling towers, air conditioners, etc.)

3. Noise created by people (sports and other outdoor activities, open-air performances, etc.)

There are a number of ways in which city noises can be controlled:

1. By following town- and community-planning methods with a desirable degree of noise abatement in mind

2. By establishing and enforcing zoning regulations and antinoise by-laws and restricting maximum permissible noise levels, particularly in residential areas

3. By requiring manufacturers of noisy mechanical and electrical equipment to test their products and supply noise ratings for them

4. By educating members of city administrations (legislators, council members, employees, etc.) to observe noise-control principles

5. By encouraging the public to complain about objectionable noises through all possible channels of communication (by complaints to the police, letters to newspapers, airport authorities, civil aeronautics administrations, through appeals to radio and television stations, etc.)

6. By educating the public to realize that a number of noise sources capable of causing great annoyance, irritation, and distress can be eliminated by careful planning and foresight and on a personal level by courtesy and consideration

Contemporary town- and community-planning authorities should observe the following principles:

1. Due consideration should be given to the fundamental fact that the provision of adequate distance between noise source and recipients is a most efficient noise-control measure.

2. Residential districts and special areas requiring quiet, such as hospital zones, should be segregated from expressways, highways, main streets, railways, playgrounds, industrial and commercial areas, and airports. The desirable separation between industrial, commercial, shopping, and residential zones should be observed.

3. A comprehensive layout of traffic arteries should be established and routed around, not through, quiet surroundings (residential districts, schools, churches, hospitals, etc.).

4. A maximum use should be made of protective greenbelts and landscaped grounds against industrial and commercial noise and near busy highways because a rich lawn produces sound absorption comparable to a high-quality carpeting and because trees, while lacking absorption, act as diffusing elements and are likely to enhance the absorption of landscaped grounds around them. Only dense, leafy shrubs and high trees or evergreens (for protection in winter) planted over a considerable area will provide an appreciable reduction of noise.

5. Noise surveys should be conducted in every major city to establish objective noise levels, particularly in downtown areas with respect to place, time, and type of noise source; to examine the various effects of noise on the population living in the area under consideration; and to provide a reliable basis for the required sound insulation of noise-sensitive buildings.

In the design of a road network, elements that contribute to traffic noise should be avoided as much as possible, for example, sloped traffic routes, level crossings, traffic lights, narrow traffic lanes, parking spaces, traffic arteries with facades along both sides of the road continuously built-in or with the buildings too close to the road.

Traffic arteries and railway tracks passing through noise-sensitive areas should be shielded by hills, cuttings, or embankments along the edges of the route and should be placed as far as possible from populated areas (Fig. 13.7). The banks along the sides facing the highway should be as steep as feasible. A highway network should be planned to permit its coordination with new residential areas as the need arises, and with the possibility of future expansion in mind so that new lanes can be added to the highway as conditions require. Residential streets should not provide shortcuts for noisy traffic. Trains should enter large metropolitan centers by underground routes.

A large sound-reflective surface, for example, the hard exterior surface of a building near a traffic-noise source, will increase the noise level by about 3 dB-A close to the sound-reflective surface. Uninterrupted facades on both sides of a street will increase the traffic noise level

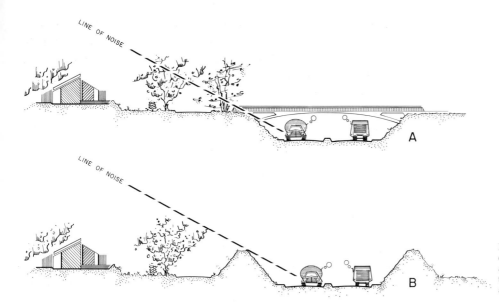

Fig. 13.7 The use of cuttings (A) or landscaped embankments (B) along both sides of traffic arteries and the provision of considerable distance between highway and populated areas are important measures against traffic noise.

by about 4 to 10 dB-A, irrespective of the height of the building. Gaps in the continuity of the facades will not substantially affect the prevailing noise level of the street. Balconies or terraces (on buildings) facing noisy traffic will reflect the street noise into the rooms below them through open doors and windows (Fig. 13.8).

While linear blocks of buildings erected at right angles to the street line reduce noise reflection along the street, they also permit the penetration and spreading of traffic noise deeper into built-up areas.

Buildings not particularly susceptible to disturbance by noise (shops, garages) can be used as baffles between noisy roads and areas needing quiet. Buildings used as baffles, however, should not become noise sources themselves. Residential streets should be so laid out that residents of the neighborhood are not unnecessarily exposed to traffic noises. Figure 13.9 illustrates a sensible layout of a quiet residential street with separated pedestrian lanes and concentrated exterior parking areas.

The design of shopping malls in suitable downtown areas with vehicular traffic banned from the mall (except for deliveries during restricted hours of the day) is a positive step toward environmental noise control.

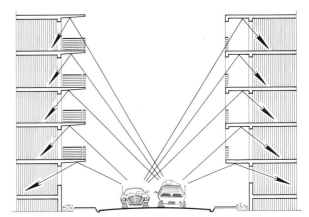

Fig. 13.8 Undersides of balconies or terraces facing noisy traffic reflect traffic noise into the rooms below through open doors and windows.

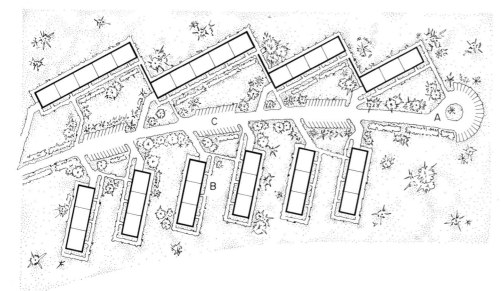

Fig. 13.9 Layout of a quiet residential street with (A) loop at the end of the street, (B) pedestrian lanes leading to the buildings, and (C) concentrated external parking areas.

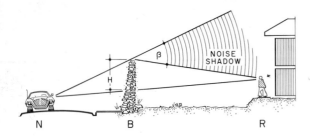

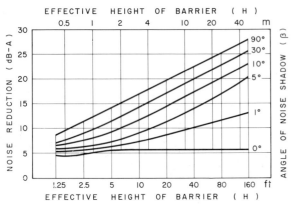

Fig. 13.10 Noise reduction by barriers placed between noise source and receiver: N, noise source; B, barrier; R, receiver.

An uninterrupted, solid, and unperforated obstruction or barrier (fence) between noise source and recipient will reduce the noise depending on the angle of noise shadow β and the effective height H of the barrier above the line connecting the noise source with the recipient (Fig. 13.10). The noise reduction will improve with increasing angle of noise shadow and barrier height. A low barrier along the traffic route will provide only negligible noise reduction in the area behind the barrier. For a barrier to be acoustically effective, it must be close either to the noise source or to the recipient to be protected against the noise. Noise reduction by a barrier increases with frequency. The perfect barrier around a noisy route is obviously a tunnel, which in turn requires interior sound-absorptive treatment in order to avoid the excessive buildup of traffic noise inside.

Traffic noise diminishes with distance, the degree of attenuation depending on the type of road surface or ground over which the noise travels. By doubling the distance, the noise will attenuate over a hard surface or in free space by about 3 dB, over grass and landscaped ground by about 5 to 6 dB. Shrubbery and rows of trees have practically no noise-reducing effect at low frequencies and reduce high frequencies by only about 1 to 2 dB. Traffic noise spreads more readily in the direction of the wind than against it.

Irregular and unexpected changes in traffic noise due to sudden stops in the regular flow of traffic (caused by stop signs, traffic lights, crossings, etc.) are always more disturbing than the more or less uniform rumble of continuous traffic. Therefore, crossings and junctions should be laid out with large radii of curvatures and with merging lanes, so that they can be negotiated at normal speeds, thus reducing low-gear driving and idling. Roads in residential areas or close to noise-sensitive buildings (schools, hospitals, churches, etc.) should be laid out to discourage speeding.

Since measured noise levels at a particular roadside vary from hour to hour or even from moment to moment, it is generally of limited use to establish "average" noise levels by taking noise-level readings for a few minutes with a sound-level meter. It is necessary to conduct measurements for a longer period of time, for example, for 8 or 24 hr, and to establish values exceeded for a given percentage of time. It has been found that the *10 percent level* and the *90 percent level* give reliable ratings of peak levels and background-noise levels, respectively. For example, if the *10 percent level* at a particular location is 80 dB-A, it means that this level has been exceeded for only 10 percent of the time. If the *90 percent level* is 40 dB-A, it means that the noise level exceeds this value for 90 percent of the time; that is, the noise level falls below the 40 dB-A value for only 10 percent of the time. The 10 percent level and the 90 percent level values provide characteristic variations occurring between different locations and traffic conditions.

For certain types of buildings (offices, schools, churches, etc.) exterior noise-level measurements are needed only by day. For others, (hospitals, residential buildings, etc.), data for nighttime noise levels are also required.

Various regulations against motor-vehicle noise issued by state or municipal authorities define the maximum legal noise level for passenger cars as about 82 to 90 dB-A, measured about 30 to 50 ft (9 to 15 m) from the vehicle, and about 90 to 95 dB-A measured at about 5 to 30 ft (1.5 to 9 m) from the vehicle. For trucks the permissible noise level is about 5 dB more. The 85-dB level is the point where a certain degree of hearing loss may occur if a person has been exposed to this level over several years, for 8 hr a day, as may be true of truck drivers. A law restricting the use of horns should also be one of the measures taken against vehicle noise.

The alarming noise usually created by motorcycles is generally higher than that of passenger cars. Any by-law enacted to control motor-vehicle noise should not ignore the highly objectionable noise caused by motorcycles.

In order to rate and evaluate traffic noise in such a way that a correlation can be established between noise level and the overall reaction (dissatisfaction) of individuals, various new traffic-noise criteria have been developed, for example, the *traffic noise index* (TNI) and the *equivalent noise level* (ENL). The TNI takes into account (1) intensity levels and characteristics of noise, (2) the effect on people and the social nuisance created, and (3) the considerable difference in the degree to which human beings tolerate noise. Individual differences in response to traffic noise is normally demonstrated by various reactions. For example, windows are closed when visitors come or at meal times, to watch television or listen to radio or to music, or when it is time for the children to go to bed, etc. To all these reactions specific values are assigned and are incorporated in the TNI.

Traffic noise at a given point can be reduced by:
1. Reducing the speed of the vehicle
2. Reducing the number of stops along the route
3. Restricting the time during which the vehicle is creating noise
4. Reducing the number of vehicles

In town planning particular consideration should be given to the control of aircraft noise. Some problems facing the planners can be solved only by international cooperation:

1. An unceasing effort must be made to develop and build quieter components for aircraft engines, even though this results in greater engine size, reduced efficiency, and increased operating cost.

2. New airports, long overdue in several cities, should be sited and developed in such a way that they do not interfere with the privacy of nearby residential or other noise-sensitive areas. Local planners should consult airport authorities with a view to regulating future extension of airport runways, maintenance, and testing facilities.

3. Owners of properties located too close to airports, and thus subjected to a high degree of aircraft noise, should be subsidized to enable them to improve the sound insulation of their property or to move out if justified.

4. New techniques in operational flight procedures (takeoff and landing) should continue to contribute to the alleviation of the disturbance created by aircraft noise. This requirement, however, must not jeopard-

ize flight safety. It involves improved ground facilities and aircraft instrumentation.

5. The methods for establishing maximum permissible aircraft noise levels in populated areas and assessing compliance with acceptable noise regulations should be internationally adopted. Scheduled flights during the night should be rigorously restricted or forbidden altogether, depending on the distance between airport and closest populated areas.

6. Since a large number of people do live close to airports, the sound-insulation requirements of new buildings in the vicinity should be established in a thoroughly professional manner and critically enforced by the civic authorities concerned, with particular regard to the future extension of the airport.

7. Maintenance and testing facilities for aircraft should be so located and operated that the noise they create does not become objectionable in the neighborhood.

Town and community planning and its implementation through strictly enforced by-laws and zoning regulations will protect the residents from the intrusion of noise on their privacy, the community against a loss in property value and tax revenue, and the noise producer from lawsuits and ensuing expenditure for noise control.

13.6.3 Site Planning Experience has shown that once a source of outdoor noise has become established in a certain area, it is difficult to eliminate. It is therefore essential that buildings requiring quiet sonic environment (schools, hospitals, churches, research institutes, etc.) be located on quiet sites, far away from highways, industrial areas, and airports.

It is advisable, where possible, to set a building back from the street in order to make use of the noise-reducing effect of the increased distance between street line and building line. If adequate distance between the building and noisy traffic route cannot be provided, rooms which do not need windows or windowless walls of habitable rooms should face the noisy road.

Buildings not particularly susceptible to noise can be used as noise baffles and can be placed between noise sources and areas requiring quiet. Car parking should be concentrated in a secluded part of the site. Residential roads should be built with loops at the end to permit turning without reversing (Fig. 13.9).

Linear blocks of buildings should be built with the end facing noisy roads, and an effort should be made to avoid the penetration of traffic noise into the area between the blocks.

13.6.4 Architectural Design Sensible architectural planning with attention to sound-control requirements is the most economical approach to effective noise control in buildings.

Rooms in which noise can be expected should be isolated both horizontally and vertically from sections of a building that can least tolerate noise, or they should be located on those parts of the site which will probably be exposed to other (interior or exterior) noises. Conversely, rooms requiring quiet should be located on the quiet part of the site or side of the building. For example, auditoriums should not be adjacent to mechanical equipment rooms. Hospital bedrooms should not face parking areas or loading platforms.

Rooms (or buildings) not particularly susceptible to noise can be located so that they act as screens or baffles between noisy and quiet areas. Adherence to the principle of separating noisy rooms from quiet ones at the planning stage will reduce to a minimum the need for sound-insulating building materials or systems, thus reducing building costs.

In the architectural design of residential buildings the rooms should be grouped into quiet quarters and noisy quarters. The quiet quarter of the building includes the habitable rooms, first the bedrooms and study, and second the living room. The noisy quarter contains the kitchen, bathroom, utility room, staircase, elevator shaft, boiler room, fan room, etc. In a residential building that is intended to be sound-controlled, the following general design rules should be observed (Fig. 13.11):

1. Quiet and noisy quarters should be grouped and separated from each other horizontally and vertically by means of adequately sound-insulating walls and floors (Chap. 14) or by rooms not particularly susceptible to noises, such as entry, corridor, staircase, and cupboards (with unlouvered doors).

2. A living room in one apartment should not be adjacent to a bedroom in another apartment. Bedrooms and living rooms in horizontal or vertical pairs of dwelling units should be adjacent to and above one another. If this layout is not feasible, the wall or floor construction separating the dwelling units must provide a higher sound insulation.

3. Bedrooms should be located in a relatively quiet part of the building and should not be adjacent to elevator shafts or mechanical rooms or overlook traffic lines or driveways.

4. Bathrooms should be efficiently separated acoustically from living rooms and should not be planned over living rooms or bedrooms, whether of the same dwelling or another. Bathroom fixtures should not be installed along walls which separate living room and bathroom.

5. Doors leading to bedrooms and bathrooms should have a reasonable sound insulation. They should have solid-core panels and be gasketed all around.

6. A staircase should not be adjacent to a bedroom. Treads of a staircase should be covered with soft materials to avoid footstep noises.

7. Uninterrupted rows of balconies along the exterior walls of buildings should be avoided. Terraces should be recessed into the building, at an adequate distance from each other.

8. A vertically staggered layout of apartments should be avoided (Fig. 13.12), because noises from a single source can penetrate several dwelling units at the same time. Also, common walls between vertically staggered dwelling units transmit footstep noises more easily into an adjacent unit than floors alone.

9. Windows should be laid out so as to minimize cross talk from one apartment to another.

A design that disregards the above requirements and yet is intended

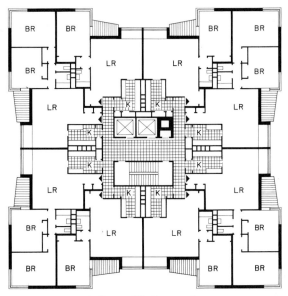

Fig. 13.11 Acoustically sensible layout of an apartment building.
PLAN

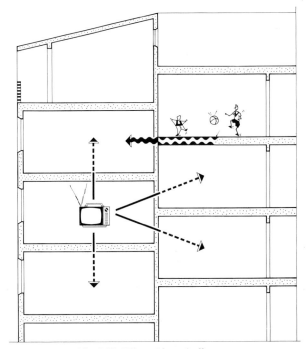

Fig. 13.12 A residential building with vertically staggered layout increases the possibility of noise transmission between dwelling units.
SECTION

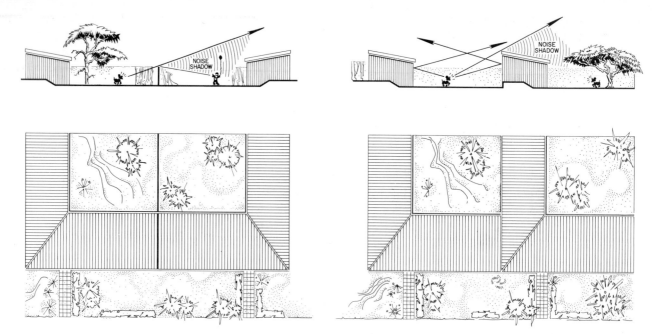

PLAN "A"   PLAN "B"

Fig. 13.13 A court-garden house provides a
relatively high degree of acoustical privacy.

to produce a soundproof building will have to use expensive sound-insulating walls and floors.

The patio house and the court-garden house provide a higher degree of acoustical privacy than the single-family detached house (Fig. 13.13).

13.6.5 Structural Design The structural engineer often has to incorporate structural noise-control measures in the structural drawings. Since the sound insulation of a floor or wall depends primarily on the thickness of the structure, neither the bearing capacity nor the strength of materials can be regarded as the sole criterion in establishing the structural dimensions. A 2- to 4-in. (50- to 100-mm) thick reinforced concrete floor slab, for example, may meet the structural requirements but be inadequate as a horizontal separation between any two occupancies, particularly if no suspended ceiling has been added to the floor construction.

A lightweight (prefabricated and prestressed) floor construction may be entirely safe for the normally predictable live and dead loads, but vibration-producing equipment installed on the floor increases the probability of resonance between equipment and the supporting lightweight floor slab. Such resonance would cause increased transmission of noise and vibration through the floor, in spite of the fact that the mechanical engineer specified vibration-proof mounts under the mechanical equipment. In addition, if the equipment is placed at the center of the span, instead of near a supporting column or wall, the probability of resonance is further increased.

Partition walls separating row houses should consist of two separated layers, extending from the bottom of the foundation to the roof (Fig. 13.14), to avoid the transmission of impact (footstep) noise from one dwelling unit into the adjacent one. The use of an inorganic isolation

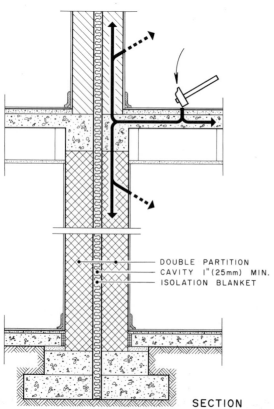

DOUBLE PARTITION
CAVITY 1"(25mm) MIN.
ISOLATION BLANKET

SECTION

Fig. 13.14 The partition wall between row houses should consist of two separate layers extending from the bottom of the foundation to the roof.

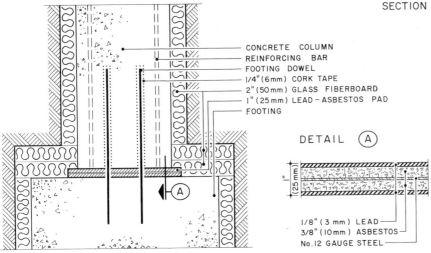

CONCRETE COLUMN
REINFORCING BAR
FOOTING DOWEL
1/4" (6mm) CORK TAPE
2" (50mm) GLASS FIBERBOARD
1" (25mm) LEAD-ASBESTOS PAD
FOOTING

DETAIL (A)

1/8" (3 mm) LEAD
3/8" (10mm) ASBESTOS
No.12 GAUGE STEEL

Fig. 13.15 Vibration-proof foundation using lead-asbestos antivibration pads.

blanket in a vertical gap at least 1 in. (25 mm) wide is essential, so that pieces of excess mortar will not drop between the separated layers and destroy the acoustical efficiency of this layout.

When buildings must be isolated against vibrations originating from adjacent railroad tracks, subways, underground railway stations, or highways, lead-asbestos antivibration pads are often used, requiring a careful integration with the foundation of the building (Fig. 13.15).

13.6.6 Mechanical and Electrical Design   Equipment and installations normally specified by mechanical and electrical engineers can be serious noise sources. The noise hazard will be greatly reduced if attention is paid to the following recommendations:

1. In the selection of a suitable heating, ventilating, or air-conditioning system and equipment, preference should obviously be given to silently operating systems, equipment, and fixtures.

2. Noise- and vibration-producing mechanical equipment (fans, motors, etc.) should be accommodated in the basement, if possible, where the equipment room can be easily surrounded with a thick load-bearing structure providing a high degree of insulation against noise and vibration.

3. Pipes, ventilating ducts, continuous perimeter heating strips, etc., should be so designed and installed that they do not short-circuit sound-insulating walls or floors.

4. Fixtures recessed back to back in partition walls (medicine cabinets, switch and outlet boxes, television-antenna outlets, etc.) should always be staggered to avoid direct transmission of sound through the partition (Fig. 13.16). All voids should be packed and holes and gaps carefully caulked around the fixtures.

5. Service pipes, mechanical appliances, and lighting fixtures should not be recessed into walls or floor-ceiling assemblies designed to provide acoustical separation. These pipes and fixtures should be resiliently attached to walls or suspended from ceilings if they are likely to transmit noise and vibration.

6. Ventilating louvers, if used, should incorporate noise filters.

Control of mechanical noise and vibration is discussed in Chap. 16.

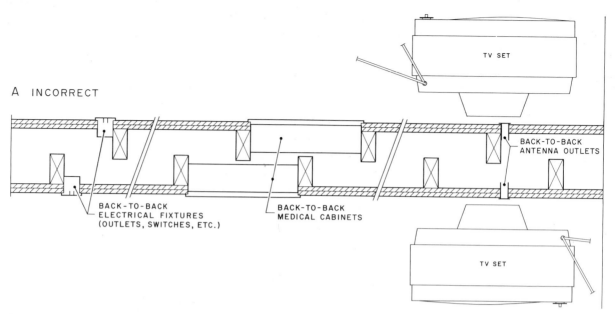

A INCORRECT

BACK-TO-BACK
ELECTRICAL FIXTURES
(OUTLETS, SWITCHES, ETC.)

BACK-TO-BACK
MEDICAL CABINETS

TV SET

BACK-TO-BACK
ANTENNA OUTLETS

TV SET

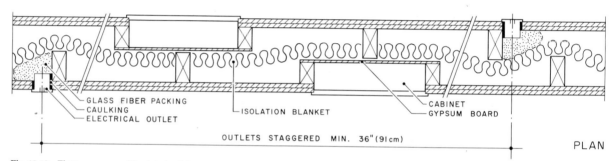

B CORRECT

GLASS FIBER PACKING
CAULKING
ELECTRICAL OUTLET

ISOLATION BLANKET

CABINET
GYPSUM BOARD

OUTLETS STAGGERED MIN. 36" (91 cm)

PLAN

Fig. 13.16 Fixtures recessed back to back in partition walls (A) should be staggered, with the voids packed and the gaps caulked (B), to avoid direct transmission of sound through the partition.

13.6.7 Organization If existing noises cannot be controlled, or if it is uneconomical to take corrective measures for their reduction, the situation can often be remedied by organization. For example, certain rooms overexposed to excessive noises can be regrouped or relocated.

Sometimes too many workers are affected unnecessarily by noisy machines scattered throughout a workshop. If the individual machines cannot be noise-controlled, it is advisable to consider their regrouping into a restricted area as far removed as possible from other activities.

In other cases, large noisy floor areas should be partitioned off from the rest of the space.

Earplugs or earmuffs should be used in excessively noisy areas where no other reasonable means of reducing noise are available or in fully automated workshops where there are practically no workers to be affected by the excessive noise.

Antinoise ordinances, if strictly enforced, constitute effective means of combating noise in communities by means of organization.

13.6.8 Sound Absorption It has been mentioned previously that the noise level in the receiving room is made up of the direct sound and the reflected or reverberant sound (Fig. 13.3). The noise level of the reverberant sound can be reduced to a limited extent by sound-absorptive treatment. This reduction of the noise level (not too close to the noise source) due to the installation of sound-absorptive treatment is given by the formula

$$\text{Reduction of noise level (dB)} = 10 \log \frac{A_2}{A_1}$$

where A_1 and A_2 are the total amount of sound absorption in the room, in square feet (square meters), before and after additional treatment, respectively. Figure 13.17, which illustrates graphically the reduction of noise level, shows that it is necessary to double the amount of existing absorption in the room in order to obtain a reduction of 3 dB in the reverberant noise level. If by the installation of various acoustical materials the absorption of the room can be increased by a factor of 10,

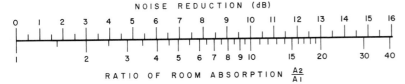

Fig. 13.17 The reduction of noise level in a room due to sound-absorptive treatment; A_1 and A_2 = total amount of absorption before and after installation of additional acoustical treatment, respectively.

the reverberant sound level will be reduced by 10 dB. Figure 13.18 illustrates that doubling the amount of absorption in the room results in a reduction in loudness of about 20 percent. When the room absorption is increased by a factor of 10, it produces a reduction in loudness of about 50 percent. Once a 10-dB reduction has been achieved, very little additional reduction in noise level can be expected in a room by the use of sound-absorptive treatment. The use of sound-absorbing materials in a room should not be regarded as a substitute or cure for deficient sound insulation.

Introducing as much sound-absorptive treatment as convenient in a room has the following advantages:

1. The room will be quieter (except for persons located in the direct sound field).

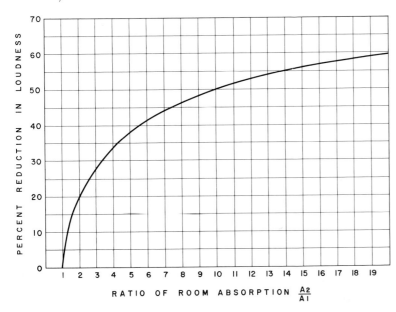

Fig. 13.18 Reduction in loudness in a room due to the use of sound-absorptive treatment; A_1 and A_2 represent the total amount of absorption before and after the installation of additional acoustical treatment, respectively.

2. The overall sound level will be reduced. Less sound energy will fall on the room enclosures, resulting in reduced noise transmission to adjacent rooms.

3. The treatment will tend to localize noises in the area of their origin. This is particularly advantageous in workshops with machines of various noise levels. The operator of a relatively quiet machine will not be so disturbed by a noisier but more remote unit.

4. The RT will be reduced. This is particularly beneficial in workrooms with sudden noises because the reverberation of these unexpected noises will be reduced. In addition, it will permit better mental localization of sound sources, reducing the feeling of confusion and improving the sense of well-being for workers in noisy rooms.

The generous use of sound-absorptive treatment in team-teaching classrooms and in landscaped offices, particularly along the floor and ceiling, is important. In these spaces no noise-reducing partitions are used; consequently sounds from different sources must drop off with distance as rapidly as possible. This is achieved by the extensive acoustical treatment along the enclosures (Chap. 17).

The use of sound-absorbing materials is beneficial in various circulation spaces, such as vestibules, lobbies, corridors, etc. Long (and particularly narrow) corridors which are acoustically untreated act as noise-transmitting tubes. Using acoustical treatment along their ceilings (and upper parts of side walls, if possible) confines the noise to the immediate vicinity of its origin and reduces the noise level throughout the corridor.

The sound-absorbing materials to be used for noise-reduction purposes are the same as those described in Chap. 5. The absorbents should be installed as close as possible to noise sources. If the available room surfaces do not provide a sufficient area for sound-absorbing materials, space absorbers are recommended (Sec. 5.4).

Since the sound absorption coefficients of acoustical materials vary with the frequency, the noise reduction achieved differs at various frequencies. This must be considered in selecting appropriate absorbent treatment.

13.6.9 Masking Noise   In many situations noise-control problems can be solved by drowning out (or masking) unwanted noises by electronically created background noise. This artificial noise is often referred to as *acoustical perfume,* although the term *acoustical deodorant* would be more appropriate. This process suppresses minor intrusions which might interrupt the recipients' privacy.

Noise from ventilating systems, from a uniform flow of traffic, or from general office activities contributes to an artificial masking noise.

In designing landscaped offices the provision of a relatively high but acceptable degree of background noise (from the ventilating or air-conditioning system) is essential in order to mask undesirable office noises created by typewriters, telephones, office machines, or loud conversation and to provide a reasonable amount of privacy.

In team-teaching classrooms the sounds produced by several learning groups and spread in various directions cancel each other out to a certain extent and create a particular type of masking noise which seems to be acceptable to the occupants.

Appropriately selected and well-distributed background music can also be considered as a type of masking noise.

13.6.10 Sound-insulating Building Construction   If the noise-control methods described so far cannot be followed for the provision of a favorable acoustical environment in a building, there is one remaining solution: an adequately sound-insulating enclosure (wall, floor, door, or window) must be used, obviously entailing increased construction costs. A detailed discussion of sound-insulating building construction will be found in Chap. 14.

BIBLIOGRAPHY

Books

Beranek, L. L.: *Acoustic Measurements*, John Wiley & Sons, Inc., New York, 1949, 914 pp.

Geiger, P. G.: *Noise Reduction Manual*, University of Michigan Engineering Research Institute, 1956, 167 pp.

Harris, C. M. (ed.): *Handbook of Noise Control*, McGraw-Hill Book Company, New York, 1957, 1184 pp.

Parkin, P. H., and H. R. Humphreys: *Acoustics, Noise and Buildings*, Frederick A. Praeger, Inc., New York, 1958, chaps. 7, 8, and 10.

Peterson, A. P. G., and E. E. Gross: *Handbook of Noise Measurement*, General Radio Co., West Concord, Mass., 1960, 132 pp.

Beranek, L. L. (ed.): *Noise Reduction*, McGraw-Hill Book Company, New York, 1960, 752 pp.

Schoenauer, N., and S. Seeman: *The Court-garden House*, McGill University Press, Montreal, 1962, 204 pp.

Lord, P., and F. L. Thomas (eds.): *Noise Measurement and Control*, Heywood & Co., London, 1963, 217 pp.

Noise: The Wilson Report, Her Majesty's Stationery Office, London, July 1963, 235 pp.

Burns, W.: *Noise and Man*, W. Clowes & Sons, Ltd., London, 1968, 336 pp.

Periodicals

Allen, W. A., and P. H. Parkin: "Acoustics and Sound Exclusion," *Architectural Review*, June 1951, pp. 377–384.

Pietrasanta, A. C.: "Aircraft Noise and Building Design," *Noise Control*, March 1957, pp. 11–18, 88.

Beranek, L. L., K. D. Kryter, and L. N. Miller: "Reaction of People to Exterior Aircraft Noise," *Noise Control*, September 1959, pp. 23–31, 60.

Kryter, K. D.: "Scaling Human Reactions to the Sound from Aircraft," *J. Acoust. Soc. Am.*, November 1959, pp. 1415–1429.

Miller, L. N.: "High Intensity Noise," *Architectural Record*, December 1959, pp. 162–165, 169–170.

Goodfriend, L. S.: "Measurement of Noise," *Noise Control*, March–April 1961, pp. 4–12.

Hubbard, H. H.: "Nature of the Sonic Boom Problem," *J. Acoust. Soc. Am.*, May 1966, pp. S1–S9.

Nixon, C. W., and P. N. Borsky: "Effects of Sonic Boom on People," *J. Acoust. Soc. Am.*, May 1966, pp. S51–S58.

Warren, C. H. E.: "Experience in the United Kingdom on the Effects of Sonic Bangs," *J. Acoust. Soc. Am.*, May 1966, pp. S59–S64.

Creighton, H.: "Noise in the External Environment," *J. RIBA*, October 1966, pp. 465–470.

Beranek, L. L.: "Noise," *Scientific American*, December 1966, pp. 66–76.

Farrell, R.: "Masking Noise: Silence Is Golden, Privacy Is Pink," *Progressive Architecture*, November 1967, pp. 152–155.

Prestemon, D. R.: "How Much Does Noise Bother Apartment Dwellers?," *Architectural Record*, February 1968, pp. 155–156.

"Noise in Scandinavia," *Build International*, September–October 1968, pp. 52–57.

Harman, D. M.: "The Role of the dB-A," *Applied Acoustics*, April 1969, pp. 101–109.

Scholes, W. E., and G. H. Vulkan: "Note on the Objective Measurement of Road Traffic Noise," *Applied Acoustics*, July 1969, pp. 185–197.

Thomas, R. J.: "Traffic Noise: The Performance and Economics of Noise-reducing Materials," *Applied Acoustics*, July 1969, pp. 207–213.

Langdon, J.: "Traffic Noise Control Criteria," *Build International*, July–August 1969, pp. 26–30.

Franken, P. A., and G. Jones: "On Response to Community Noise," *Applied Acoustics*, October 1969, pp. 241–246.

Hewling, M.: "Town Planning and Traffic Noise," *Applied Acoustics*, October 1969, pp. 247–257.

Bottom, C. G., and D. J. Croome: "Road Traffic Noise: Its Nuisance Value," *Applied Acoustics*, October 1969, pp. 279–296.

Schaudinischky, L. H., N. Moses, and A. Schwartz: "General Graphical Method for Aircraft Noise Evaluation," *Applied Acoustics*, October 1969, pp. 297–308.

Scholes, W. E.: "Traffic Noise Criteria," *Applied Acoustics*, January 1970, pp. 1–21.

Digests and Reports

Northwood, T. D.: *Noise Transmission in Buildings*, Canadian Building Digest 10, National Research Council, Ottawa, October 1960, 4 pp.

Northwood, T. D.: *Sound and People*, Canadian Building Digest 41, National Research Council, Ottawa, May 1963, 4 pp.

Parkin, P. H., H. J. Purkis, R. J. Stephenson, and B. Schlaffenberg: *London Noise Survey*, Building Research Station, London, 1968, 60 pp.

Leach, S. J.: *Noise*, Building Research Station News, Garston, Autumn 1970, pp. 16–17.

If for one reason or another none of the noise-control methods described in Chap. 13 can be implemented, the transmission of airborne noise, structure-borne (impact) noise, or vibration must be intercepted; that is, the desired acoustical privacy must be achieved by using sound-insulating walls, floors, doors, or windows.

In the past, heavy and space-consuming building materials were used for the construction of sound-insulating enclosures: the heavier and thicker they were, the more efficient their sound insulation.

In contemporary buildings thick and heavy walls and floors should be avoided in order to gain more space; to save construction loads, thus reducing building costs; to shorten the construction time; and to provide flexibility in design. These requirements have stimulated the demand for thin, lightweight, prefabricated, and movable building elements, creating serious acoustical problems for the architect and all too often a considerable loss of privacy for the occupants of the building.

In subsequent discussions, the term *partition* means any enclosure (wall, floor, door, or window) that separates any two spaces horizontally or vertically.

14.1 Insulation against Airborne Sound

14.1.1 Sound Transmission Loss   The *sound transmission loss,* or simply *transmission loss* (TL), of a partition, stated in decibels, is a measure of its sound insulation. It is equal to the number of decibels by which sound energy incident on the partition is reduced in passing through the structure. The numerical value of the TL depends only on the construction of the partition and varies with the frequency of the sound. It is independent of the acoustical properties of the two spaces separated by the partition.

The TL of a partition can be determined in an acoustical laboratory or in the field as follows: a steady sound is generated in the source room at one side of the partition to be tested; the sound levels are then measured at both sides of the partition, that is, in both source room and receiving room. The TL of the partition is determined from the difference between measured sound levels on both sides of the partition (Fig. 14.1).

14.1.2 Single-leaf Partitions   The TL of homogeneous, *single-leaf partitions* depends primarily on the surface weight of the partition and the frequency of sound transmitted. The TL of such partitions can be determined from the *mass-law curve,* illustrated in Fig. 14.2. This curve assumes that the sound hits the partition uniformly from all directions (random incidence). The figure shows that for single-leaf partitions the TL increases about 5 to 6 dB for each doubling of frequency or doubling of weight. It must be noted that the TL for single-leaf partitions, regardless of their weight, cannot be increased to an unlimited extent because of unpredictable paths of flanking transmission.

To achieve an effective TL of a partition, it must be impervious to airflow. Walls of porous concrete blocks will not yield a TL in propor-

CHAPTER FOURTEEN

Sound-insulating Construction

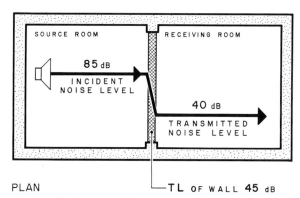

PLAN   └─ TL OF WALL **45** dB

Fig. 14.1   The TL of a partition, or measure of its sound insulation, is equal to the number of decibels by which sound energy incident on the partition is reduced in passing through the structure.

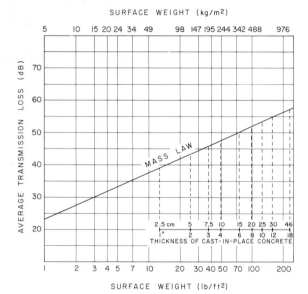

Fig. 14.2 The approximate average TL of solid single-leaf partitions can be estimated from this mass-law curve.

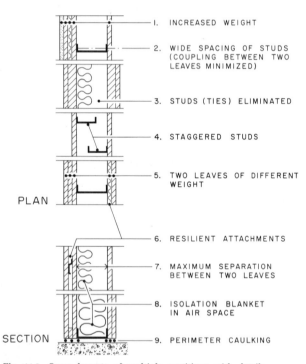

SOUND INSULATION INCREASES WITH :

1. INCREASED WEIGHT

2. WIDE SPACING OF STUDS (COUPLING BETWEEN TWO LEAVES MINIMIZED)

3. STUDS (TIES) ELIMINATED

4. STAGGERED STUDS

5. TWO LEAVES OF DIFFERENT WEIGHT

PLAN

6. RESILIENT ATTACHMENTS

7. MAXIMUM SEPARATION BETWEEN TWO LEAVES

8. ISOLATION BLANKET IN AIR SPACE

SECTION

9. PERIMETER CAULKING

Fig. 14.3 Some layouts of multiple partitions with details contributing to increased sound insulation.

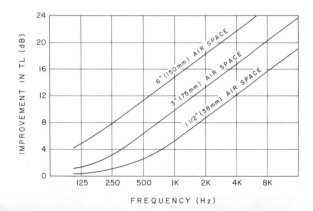

tion to their weight, as evident from Fig. 14.2, because of their porosity. However, the TL of a porous partition may be considerably improved by sealing its exposed surfaces with plaster, oil paint, cement-base paint, etc.

A limitation to the mass-law curve results from a special condition called the *coincidence effect*. Under this condition, as normally happens in practice, the effective TL of a partition is considerably lower at certain frequencies than the mass law would predict. The coincidence effect becomes detrimental if the critical frequency range (called *coincidence frequency*), at which the partition is substantially transparent to the passage of sound, falls in the range of audibility. The coincidence effect can be reduced or limited if the coincidence frequency can be kept outside the important range of frequencies. This can be achieved by using relatively thick and very stiff walls or heavy and limp walls with reduced stiffness.

14.1.3 Multiple Partitions To achieve a significant improvement in the TL value of a single-leaf partition requires doubling or tripling its mass. Such an increase in the weight and thickness of an enclosure is obviously difficult to achieve for functional, spatial, structural, and economical reasons.

If a high degree of sound insulation is required, it is therefore advisable to use a *multiple partition* built of two or three separated leaves.

Multiple partitions (Fig. 14.3) provide a higher TL than would be expected from their total weight, particularly at the higher frequencies, if the following precautions are observed:

1. The total weight has been established as a reasonable maximum.
2. The separation between the leaves has been consistently secured.
3. A maximum distance has been established between the leaves.
4. A continuous layer or patches of sound-absorbing blanket have been mounted in the air space.
5. The leaves have been built of different materials or of the same material but with differing thicknesses.
6. The leaves have been resiliently attached to the studs or to one another.
7. Noise leaks, particularly around perimeter edges, have been carefully avoided.
8. The stiffness of the partition has been so established as to minimize the coincidence effect.

Figure 14.4 shows the improvement in TL for multiple partitions with air space over single-leaf partitions of the same total weight. Figure 14.5 illustrates the approximate average TL of multiple partitions with various air spaces and with unconnected leaves.

It must be noted that the curves shown in Figs. 14.4 and 14.5 do not indicate the sometimes surprising dips which can occur in the TL of multiple partitions at certain frequency ranges. These dips result from such specific conditions as stiffness, structural connection, and resonance between layers; damping; and edge fixing. Therefore, in the preliminary acoustical assessment of multiple partitions, the diagrams in Figs. 14.2, 14.4, and 14.5 should be used with caution. By selecting the proper

Fig. 14.4 Approximate improvement in the TL of multiple partitions with various air spaces over single-leaf partitions of the same total weight.

material and a layout with adequate separation between leaves, these effects should be minimized and the dips in the TL curve shifted to less critical frequency ranges.

Figure 14.6 illustrates the beneficial effect of using an isolation blanket within a multiple dry-wall partition. The acoustical rating, called the *sound transmission class* rating (Sec. 14.1.6) of this wall is 47 dB when an isolation blanket is used between the two layers of gypsum boards (Fig. 14.6A). The acoustical rating drops to 39 dB when no isolation blanket is applied (Fig. 14.6B). Details of this dry-wall partition are shown in Fig. B.7 of Appendix B (wall 43). It must be stressed, however, that an isolation blanket is particularly beneficial only for a lightweight multiple wall; the same blanket in a cavity brick wall increases the acoustical rating only slightly.

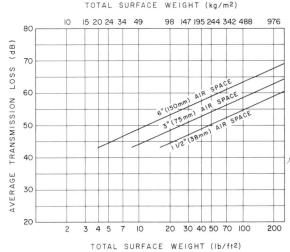

Fig. 14.5 Approximate average TL of multiple partitions with different air spaces.

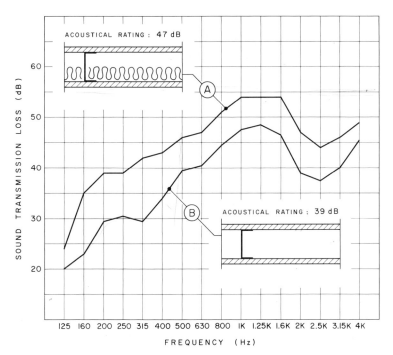

Fig. 14.6 Dry-wall partitions with ⅝-in. (16-mm) gypsum boards on both sides of metal studs (A) with isolation blanket in the air space, where the acoustical rating is 47 dB, and (B) without isolation blanket, where the rating drops to 39 dB.

Figure 14.7 shows the acoustical effect of horizontally installed resilient bars used in a multiple dry-wall partition. The acoustical rating is 39 dB with resilient bars, but it drops to 34 dB when no resilient bars are used. Details of this partition are shown in Fig. B.3 (walls 18 and 21).

Wall 5 of Fig. B.1 compares cavity-brick walls with and without wire ties between the two leaves. The superiority of alternative *b*, without wire ties, is evident: it has an acoustical rating of 54 dB, while alternative *a*, with wire ties, has an acoustical rating of only 49 dB.

In Figs. B.1 to B.9 additional practical examples illustrate the effect of different elements in increasing sound insulation. For example, in multiple-wall constructions flexible thin metal studs create a less rigid linkage between the two layers of the wall, making them preferable to wooden studs.

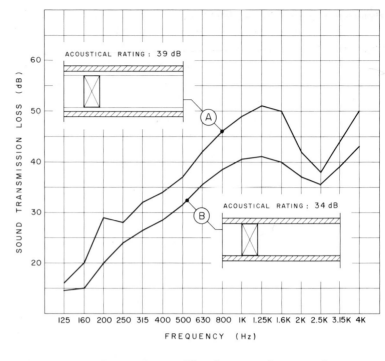

Fig. 14.7 Dry-wall partitions with ⅝-in. (16-mm) gypsum boards on both sides of wood studs (A) with horizontal resilient bars between studs and gypsum boards, where the acoustical rating is 39 dB, and (B) without resilient bars, where the rating drops to 34 dB.

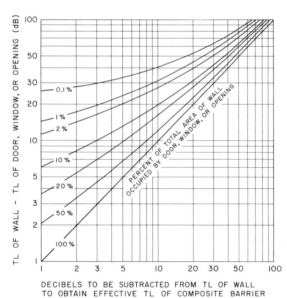

Fig. 14.8 Chart for calculating the effective sound insulation of composite barriers.

14.1.4 Composite Barriers   If a door, window, or other opening is to be incorporated into a wall, the eventual overall sound insulation of the resulting *composite partition* is determined primarily by its weakest element. Figure 14.8 shows the procedure for calculating the overall TL of a composite partition. According to this figure, when, for example, a folding door with an acoustical rating of 30 dB occupies 50 percent of a wall which has a rating of 50 dB, the eventual TL of the composite partition will be about $50 - 18 = 32$ dB. In order to achieve a higher overall sound insulation for the same composite barrier, a folding door with a much higher acoustical rating would be needed. On the other hand, if an overall acoustical separation of 32 dB is acceptable, it would be more sensible to incorporate the same folding door in a partition that has an acoustical rating of only about 45 dB.

Figure 14.8 also reveals that only negligible sound insulation can be expected from a partial-height partition, for example, in an office. In this case the solid partition with the opening above constitutes the composite barrier.

14.1.5 Measurement of Transmission Loss   Since the TL, that is, the airborne-sound insulation of any partition, varies with frequency, TL measurements must be made over a frequency range between 125 and 4000 Hz. Measurements of TL can be made in a laboratory or in the field.

Laboratory measurements should be performed in accordance with the current practice endorsed by the American Society for Testing and Materials, the American National Standards Institute, and the International Organization for Standardization. The method of testing is described in the recommendation designated as ASTM E90-66T, "Tentative Recommended Practice for Laboratory Measurement of Air-borne

Sound Transmission Loss of Building Partitions." According to the recommended procedure, a test panel typifying a wall or floor should be large enough to include all the essential constructional elements. For testing, the panel is normally installed in testing frames positioned in an opening between two testing (reverberant) chambers, simulating an actual construction. Measurements of the TL are made at several (usually 16) test frequencies between 125 and 4000 Hz. The TL of the test panel is given by the formula

$$TL = L_1 - L_2 + 10 \log S - 10 \log A_2$$

where L_1 = average sound pressure level in source room, dB
L_2 = average sound pressure level in receiving room, dB
S = area of test panel, sq ft (sq m)
A_2 = total absorption of receiving room, sq-ft sabins (sq-m sabins)

In the past, an arithmetical average TL was given in the laboratory report of the test. This was a convenient but often misleading method of rating because it gave equal significance to all test frequencies, regardless of their importance, and because it gave equal significance to both high and low TL values, implying that particularly high values at certain frequencies could compensate for low values at other frequencies.

14.1.6   Sound Transmission Class   To avoid the misleading nature of an average TL value and to provide a reliable single-figure rating for comparing partitions, the current ASTM E90-66T recommendation has adopted a different procedure for single-figure rating, called *sound transmission class* (STC) rating. According to this procedure, the STC of a partition can be determined by comparing the 16-frequency TL curve with a standard reference contour, the *sound transmission class contour* (Fig. 14.9). The STC contour consists of a horizontal segment from 1250 to 4000 Hz, a middle segment, which decreases by 5 dB from 1250 to 400 Hz, and a low-frequency segment, which decreases by 15 dB from 400 to 125 Hz. The STC rating for a given partition is determined by comparing the measured TL curve against the STC contours,

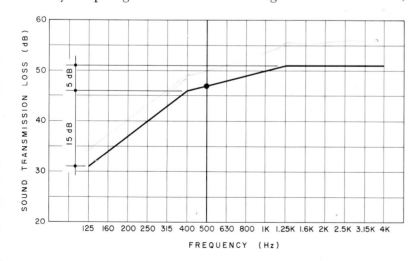

Fig. 14.9   Typical sound transmission class contour (STC 47).

that is, shifting the STC contour vertically relative to the TL curve until some of the measured TL values fall below those of the STC contour and the following conditions are fulfilled: (1) the sum of the deficiencies, that is, the deviations below the contour, do not exceed 32 dB (average of 2 dB for each of the 16 test frequencies); and (2) the maximum deficiency at any single test frequency does not exceed 8 dB.

When the contour is adjusted to the highest value (in integral decibels) that meets the above requirements, the STC rating for the wall or floor construction under consideration is the TL value corresponding to the intersection of the contour and the 500-Hz ordinate.

The following example will illustrate how misleading the average TL value of a partition can be in evaluating its sound-insulating performance. Two different partitions with different TLs at vital frequency readings but with the same average TL value can be erroneously considered as acoustically identically effective against airborne noises if their average TL is regarded as a characteristic of their sound insulation. Figure 14.10A and B shows the TL curves of two such partitions, both having by chance a 16-frequency average TL rating of 42 dB. On the basis of their average TL ratings these two partitions seem to be equal even though diagram B shows a serious deficiency (dip) in the vital frequency range of 1250 to 4000 Hz. Corresponding STC contours superimposed on TL curves A and B, however, reveal that partition A, with an STC rating of 45 dB, is superior to partition B, which has an STC rating of only 38 dB.

14.1.7 Noise Reduction of Partitions   As mentioned previously, the TL is determined by the physical properties of a partition, irrespective of the acoustical properties of the rooms separated by the partition.

Noise reduction (NR) is a more general term than TL for specifying sound insulation between rooms because it takes into account the effects of the various transmission paths between source room and receiving room and also the acoustical properties of these rooms.

Fig. 14.10 Comparison of the sound-insulating performance of two partitions. The average TL values of partitions A and B are equal, but corresponding STC contours reveal the superiority of partition A.

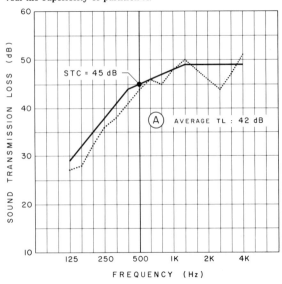

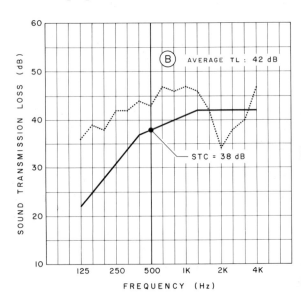

The NR, expressed in decibels, is given by

$$NR = L_1 - L_2$$

or

$$NR = TL + 10 \log \frac{A_2}{S}$$

where L_1 = average sound pressure level in source room, dB
L_2 = average sound pressure level in receiving room, dB
TL = transmission loss of partition, dB
A_2 = total absorption of receiving room, sq-ft sabins (sq-m sabins)
S = area of partition, sq ft (sq m)

The NR may be higher or lower than the TL, depending on the relationship between partition area and sound absorption in the receiving room. With increasing partition area, there is a greater transmission of noise, and with increased sound absorption, there is a lesser transmission of noise into the receiving room. If all boundary surfaces in the receiving room are completely absorbent, the NR will exceed the TL by about 5 dB, in which case NR = TL + 5 dB.

The NR provided by a partition between source room and receiving room will be often reduced by so-called *flanking transmission*, that is, by the sound traveling through flanking paths, such as side walls, floors, openings in the partition (due to joints or gaps), doors, joints between partitions and mullions, ceiling plenums, ducts, recessed fixtures, cross-connected heating units, etc. Many of these transmission paths are shown in Fig. 13.6.

14.2 Insulation against Structure-borne (Impact) Noise

Insulation against structure-borne (or impact) noise can be achieved by the use of:

1. Soft floor finish (carpet, cork, vinyl, rubber, etc.)
2. Floating floor
3. Resilient (antivibration) mounts
4. Resiliently suspended solid ceiling

The addition of a soft floor finish does not provide extra insulation against airborne sound but merely reduces or eliminates impact noise, such as footstep noise, at the source. On the other hand, a floating floor or a resiliently suspended ceiling also improves the airborne-sound insulation of floor assemblies.

14.2.1 Measurement of Structure-borne (Impact) Noise
The measurement of structure-borne, or impact, noise is different from that of airborne noise. According to the recommendation of the International Organization for Standardization (ISO R 140-1960E), the insulation against impact noise provided by a given floor must be determined by means of a standard *tapping* machine, which produces a series of uniform impacts at a constant rate on the floor being tested by means of five small hammers which fall freely at a specified rate on the floor. The

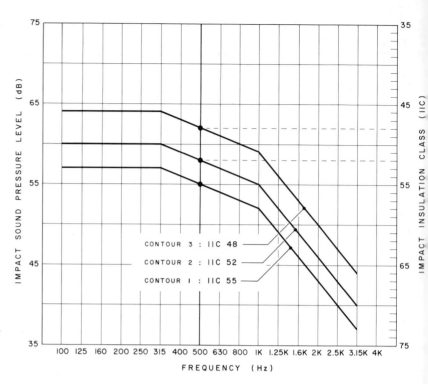

Fig. 14.11 IIC contours recommended by the Federal Housing Administration.

sound pressure levels of the impact noise transmitted into the receiving room, beneath the floor, are measured with a sound-level meter in sixteen $\frac{1}{3}$-octave bands with center frequencies between 100 and 3150 Hz. The measurements are normalized to a receiving room RT of $T_0 = 0.5$ sec because the amount of sound-absorbing material has a bearing on the measured sound levels.

The measured *impact sound pressure* (ISP) levels are then compared to a standard *impact-noise reference contour*. Figure 14.11 illustrates three impact-noise reference contours, *contour 1, contour 2,* and *contour 3,* presently used by the National Bureau of Standards, Washington, D.C., and recommended for use by the Federal Housing Administration. These contours consist of a horizontal low-frequency segment from 100 to 315 Hz, a middle segment which decreases by 5 dB from 315 to 1000 Hz, and a high-frequency segment which decreases by 15 dB from 1000 to 3150 Hz. The three reference contours of Fig. 14.11 represent criteria to be observed in different environments, for example, in rural, suburban, urban, or downtown areas, with differing noise conditions. The ordinate scale on the left shows *impact sound pressure* (ISP) levels; the ordinate scale on the right shows *impact insulation class* (IIC) levels providing a suitable scale for the single-figure rating of the structure-borne (impact) insulation of floors. A floor construction will meet the requirements of a particular IIC contour if some of the measured SPL values for the test floor fall above those of the IIC contour and if (1) the sum of the deficiencies, that is, the deviations above the contour, are not greater than 32 dB (average of 2 dB for the 16 test frequencies) and (2) the maximum deficiency at any frequency does not exceed the contour by more than 8 dB.

Under these conditions the IIC rating for the test floor is the value of the IIC scale at 500 Hz of the lowest reference contour for which the above requirements are met.

The use of the simple single-figure STC and IIC ratings will be of great help to architects in the quick but accurate evaluation and selection of wall and floor constructions. In the illustrations of walls and floors included in Appendixes B and C (Figs. B.1 to B.9 and C.1 to C.4) pertinent STC and IIC ratings have been indicated.

While there has been some objection to the tapping machine as a noise source in establishing the impact insulation rating of floors, no better method is available. Although some authorities have claimed that the tapping machine does not sufficiently simulate footstep noise made by women wearing high-heeled shoes, thanks to the change in fashion this particular noise has almost disappeared, at least for the time being.

14.3 Laboratory vs. Field Measurements

The purpose of conducting field measurements is to make sure that the acoustical performance of a partition (wall, floor, door, or window) meets the specified acoustical criteria. Early field measurements of the sound insulation of walls and floors were normally conducted under unfavorable conditions and with unreliable methods. The acoustical ratings achieved on a site were 5 to 10 dB lower than those measured in a closely controlled laboratory, under ideal testing conditions, and according to a predetermined, well-organized procedure.

During a laboratory test sound is transmitted only through the test panel, without any indirect or flanking path around the panel. Repeated measurements conducted on several test panels (of nominally identical partitions) in the same laboratory (or in any other accredited laboratory whose standards are the same) will yield results which are in agreement, at any given frequency.

The results of field tests differ from laboratory tests for the following reasons:

1. The enclosure under a field test is structurally joined to the surrounding walls and floors and connected with ducts, plenums, conduits, etc.; consequently, flanking paths for the transmission of noises are unavoidable.

2. Many invisible sound leaks exist in an actual installation along penetrations of ducts or pipes, joints, perimeters, etc., causing direct noise transmission.

3. Wide variations exist in the size of tested enclosures and in the diffusive and absorptive characteristics of adjoining rooms, resulting in considerable disagreement in the results.

4. Excessive or unsteady background noise may prevail on the site, jeopardizing the accuracy of field measurements.

All these conditions and circumstances reduce the accuracy and reliability of field measurements and create the false impression that no matter how much attention is paid to details, the acoustical performance of any partition measured on the site is bound to be inferior to that of an identical panel tested in the laboratory.

The following measures will help ensure that the acoustical performance of field installations meets the specified criteria and improve agreement between laboratory and field measurements:

1. The installation of a test panel in the laboratory should simulate job conditions as closely as possible.

2. All paths for flanking transmission and leakage in the field installation should be eliminated or at least reduced to an absolute minimum.

3. Field measurements should be conducted in unfurnished and preferably reverberating rooms, entirely enclosed, and with a low background-noise level.

4. Laboratory and field measurements for airborne and impact-noise transmission should be conducted in accordance with the current practice recommended by the major standardization organizations, such as the American Society for Testing and Materials (ASTM designation E 90-66T and E 336-67T) or the International Organization for Standardization (ISO R 140-1960E).

5. Results obtained from field measurements should be normalized to the same reference base as that used for laboratory measurements.

In spite of the discrepancies found between laboratory and field testing, field measurements constitute an important tool in evaluating the acoustical performance of enclosures. This applies particularly to floor-ceiling assemblies which are rigidly connected with the surrounding structure, creating a much larger number of flanking paths for impact noise than in a laboratory, where the floor-ceiling assembly is structurally isolated from the receiving room.

14.4 Sound-insulating Building Constructions

In the selection of a wall or floor construction, three factors must normally be considered: (1) the existing or predictable noise level on the source side or in the source room, (2) the acceptable (or desirable) background-noise level in the receiving room, and (3) the ability of the selected enclosure to reduce the exterior noise to an acceptable level.

The acceptable (or desirable) background-noise level can be expressed in terms of noise criterion (NC) level, specified in terms of *noise criterion curves* (Chap. 15). The basic objective is that the transmitted portion of the exterior noise be reduced on the receiving side just below background-noise level, provided that the background noise is within the permissible or acceptable range. For example (Fig. 14.12), if an exterior noise of 70 dB must be reduced by using a partition below a background noise level of 20 dB to about 15 dB, the partition must have an acoustical rating (STC value) of $70 - 15 = 55$ dB. Figure 14.12 also shows that if the background-noise level can be raised to 35 dB instead of 20 dB, provided that this is still within the acceptable range, a more economical 40-dB (instead of 55-dB) partition will render the transmitted noise inaudible.

Background noise is a mixture of various existing noises in the unoccupied room created by the mechanical and electrical services of the building, by exterior vehicular traffic, by general office activities in spaces adjacent to the receiving room, etc. In rural or suburban areas the background noise is naturally lower.

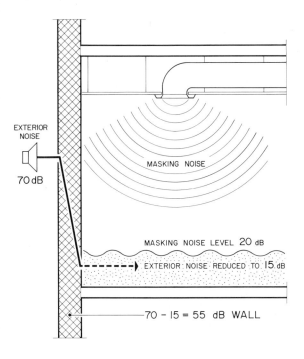

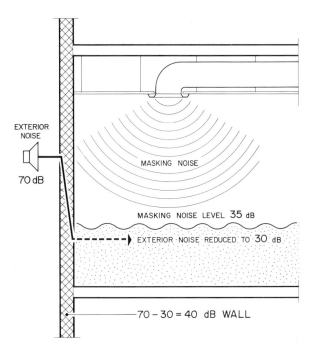

Fig. 14.12 With a relatively high but acceptable background-noise level in a room, the reduction of exterior noises can be achieved at a lower cost.

It is generally agreed that a reasonable amount of background noise, or masking noise, when properly controlled (or artificially produced by electronic devices), will beneficially mask other disturbing noises, provided that the masking noise is (1) continuous, (2) not too loud, (3) unobtrusive, and (4) carries no information, such as intelligible speech or identifiable music.

An excessive masking noise will impair audibility or intelligibility by drowning out faint speech, soft music, or other very low-intensity sounds one might want to hear, for example, in a demonstration room.

14.4.1 Walls Optimum performance against airborne noises can be expected from a wall only if the following conditions are satisfied:

1. It has a reasonable and uniformly distributed mass over its entire area.

2. It is constructed both horizontally and vertically as an uninterrupted, complete barrier.

3. It is effectively sealed around its periphery (Fig. 14.13), between its elements, and around openings made for outlets, switches, etc. (Fig. 13.16).

Fig. 14.13 Acoustical tests conducted on a dry-wall partition (wall 45 of Fig. B.7, Appendix B) reveal that the STC rating of dry-wall partitions depends to a large extent upon the effectiveness of caulking around the edges.

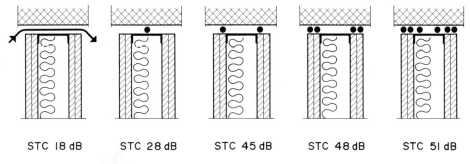

STC 18 dB   STC 28 dB   STC 45 dB   STC 48 dB   STC 51 dB

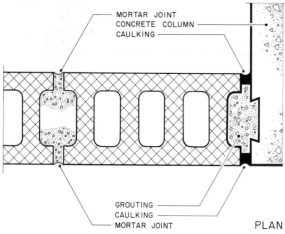

MORTAR JOINT
CONCRETE COLUMN
CAULKING

GROUTING
CAULKING
MORTAR JOINT

PLAN

Fig. 14.14 Airtight sealing of horizontal and vertical joints in masonry construction is indispensable for effective sound insulation.

Fig. 14.15 The practical application of semiresilient attachments in multiple walls, contributing 2 to 5 dB to the STC rating of partitions.

4. It is built from structural slab to structural slab, or when attached to a suspended ceiling only, adequate measures have been taken for the acoustical restoration of its missing portion above the suspended ceiling.

The sealant should be a nonsetting, nonskinning, and nonhardening caulking compound; gasketing alone is not as effective as caulking. Loose and void mortar joints should be carefully avoided in masonry-wall construction because they create noise leaks (Fig. 14.14). If no plaster is specified for a masonry wall, its exterior surfaces should be painted, possibly with two layers. Gypsum boards used in dry-wall construction should be carefully sealed and taped.

Since it is necessary to double the weight of a single-leaf partition to provide about 5 to 6 dB improvement in its STC rating, using a multiple partition is recommended where a high degree of sound insulation is required. A multiple partition should include as many of the useful features illustrated in Fig. 14.3 as possible. Resilient layers (fiberboard, glass-fiber board, etc.), semiresilient attachments, or resilient clips between individual layers and the inner framing or core of the wall are particularly recommended. These elements are inexpensive, do not require excessive labor, and contribute about 2 to 5 dB to the STC rating of a multiple wall (Fig. 14.15).

Every attempt should be made to increase the weight of a wall without rendering it too stiff. As mentioned before, the stiffness of a wall tends to counteract the acoustically beneficial effect of the mass and of the separation between individual layers of the wall. Using sheet lead, a relatively heavy and limp material, in walls and floors is recommended to increase the weight without rendering the partition harmfully stiff (Fig. 14.16).

Appendix B includes useful architectural-acoustical information on a number of wall constructions.

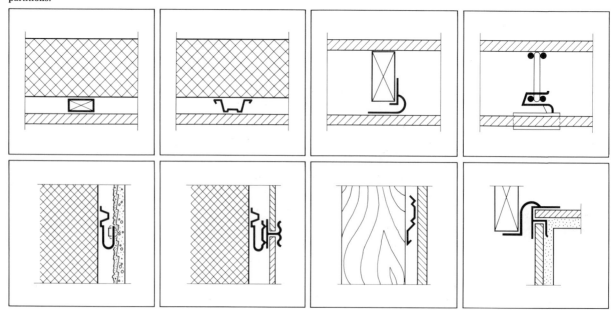

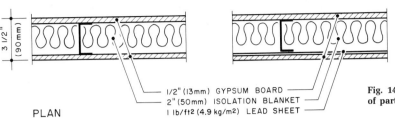

STC 44 dB   STC 48 dB

3 1/2"
(90 mm)

PLAN

1/2" (13mm) GYPSUM BOARD
2" (50mm) ISOLATION BLANKET
1 lb/ft2 (4.9 kg/m2) LEAD SHEET

Fig. 14.16 Sheet lead improves the sound insulation of partitions.

14.4.2 Floors and Ceilings   While airborne noises must primarily be isolated by walls, an acoustically efficient floor construction should provide adequate protection against both airborne and impact noises. A floor with thick carpeting which adequately reduces impact noises is not necessarily satisfactory against airborne noises. On the other hand, a thick, bare concrete slab which gives satisfactory insulation against airborne noises will not provide adequate protection against impact noises originating from the room above.

The sound insulation of floors can be improved in the following ways:

1. A soft *resilient surface*, such as carpeting, cork tile, rubber, or vinyl tile, greatly improves the impact-noise insulation of the floor but provides only negligible insulation against airborne noise.

2. A *floating floor* considerably improves the sound insulation against both airborne and impact noises.

3. A solid *suspended ceiling* improves the insulation against both airborne and impact noises, the extent depending on the weight of the suspended ceiling and the degree of resiliency with which the ceiling is attached to the structural floor.

Hard, rigid finishes over a concrete floor, such as wood, linoleum, vinyl-asbestos tile, asphalt tile, etc., do not improve the impact-noise insulation of the floor. Whenever possible, laying a carpet (Chap. 5) is unquestionably the most sensible measure for eliminating impact (footstep) noises.

Floating floors can be supported by a continuous layer of resilient blanket, resilient mounts, or sleepers, which rest on a resilient blanket or are carried in resilient chairs (Figs. 14.17 and 14.18).

In all cases the floating floor assembly rests on the structural slab. Floating wood floors should be carefully nailed to the supporting sleepers only, in order not to short-circuit the resilient blanket beneath the sleepers. A floating concrete slab should be at least 3 in. (75 mm) thick, on top of an adequately resilient blanket. Floating concrete slabs are more effective than floating wood floors.

In order to obtain maximum efficiency it is essential not only to provide a consistent and uninterrupted acoustical separation between floating floor and structural slab, but also to avoid any rigid contact between floating floor and surrounding walls. The resilient blanket beneath the floating slab must be adequately protected by a waterproof membrane (roofing felt or polyethylene) against moisture originating from the pouring of the floating slab. Protection of the waterproof membrane (by plywood) may also be necessary against such potential

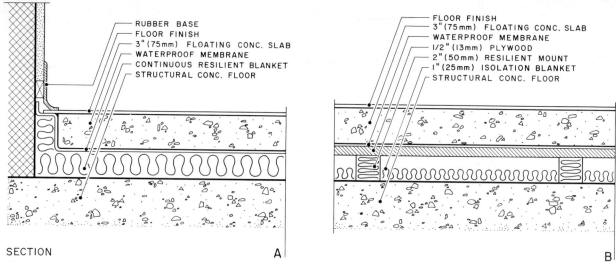

SECTION   A   B

Fig. 14.17 Floating concrete floors supported by (A) a continuous layer of resilient blanket and (B) distributed resilient mounts.

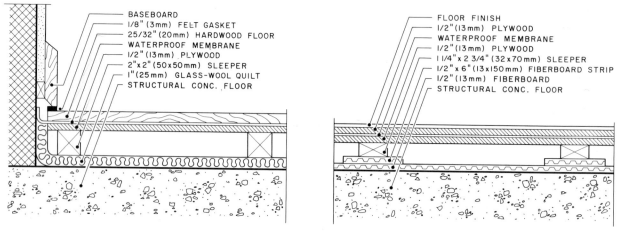

SECTION

Fig. 14.18 Floating wooden floors supported by resiliently mounted sleepers.

damages as rupture during reinforcement and concrete pouring. Once the area of the floating concrete slab exceeds 130 to 150 sq ft (12 to 14 sq m) suitably spaced expansion joints and reinforcing bars should be provided. All pipes, ducts, conduits, etc., which penetrate through floating floors should be isolated all around to avoid short-circuiting between structural floor and floating slab (Fig. 14.19).

When floating floors are used to protect certain areas against impact noises from above, it is important to make sure that no impact noise enters the protected area through any other path (Fig. 14.20).

Suspended ceilings attached to the structual floor contribute substantially to the sound insulation of a floor against both airborne and impact noises. In order to increase their effectiveness the following recommendations should be observed:

1. The ceiling membrane should weigh not less than 5 lb per sq ft (25 kg per sq m). If an absorbent blanket (mineral or glass wool) is used in the air space above the ceiling, the weight of the ceiling membrane can be somewhat reduced.

2. The ceiling membrane should not be too rigid.

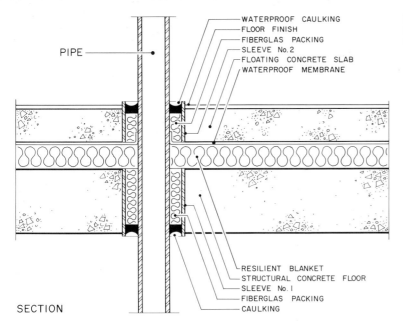

PIPE

WATERPROOF CAULKING
FLOOR FINISH
FIBERGLAS PACKING
SLEEVE No. 2
FLOATING CONCRETE SLAB
WATERPROOF MEMBRANE

RESILIENT BLANKET
STRUCTURAL CONCRETE FLOOR
SLEEVE No. 1
FIBERGLAS PACKING
CAULKING

SECTION

Fig. 14.19 Pipes penetrating through floating floors should be sleeved and acoustically isolated to avoid short-circuiting.

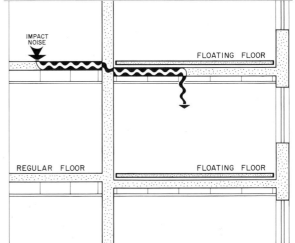

IMPACT NOISE

FLOATING FLOOR

REGULAR FLOOR

FLOATING FLOOR

SECTION

Fig. 14.20 Impact noises generated on acoustically untreated floors may reach areas protected by floating floors against impact noises from above.

3. Direct paths of noise transmission through the ceiling should be avoided by the use of a solid, airtight membrane.

4. Gaps between ceiling and surrounding structure should be sealed, thus avoiding noise penetration through direct air paths.

5. The air space between ceiling membrane and structural floor should be increased to a reasonable maximum, and an isolation blanket placed in the air space.

6. The number of points of suspension from the structural floor above should be reduced to a minimum. Resilient hangers are preferable to rigid ones.

When a suspended ceiling is used to improve the airborne or impact-sound insulation of a floor, the application of a lightweight and sound-absorptive but sound-transparent acoustical ceiling is useless and should be avoided. The ceiling membrane should consist of a minimum $3/4$-in. (20-mm) solid cement-plaster layer with hermetically sealed (caulked) joints all around. If the reduction of undesirable noises within a sound-insulated room is required, the installation of sound-absorptive treatment along the underside of the solid ceiling membrane should be considered.

Figure 14.21 shows various hangers used in resiliently suspended

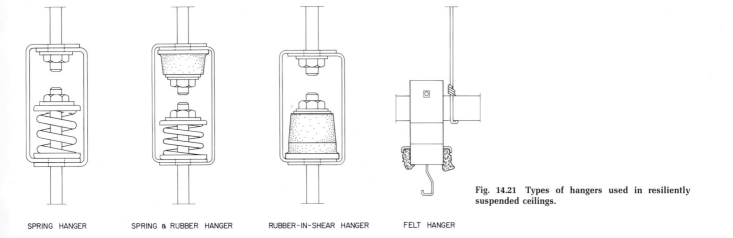

SPRING HANGER   SPRING & RUBBER HANGER   RUBBER-IN-SHEAR HANGER   FELT HANGER

Fig. 14.21 Types of hangers used in resiliently suspended ceilings.

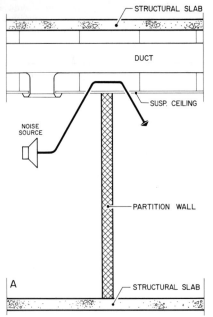

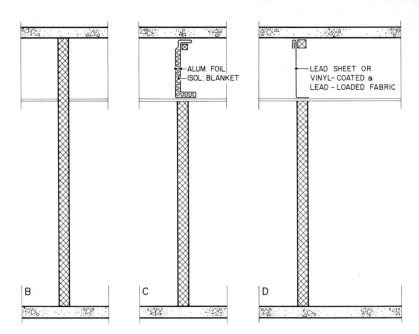

SECTION

Fig. 14.22 To avoid noise transmission above partitions built up to suspended-ceiling height (A), walls should be constructed up to the structural slab above (B), or an adequate sound barrier should be installed in the ceiling space above the partition (C, D).

ceilings. A semiresilient separation between structural floor and suspended ceiling, achieved by the use of "resilient" clips, does not contribute nearly as effectively to the sound insulation of floor-ceiling assemblies as fully resilient hangers do (Fig. 14.21).

Walls built only up to suspended-ceiling height suffer a serious reduction in TL. Manufacturers of various suspended-ceiling assemblies seem insufficiently concerned about this reduction. This is understandable because any objection to the reduced acoustical performance of a suspended ceiling would undermine the manufacturers' claim for complete flexibility and demountability. It is therefore essential that the space between a suspended ceiling and structural soffit, above the line of the partition wall, be adequately sealed (Fig. 14.22).

It is an interesting acoustical phenomenon that noise transmission through the plenum above a suspended ceiling is rather difficult to detect. This is due to the so-called *Haas effect;* that is, if the same speech sound is picked up from two directions, the sound that arrives first determines the apparent direction. In the present case, if speech sound can travel simultaneously through the partition and through the plenum above the suspended ceiling, the partition offers the shorter path for the sound and it will therefore appear as though the sound were coming through the partition, creating the illusion that the partition and not the ceiling is the noise transmitter.

The yearly *Bulletin* of the Acoustical and Insulating Materials Association (Park Ridge, Ill.) includes the noise-attenuation factors of most suspended acoustical (sound-absorptive) ceilings used in North America.

Figure 14.23 summarizes the guidelines described so far to improve the airborne and impact-sound insulation of cast-in-place and precast concrete floors. Alternative *A* shows that if no suspended ceiling is used, the application of a heavy concrete slab at least 6 in. (150 mm) thick, or 72 lb per sq ft (350 kg per sq m), with carpet will give adequate insulation in most cases. Alternative *B* illustrates the use of a minimum

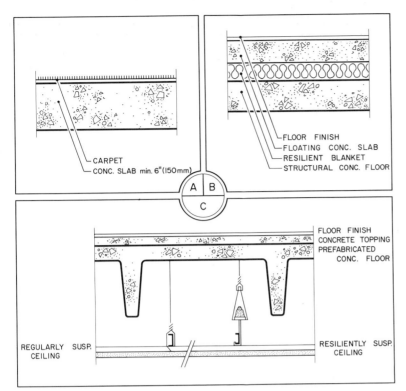

A B
C

CARPET
CONC. SLAB min. 6"(150mm)

FLOOR FINISH
FLOATING CONC. SLAB
RESILIENT BLANKET
STRUCTURAL CONC. FLOOR

FLOOR FINISH
CONCRETE TOPPING
PREFABRICATED
CONC. FLOOR

REGULARLY SUSP.
CEILING

RESILIENTLY SUSP.
CEILING

Fig. 14.23 Simplified illustration of the measures necessary to improve the sound insulation of concrete floors against both airborne and impact noises: (A) using carpet on an adequately thick and heavy concrete slab; (B) using a floating floor; (C) using a regularly or resiliently suspended ceiling beneath excessively thin and lightweight structural slabs.

3-in. (75-mm) floating concrete floor without an additional suspended ceiling beneath the floor. Alternative *C* shows the application of a regularly suspended and a resiliently suspended ceiling beneath excessively thin and lightweight (prefabricated or prestressed) concrete slabs, depending on the degree of privacy to be achieved.

Figure 14.24 illustrates the practical application of a floating wooden floor and a regularly suspended ceiling in an apartment building to improve the sound insulation of a prefabricated concrete floor.

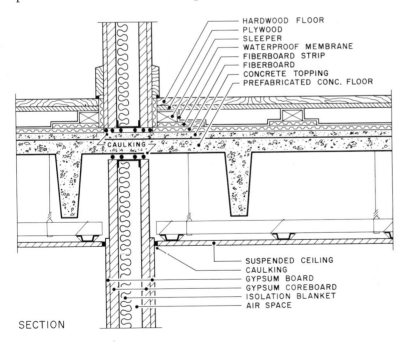

HARDWOOD FLOOR
PLYWOOD
SLEEPER
WATERPROOF MEMBRANE
FIBERBOARD STRIP
FIBERBOARD
CONCRETE TOPPING
PREFABRICATED CONC. FLOOR

CAULKING

SUSPENDED CEILING
CAULKING
GYPSUM BOARD
GYPSUM COREBOARD
ISOLATION BLANKET
AIR SPACE

SECTION

Fig. 14.24 Practical application of a floating wooden floor and a regularly suspended ceiling in an apartment building to improve the inadequate sound insulation of a prefabricated concrete floor.

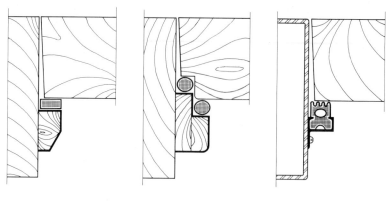

GASKETED DOOR STOP   DOUBLE-GASKETED DOOR STOP   ADJUSTABLE DOOR STOP

Fig. 14.25 Door stops used at the jambs and heads of sound-insulating doors.

Appendix C includes useful architectural-acoustical information on a number of floor constructions.

14.4.3 Doors and Movable Partitions Doors constitute acoustically weak elements of walls because (1) their surface weight is normally less than that of the wall into which they are built, (2) the gaps around their edges, unless sealed, offer an easy passage for the transmission of noise, and (3) they are considerably smaller than an average partition, consequently their low-frequency resonances occur at a more critical range of the audio-frequency spectrum.

Sound-insulating doors should be of solid-core and heavy (rather than hollow-core and light) construction, with all edges well sealed. Lightweight, hollow-core wooden doors are dimensionally unstable and can warp, destroying the seal along the perimeter of the door. Rubber, foam-rubber, or foamed plastic strips, adjustable or self-aligning stops, and gaskets can be used for sealing the edges of doors (Fig. 14.25). They should be installed so that they are slightly compressed between door and stop when the door is in a closed position. In simple cases the bottom edges can have a replaceable strip of felt or foam rubber attached to minimize the gap between door and floor. A more effective alternative is to install drop-bar draft excluders, called *automatic threshold closers* (Fig. 14.26).

Fig. 14.26 Automatic drop-bar threshold closers used for sound-insulating doors.

SECTION

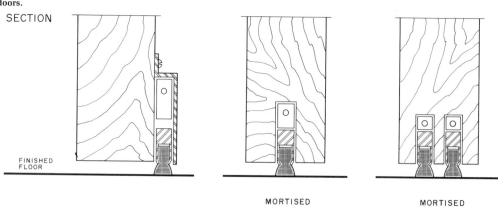

SURFACE-MOUNTED   MORTISED SINGLE DROP-BAR   MORTISED DOUBLE DROP-BAR

If doors must have an unusually high degree of sound insulation, they are built so that a separation between the two faces of the door is carried through uninterruptedly from edge to edge in both directions, and, in addition, damping treatments are inserted between individual layers of the doors. Ordinary doors with surface leather padding do not contribute to the reduction of airborne noises between source room and receiving room; they provide a negligible degree of sound absorption only in the room facing the leather padding.

The use of automatic door closers is recommended whenever feasible and applicable, in order to avoid the annoying sound of doors slamming. Similarly, door chimes are preferable to door knockers.

In the acoustical evaluation of a sound-insulating door, distinction should be made between the panel value and the operating value of its STC rating. Panel values are obtained when the door is tested with hermetically sealed edges. Operating values (always lower than panel values) obtained from tests simulating conditions of field installation in every respect reflect a more realistic acoustical performance.

Doors always reduce the overall TL of walls in which they are installed (Fig. 14.8). In order to keep this reduction to a minimum, it is recommended that the difference between the TL of the wall and that of the door should not exceed 5 to 10 dB. Figure 14.27 illustrates a sound-insulating double door with steel frame and perimeter absorption between the doors. Figure 14.28 compares the TL diagrams of various door constructions.

In apartment buildings, offices, and institutional buildings where rooms are located along both sides of corridors, doors should be staggered so that noise from one room will not penetrate directly across into another (Fig. 14.29). Staggered doors give sound a longer distance to travel so that sound waves are absorbed in the corridor to a certain extent before reaching adjacent rooms.

When a particularly high degree of acoustical privacy is required for a room, the need for a highly effective and expensive sound-insulating door may be avoided using two moderately sound-insulating doors, or a sound lock (Fig. 14.30). All wall, floor, and ceiling surfaces within a sound lock should be rendered sound-absorptive, in order to achieve a maximum attenuation of noise transmission through the sound lock.

In auditoriums, classrooms, convention halls, hotels, motels, etc., flexible utilization of large, acoustically sensitive spaces often requires the use of room dividers, or *movable partitions*. These are large folding, sliding, or side-coiling doors which provide various degrees of sound insulation between the separated spaces.

Depending on the basic functions they have to fulfill, movable partitions should meet the following requirements, in addition to those outlined in Sec. 5.9:

1. They should combine visual separation with acoustical privacy to the required degree.

2. They should be capable of dividing an area into two or more spaces, easily and quickly, without the need for additional manpower.

3. They should require a minimum of maintenance and servicing.

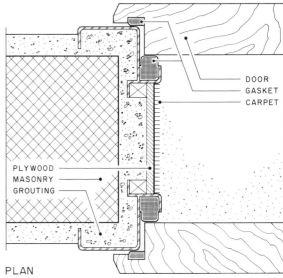

PLAN

Fig. 14.27 Sound-insulating double door with steel frame and perimeter absorption.

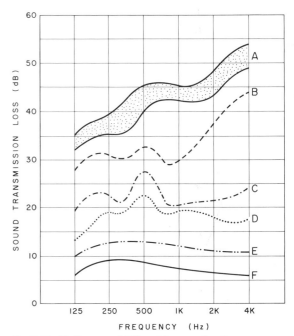

Fig. 14.28 TL diagrams of different door constructions: (A) soundproof door (spread of TL values); (B) solid-core door gasketed; (C) hollow-core door gasketed; (D) ungasketed hollow-core door; (E) louvered door (25 percent open); (F) open door.

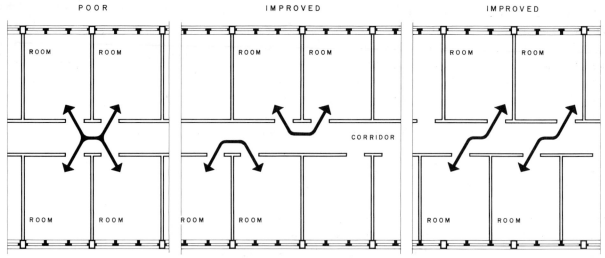

Fig. 14.29 Staggered doors contribute effectively to the acoustical privacy of occupancies located along the two sides of a corridor.

PLAN

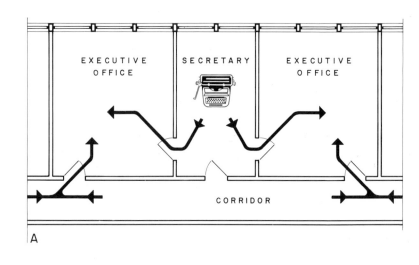

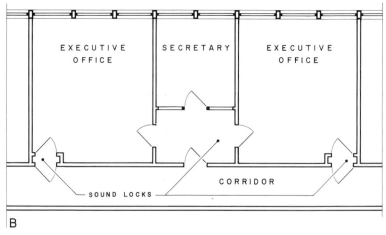

PLAN

Fig. 14.30 Ordinary doors (A) seriously reduce the acoustical qualities of sound-insulating walls around executive offices. In order to avoid the use of expensive sound-insulating doors, sound locks (B) can be used.

4. Their shape should conform to any unavoidable irregularities in the floor without loss of acoustical efficiency.

5. The elements (panels) should not warp or twist even under conditions of unfavorable temperature and humidity.

6. The bottom seal should not mar the finished (or carpeted) floor.

7. The elements, when retracted, should not require space-consuming storage areas.

8. The surface treatment of the elements should offer a reasonable variety for the interior decorator of the rooms concerned.

The acoustical performance of movable partitions extends over a wide range, and their STC ratings can go as high as 55 dB.

14.4.4 Windows

Like doors, windows constitute weak components in exterior walls and enclosures because their surface weight is much below that of the exterior wall and their connection with the wall, unless adequately sealed, constitutes a direct path for the penetration of exterior noise. However, windows do provide some acoustical advantage by allowing exterior masking noises to enter the building, thereby covering up some of the noises that may come through adjoining walls or floors.

The TL of windows depends on the number, thickness, and relative positions of the panes and on their edge connection to the wall (Fig. 14.31). Double glazing, well-sealed edges, and a minimum distance of 4 to 5 in. (100 to 125 mm) between the panes are basic features of sound-insulating windows.

If a high degree of sound insulation is expected from a window, double- or triple-pane construction is preferable to a very thick single pane. The distance between the panes has a distinct effect on the TL of the window, particularly at low frequencies, and the TL improves with increasing distance between the panes (Fig. 14.31). If a reasonable distance cannot be secured between the panes, it is advisable to increase the thickness, that is, the weight of the panes. Figure 14.32 illustrates range of sound insulation of single- and double-glazed windows.

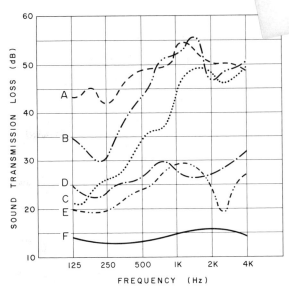

Fig. 14.31 TL values of various window constructions with weather-stripped and sealed edges: (A) double window, ½-in. (13-mm) plate glass and 8-in. (20-cm) air space; (B) double window, 24-oz (3-mm) glazings and 8-in. (20-cm) air space; (C) double window, 24-oz (3mm) glazings and 4-in. (100-mm) air space; (D) single window, ½-in. (13-mm) plate glass; (E) single window, 24-oz (3-mm) glazing; (F) open window. All double windows (A, B, and C) have sound-absorptive reveals.

Fig. 14.32 Ranges of sound insulation of single- and double-glazed windows. Values on the left represent windows that can be opened; values on the right represent fixed windows.

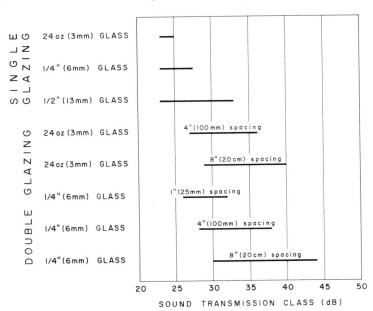

In air-conditioned buildings the TL of fixed windows, with thick double panes well spaced and structurally isolated from each other, may approximate that of the surrounding wall.

Adding sound-absorbing treatment around the perimeter between the panes, mounting panes in an elastic material (cork, felt, sponge, rubber, neoprene, etc.), and eliminating parallelism between panes will result in a reasonable increase in the TL of windows. Each glass should be of a different thickness or weight per unit area in order to eliminate acoustical coupling and resonance. These methods of increasing the sound-insulating quality of windows are used in the installation of control and observation windows in radio, television, and recording studios (Fig. 14.33).

Windows which are moderately sound-retarding and manufactured mainly for thermal-insulation purposes are available on the market (Twindow, Thermopane, etc.).

Fig. 14.33   Control window between a radio or recording studio and a sound-control room.

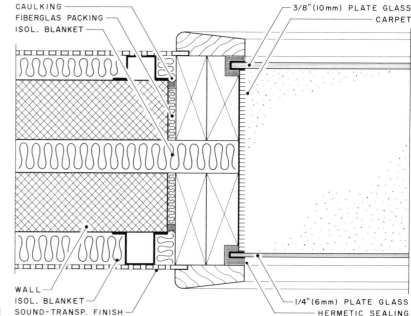

14.4.5 Discontinuous Construction   If in a room or in part of a building a particularly high degree of insulation is required against airborne noises, structure-borne noises, and vibrations, all the measures discussed so far in this chapter must be incorporated into a single design, called *discontinuous construction*, or *box within a shell*. Basic elements of such an arrangement are shown in Fig. 14.34. The room illustrated in this figure could be used for audiometric tests, as a radio or recording studio, or for any other purpose where an extraordinary degree of acoustical privacy must be achieved. Such a room is normally accessible through a sound lock and has a floating floor on top of the structural slab; the walls built on the floating floor are separated from the load-carrying exterior walls. The ceiling is resiliently suspended from the structural floor above. The acoustical separation of the inner shell from the building structure must not be short-circuited by rigid, connecting links, such as wall ties, ducts, pipes, or unisolated windows.

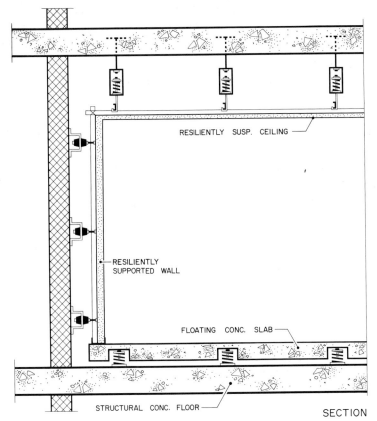

RESILIENTLY SUSP. CEILING

RESILIENTLY
SUPPORTED WALL

FLOATING CONC. SLAB

STRUCTURAL CONC. FLOOR

SECTION

Fig. 14.34 Discontinuous construction with floating floor, isolated wall, and resiliently suspended ceiling.

BIBLIOGRAPHY

Books

Harris, C. M. (ed.): *Handbook of Noise Control*, McGraw-Hill Book Company, New York, 1957, 1184 pp.

Parkin, P. H., and H. R. Humphreys: *Acoustics, Noise and Buildings*, Frederick A. Praeger, Inc., New York, 1958, chap. 8.

Parkin, P. H., H. J. Purkis, and W. E. Scholes: *Field Measurements of Sound Insulation between Dwellings*, Her Majesty's Stationery Office, London, 1960, 571 pp.

Berendt, R. D., and G. E. Winzer: *Sound Insulation of Wall, Floor, and Door Constructions*, National Bureau of Standards Monograph 77, Washington, D.C., November 1964, 49 pp.

Berendt, R. D., G. E. Winzer, and C. B. Burroughs: *A Guide to Air-borne, Impact, and Structure-borne Noise Control in Multifamily Dwellings*, U.S. Department of Housing and Urban Development, Washington, D.C., September 1967.

Periodicals

Rettinger, M.: "Sound-reducing Doors," *Progressive Architecture*, April 1955, pp. 120–122.

Hamme, R. N.: "Sound Transmission through Suspended Ceilings over Partitions," *Noise Control*, January 1959, pp. 64–69, 76.

Rettinger, M.: "Sound-retarding Windows," *Progressive Architecture*, March 1960, pp. 184–186.

Farrell, R.: "Designing Sound Insulation into Buildings," *Architectural and Engineering News*, March 1964, pp. 36–49.

Rettinger, M.: "Noise Abatement by Barriers," *Progressive Architecture*, August 1965, pp. 168–169.

Olynyk, D., and T. D. Northwood: "Subjective Judgements of Footstep-noise Transmission through Floors," *J. Acoust. Soc. Am.*, December 1965, pp. 1040–1042.

Doelle, L.: "Architectural Noise Control," *J. RAIC*, May 1966, pp. 34–38.

Utley, W. A., and K. A. Mulholland: "The Transmission Loss of Double and Triple Walls," *Applied Acoustics*, January 1968, pp. 15–20.

Scholes, W. E., and P. H. Parkin: "The Insulation of Houses against Noise from Aircraft in Flight," *Applied Acoustics*, January 1968, pp. 37–46.

Fischer, R. E.: "Some Particular Problems of Noise Control," *Architectural Record*, September 1968, pp. 185–192.

Utley, W. A., and B. L. Fletcher: "Influence of Edge Conditions on the Sound Insulation of Windows," *Applied Acoustics*, April 1969, pp. 131–136.

Lange, P. A.: "Sound Insulation of Glazing with Respect to Traffic Noise," *Applied Acoustics*, July 1969, pp. 215–236.

"Lead," *Progressive Architecture*, October 1969, pp. 174–183.

Farrell, R.: "Lab Tests and Field Tests: The Accuracy Gap," *Architectural and Engineering News*, February 1970, pp. 26–32.

Goodfriend, L. S.: "Leaks and Seals," *Architectural and Engineering News*, February 1970, pp. 36–37.

Higginson, R. F.: "Sound Insulation between Rooms Having Resilient Linings on the Walls," *Applied Acoustics*, April 1970, pp. 133–143.

Digests and Reports

Solutions to Noise Control Problems in the Construction of Houses, Apartments, Motels, and Hotels, Owens-Corning Fiberglas Corporation, Toledo, Ohio, February 1964, 63 pp.

Northwood, T. D., and D. M. Clark: *Frequency Considerations in the Subjective Assessment of Sound Insulation*, National Research Council, Ottawa, Research Paper 391, May 1964, 4 pp.

Wooley, R. M.: *Sound Insulation of Windows*, Building Research Station, Garston, Herts, October 1967, 6 pp.

Northwood, T. D.: *Transmission Loss of Plasterboard Walls*, National Research Council, Ottawa, Building Research Note 66, October 1968, 9 pp.

Sewell, E. C.: *Sound Transmission within Buildings*, Building Research Station News, Garston, Herts, Autumn 1970, pp. 9–11.

The need for effective noise control in buildings results because noise affects people by being so loud that it causes temporary or permanent ear damage, interfering with listening to speech or music, causing deterioration of work performance, or simply being distracting and annoying.

The distracting and annoying effects of noise cause different reactions in people, as described in Sec. 13.1. When it is a question of damage to hearing or interference with listening to speech or music, a person's reaction is more limited.

A basic problem in noise control is to predict how the expected noise is likely to interfere with the occupancy of the room under consideration and then to set limits to the path of intruding or spreading noise in order to avoid any harmful interference. To do so, various criteria discussed briefly in this chapter must be considered, depending on the type and circumstances of the noise-control problem.

15.1 Damage to Hearing

Noises so loud (about 140 to 150 dB) that they cause immediate damage to hearing normally do not occur in buildings; they may occur, however, near airports. In such special cases precautions are required to avoid the risk of people accidentally entering the damage zone without earmuffs.

Noise levels high enough to cause temporary or permanent deafness occur in industry. Various criteria have been established giving the maximum noise levels which must not be exceeded if complete or partial deafness is to be avoided. If existing noise levels measured in a very noisy room exceed the danger levels established in the corresponding criteria, measures will have to be taken (Chap. 13) in order to reduce the noise and to protect the workers. It is essential that an effective hearing-conservation program be administered in any noisy industry, including regular audiometric checks of employees' hearing.

In the United States the Walsh-Healey Public Contracts Act (revised in 1969) requires that when the level of industrial noise, measured on the A scale of a sound-level meter, exceeds values listed in Table 15.1, effective administrative or engineering measures must be taken to reduce the prevailing noise level below the levels of the table. If these measures fail to reduce the noise level adequately, protective equipment (earmuffs or earplugs) must be provided for the workers.

The requirements specified in the Walsh-Healey Public Contracts Act apply to firms which hold federal supply contracts in any amount exceeding $10,000.

15.2 Maximum Permissible Background-noise Levels

When the existing or probable level of an exterior noise source has been determined (by measurement, estimation, or analogy), the acceptable background-noise level in the receiving room has to be established. The difference between existing or probable level at the source and acceptable background-noise level at the recipient's position indicates

CHAPTER FIFTEEN

Noise Criteria

TABLE 15.1 Permissible Noise Exposures as Specified in the Walsh-Healey Public Contracts Act (United States)

Duration per day, hr	Sound level, dB-A
8	90
6	92
4	95
3	97
2	100
1½	102
1	105
½	110
¼ or less	115

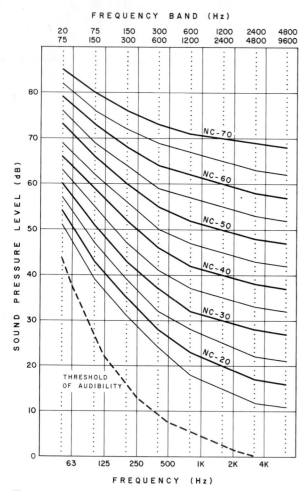

FREQUENCY BAND (Hz)

Fig. 15.1 Noise-criterion (NC) curves for determining the acceptable or desirable background-noise levels in rooms.

the degree of noise reduction to be achieved. Criteria developed after extensive investigations make it possible to specify those permissible background-noise levels which will provide a satisfactory environment for listening to speech and music or for any other activity.

The recommended maximum permissible background-noise levels in various occupancies can be specified in terms of *noise criterion* (NC) curves, illustrated in Fig. 15.1. The individual NC curves, as illustrated in this figure, are designated by their sound-pressure-level values in the important 1200- to 2400-Hz frequency band. These NC curves are recommended for the specification of the desired amount of background-noise levels for various occupancies. Table 15.2 shows the permissible background-noise levels in various occupancies, with any ventilating or air-conditioning systems operating and with normal outside traffic conditions; these levels can be specified in terms of NC curves. It is assumed that the infiltrating exterior noise is meaningless; if the intruding noise constitutes meaningful communication (for example, speech or music), other criteria apply.

The implications of Table 15.2 are illustrated graphically in Fig. 15.2.

A very low level of background noise often provides inadequate masking and will not secure sufficient privacy against interfering noises coming from adjacent rooms. In such cases the NC levels can be used to specify the desirable lowest limit under which the background noise must not fall. It is then the responsibility of the consulting mechanical engineer to make sure that background noise levels fall between a desirable minimum and a permissible maximum limit, depending on

TABLE 15.2 Recommended Background-noise Criteria for Rooms

Type of room	NC number
Concert hall	15–20
Radio or recording studio	15–20
Opera house	20
Legitimate theater	20–25
Music room	20–25
Television studio	20–25
Executive office	20–30
Classroom or lecture hall	25
Motion-picture studio	25
Conference room	25–30
Church or synagogue	25–30
Courtroom	25–30
Assembly hall or school auditorium	25–35
Home (sleeping areas)	25–35
Hotel or motel	25–35
Motion-picture theater	30
Hospital	30
Semiprivate office	30–35
Library	30–35
Business office	35–45
Restaurant	35–50
Drafting room	40–45
Gymnasium	45–50
Typing or accounting office	45–60
Coliseum	50

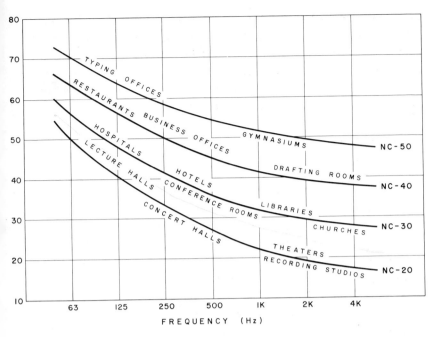

Fig. 15.2 Recommended background-noise criteria for certain rooms.

the function of the rooms; both levels can be expressed in terms of NC curves.

The general configuration of the NC curves is quite similar to the noise rating (NR) curves established by the International Organization for Standardization, used mostly in European practice.

15.3 Criteria for Residential Buildings

Establishing acceptable background-noise levels in residential buildings is not as straightforward as in other types of buildings because of wide differences in the location of residential developments, their economic range, etc., and also of the differing activities which take place in them. Table 15.3 shows recommended NC values for homes in different locations.

15.4 Criteria for Office Spaces

In the noise control of office spaces the problem is not merely whether or not a noise is excessive but also what the noise conveys. In addition to providing an adequately low background-noise level, the transmission, or spreading, of intelligible and identifiable noises must also be controlled. In an office this is essential for both listener and speaker, because the distracting effect of an identifiable noise (speech sounds) is intensified when the noise becomes intelligible and because the person speaking does not like to be overheard. When the occupant of an office or other space is reasonably well protected against intelligible speech originating from an adjacent or nearby area of the same room and has the assurance that he is not being overheard, he is said to have *acoustical privacy* or *speech privacy*.

A large amount of research has been carried out, and new studies are in progress to establish noise criteria acceptable to the majority

TABLE 15.3 Recommended Background-noise Criteria for Homes

Location	NC number, dB	
	Bedroom	Living room
Rural	20	25
Suburban	25	30
Urban	30	35
Near heavy traffic	35	40
Near heavy industry	40	45

of office workers. It appears that in the selection of an appropriate NC curve (Table 15.2) or any other suitable criterion for the noise control of offices, the architect will have to make a judicious decision because of the wide range of functions and sizes of office spaces, potential noise sources and their fluctuations in various offices, and individual differences in noise tolerance.

BIBLIOGRAPHY

Books

Harris, C. M. (ed.): *Handbook of Noise Control*, McGraw-Hill Book Company, New York, 1957, chaps. 7, 38, 39, and 40.
Parkin, P. H., and H. R. Humphreys: *Acoustics, Noise and Buildings*, Frederick A. Praeger, Inc., New York, 1958, chap. 10.
Beranek, L. L. (ed.): *Noise Reduction*, McGraw-Hill Book Company, New York, 1960, chaps. 19 and 20.

Periodicals

Beranek, L. L.: "Revised Criteria for Noise in Buildings," *Noise Control*, January 1957, pp. 19–27.
Kryter, K. D.: "Noise Control Criteria for Buildings," *Noise Control*, November 1957, pp. 14–20.
Farrell, W. R.: "Acoustical Privacy: What It Is and How It Can Be Achieved Economically," *Architectural Record*, June 1959, pp. 226–231.
"Criteria for Noise Control," *Architects' Journal*, February 27, 1963, pp. 491–492.
Rose, J. A.: "Acoustical Design, Criteria, and Planning," *Architectural Science Review*, September 1964, pp. 98–109.
Stewart, K. C.: "Noise and the Law," *Architectural and Engineering News*, February 1970, p. 40.

Although today mechanical equipment and machinery render the lives of the occupants of buildings more comfortable, more enjoyable, and more productive, these machines and equipment are fundamental contributors to noise in buildings. In addition, the need for optimum utilization of space within a building frequently results not only in less than adequate room for mechanical equipment and ductwork but also in the highly undesirable proximity of machinery to noise-sensitive areas.

In the control of mechanical noise complete elimination is seldom, if ever, the objective. Technically this would be difficult, uneconomical, and unnecessary. Instead, the general objective is the attenuation of mechanical noise to an acceptable level, depending on various conditions, such as anticipated activity in the room, the required degree of privacy, etc.

Mechanical noises are generated by plumbing systems, by ventilating and air-conditioning systems, and by machinery.

The satisfactory control of mechanical noise and vibration is the responsibility of the consulting mechanical engineer, but familiarity with the most important aspects of this subject will be helpful for the architect as well.

16.1 Noise from Plumbing Systems

Plumbing noises are seldom excessively loud; nevertheless they can be annoying and embarrassing, for example, when they originate from bathroom fixtures. The following are the main sources of plumbing noise:

1. Turbulent flow of water
2. Water-hammering caused by the sudden interruption of water flow
3. Pump noise caused by motor-driven pumps
4. Loose or defective parts of fixtures
5. Expansion and contraction of piping
6. Draining of water from bathtubs, toilets, sinks, and lavatories
7. Running and splashing of water when a bathtub is being filled or a shower is used
8. Entrapped air in the plumbing system

As in so many cases of noise control, the best procedure is to suppress the noise at the source, for example, by installing supply and drain pipes as far as possible from quiet areas of the building or by selecting and installing quietly operating fixtures. As a next step, an attempt must be made to prevent noise from penetrating into the water pipe or to prevent its transmission from the pipe to the building structure. Transmission along the pipe can be reduced considerably by inserting a flexible (rubber, rubber-and-fabric, plastic, etc.) pipe between the source and the metal pipe.

If noise is transmitted through a pipe, the amount of noise that is radiated by the pipe itself is negligible; most of the disturbing sound is radiated by the building structure (partitions, slabs, ceilings, etc.) to which the pipe is attached. To eliminate this noise radiation, pipes should be attached to massive structural elements (masonry walls) or resiliently mounted, that is, adequately insulated from their supports

CHAPTER SIXTEEN

Control of Mechanical Noise and Vibration

by being wrapped in felt, asbestos, rubber, neoprene, mineral wool, or some other suitable material. If the noise-reducing measures recommended above cannot be utilized to the required extent, the noise-conducting pipes should be screened from the affected rooms by building them into suitable ducts or shafts. One must make sure that these pipe ducts or shafts do not conduct other airborne noises from one part of the building to another.

In high-rise buildings the use of pressure reducers or regulators should be considered.

If the complete elimination of plumbing noise is necessary, noise-producing fixtures (bathtubs, showers) should be installed on floating floors or resilient underlays (cork, rubber, or neoprene).

16.2 Noise from Ventilating and Air-conditioning Systems

In rooms where listening to speech or music is important, the noise level created by an air-handling system should be about 5 to 15 dB below the desired level of background noise in order to avoid interference of ventilation noise with the intelligibility of speech or with the enjoyment of music.

In certain rooms, on the other hand, such as offices, hospital rooms, restaurants, etc., the aim in the control of mechanical noise is not to eliminate all the noise caused by the system but to create a balanced acoustical environment. The noise should be reduced only to the degree necessary to allow the anticipated activity in the room to take place at a comfortable level. To reduce mechanical noise below this level is wasteful. In addition, as mentioned above, excessive noise reduction would remove that artificial masking noise which can beneficially cover up intruding weaker sounds and render them inaudible. Noise control by means of masking sounds has been outlined in Secs. 13.6.9 and 14.4.

The noise control of air-handling systems should start, therefore, with a critical determination of criteria for the desired background-noise levels in all rooms, depending on the particular activities in each. Criteria for noise in various spaces were discussed in Chap. 15.

16.2.1 Sources of Mechanical Noise and Vibration   Noises encountered in mechanical systems can be grouped as follows:

1. Mechanical-equipment noise caused by individual ventilating and air-conditioning units and by the fans, motors, compressors, pumps, etc., of large centralized systems. These noises transmitted through the ducts and through the building structure (Fig. 16.1) can affect even rooms not served by the system.

2. *Self-noise* caused by high-velocity airflow, pulses created by the fan blades, airflow around sharp bends, or turbulences created by grilles, diffusers, dampers, and pressure regulators.

3. Cross talk from one space to another, for example speech sound that enters a supply or return air grille in one room travels through the duct or plenum and emerges in a nearby room through another grille, entirely irrespective of the direction of airflow.

4. Noise transmitted from exterior sources via an exposed part of the duct into the building.

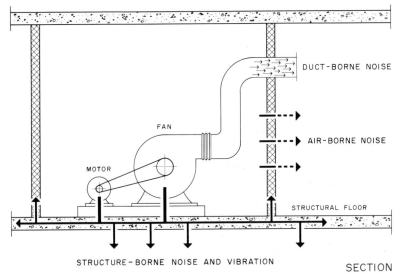

DUCT-BORNE NOISE

FAN

AIR-BORNE NOISE

MOTOR

STRUCTURAL FLOOR

STRUCTURE-BORNE NOISE AND VIBRATION

SECTION

Fig. 16.1 Principal noise sources of air-handling systems.

16.2.2 Noise-reducing Components

In the control of ventilating and air-conditioning noise attention must be given to the three principal noise-producing parts of the system: (1) the central mechanical equipment, (2) the supply and return ducts, and (3) the supply and return grilles.

The installation of quietly operating equipment, far removed from noise-sensitive rooms or floors (possibly in the basement or in a separate building), is an important point to remember in striving to reduce mechanical noises. Additional methods are as follows:

1. Absorption of noise in duct wall linings (Fig. 16.2)
2. Reduction of noise by means of bends
3. Division of noise into several branches of the duct system
4. Using heavy-gauge metal for ducts, properly braced and stiffened

Fig. 16.2 Methods of reducing noise by using sound-absorptive lining in the ductwork of air-handling systems.

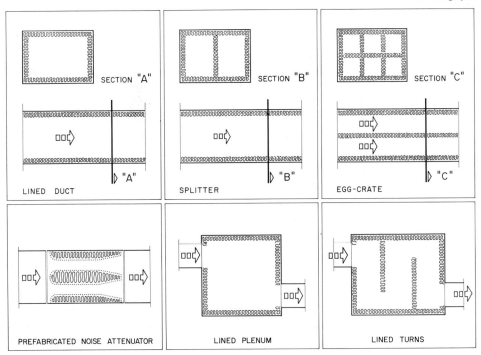

SECTION "A"

SECTION "B"

SECTION "C"

LINED DUCT

"A"

SPLITTER

"B"

EGG-CRATE

"C"

PREFABRICATED NOISE ATTENUATOR

LINED PLENUM

LINED TURNS

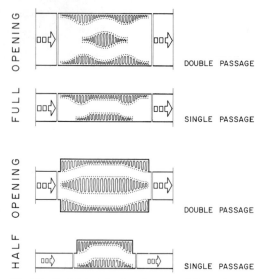

FULL OPENING — DOUBLE PASSAGE

FULL OPENING — SINGLE PASSAGE

HALF OPENING — DOUBLE PASSAGE

HALF OPENING — SINGLE PASSAGE

Fig. 16.3 Prefabricated noise attenuators (silencers) used in ductworks of air-handling systems.

5. Supporting ducts by resilient hangers

6. Acoustical separation of ducts from walls and floors at points of penetration, by means of resilient packing with fiber glass, rubber, and neoprene and by caulking the exposed end of the packing

7. Using boxed-in ducts between gypsum-board enclosures or in shafts

8. The use of properly shaped, streamline-contoured, and carefully distributed fixtures (grilles) at the discharge end of the duct, with adequately low air velocity

9. Spreading noise into the room at supply or return air grilles

10. Absorption of noise within the room supplied with air

Thermal insulation installed along the outside surface of a duct wall will contribute, to a certain degree, to the TL of the duct wall.

Sound-absorbing materials, such as glass-fiber or mineral-fiber boards, installed along the inside of rectangular or tubular ducts, will increase the attenuation of noise along the duct. Sound-absorbing materials used for duct lining should have a high absorption coefficient, a smooth surface for low air friction, adequate strength to resist disintegration due to airflow, and adequate resistance against fire, rot, vermin, and odor.

The incorporation of a plenum (an expanded section of the duct) into the duct system with a sound-absorptive interior surface contributes to the reduction of noise within the ductwork. Plenum chambers are used when a large number of smaller ducts are fed by one main supply fan.

Ducts with small cross sections are more effective noise attenuators than those with larger cross sections. Therefore, when a duct is too short to provide satisfactory reduction of noise, added attenuation can be obtained (at the expense of increased pressure drop) by dividing the duct into a number of smaller lined ducts (egg-crate-type sound-absorbing cells, splitters, etc., Fig. 16.2) or by using prefabricated (package) attenuator units, called *silencers* (Fig. 16.3).

Since the noise level close to the duct exit is greater than at a distance from the grille, the duct opening in auditoriums should be as far as possible from the listeners.

16.2.3 Attenuation of Mechanical Noise In order to achieve the required attenuation of ventilating and air-conditioning noise below the acceptable background-noise level in a room, the following steps should be considered:

1. The noise level produced by individual units of the equipment at the source must be determined.

2. The attenuation of this noise level due to ducts, walls, floors, ceilings, distance between supply grille and occupant, etc., must be calculated next; that is, the noise level at the occupant's position has to be checked.

3. For each room to be served by the air-handling system, the NC level must be established (Chap. 15) below which the noise level (item 2) will eventually have to be reduced.

4. If the mechanical noises have not been reduced to the required

extent, that is, below NC levels (item 3), further attenuation will have to be achieved by additional measures.

There are several means of obtaining the required additional attenuation:

1. The noise can be further reduced at the source.

2. The duct layout can be modified by lengthening the ductwork.

3. Additional sound-absorptive lining can be used along the interior surface of the ducts.

4. Prefabricated noise attenuators (silencers) can be used, preferably at partition wall junctions.

Besides the reduction of duct-borne noise, the elimination of cross talk between the rooms served by the system is also important (Fig. 16.4).

It must be stressed again that a most effective and economical means of controlling ventilation noise is achieved by concentrating and locating

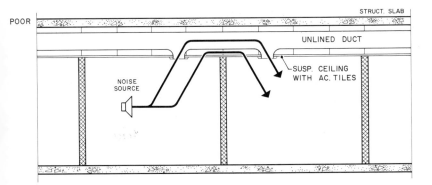

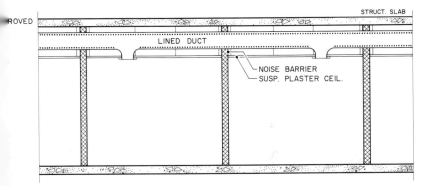

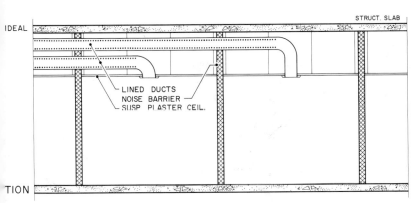

Fig. 16.4 Layouts of supply or return air ducts to reduce the undesirable transmission of noise (cross talk) between nearby rooms.

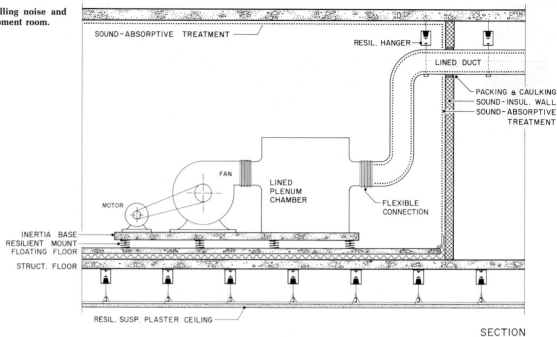

Fig. 16.5 Measures for controlling noise and vibration of a mechanical-equipment room.

SOUND—ABSORPTIVE TREATMENT

RESIL. HANGER

LINED DUCT

PACKING & CAULKING
SOUND—INSUL. WALL
SOUND—ABSORPTIVE TREATMENT

FAN

LINED PLENUM CHAMBER

MOTOR

FLEXIBLE CONNECTION

INERTIA BASE
RESILIENT MOUNT
FLOATING FLOOR

STRUCT. FLOOR

RESIL. SUSP. PLASTER CEILING

SECTION

the noise-producing equipment as far as possible from the rooms requiring a high degree of quiet and in a part of the building where noise and vibration can be relatively well tolerated.

16.3 Machinery Noise

Heating chambers (boilers), diesel generators, pumps, compressors, cooling towers, motors, pneumatic devices, electric-circuit equipment, elevator hoist equipment, transformers, swimming-pool equipment (on rooftops), etc., are notorious sources of machinery noise. Sometimes such machinery is placed in the basement of buildings, although in high-rise buildings it is frequently necessary for the mechanical-equipment floor to be located on top of the building or somewhere between the typical floors.

The required degree of noise control in rooms close to machinery will depend on the noise level produced by the machinery and the level which can be tolerated in the room under consideration.

In order to provide adequate noise reduction between the mechanical-equipment room and adjoining occupancies, the following noise paths will have to be checked:

1. Airborne paths between the noisy equipment room and the adjoining or nearby occupancies through walls, floors, ceilings, etc.

2. Structure-borne paths between vibrating equipment and adjoining areas through the building structure

3. Duct-borne paths for the transmission of fan noise and airflow noise into adjacent rooms serviced by the ventilating or air-conditioning equipment

To secure the required attenuation of machinery noise somewhat below NC levels in the rooms close to an equipment room, the following measures should be considered (Fig. 16.5):

1. The installation of a floating floor beneath the entire equipment room

2. The efficient installation of all pieces of equipment and machinery on top of the floating slab, if necessary, on a properly designed and constructed inertia base with vibration-isolating mounts

3. Use of a lined plenum chamber on the discharge side of the fan

4. Provision for a resiliently suspended dense ceiling in the rooms beneath the machinery floor

5. Control of duct-borne fan noise and airflow noise

6. Using sound-insulating walls, floors, and doors around the noise-producing equipment room

7. Applying sound-absorptive treatment along the ceiling and walls of the equipment room

16.4 Vibration

The increased use of thin and lightweight building constructions, the demand for high-pressure and high-speed air-conditioning systems, and the accommodation of large, centralized mechanical equipment rooms in the more flexible, long-span upper floors of buildings have all increased the occurrence of vibration in modern buildings.

Vibration (the movement of a structure or any other solid body caused by some alternating force, for example, an out-of-balance rotating part of a machine) may be transmitted readily to distant parts of the structure and reradiated from large surfaces (walls, ceilings, windows) as irritating noise; it may even be transmitted to other nearby buildings.

Vibration may have the following effects:

1. It may damage buildings.

2. It may be annoying to the occupants.

3. It may interfere with work and harm precision instruments.

4. It may cause noise if the rate of vibration is within the audio-frequency range.

There are two types of applications of vibration isolation: (1) *active isolation*, in which the transmission of unbalanced forces from a machine to its foundation is prevented, and (2) *passive isolation*, in which harmful motion from a substructure to a device mounted on it is reduced. This is used for the installation of precision instruments, allowing their placement wherever space is available or where work flow requires. In either case, the vibration isolation is designed according to the same principles.

The source of vibration usually has a predominant frequency at which it vibrates, called the *disturbing frequency* or *driving frequency*. The resilient mount with the weight of the equipment or machine on it will have its own *resonant frequency* or *natural frequency of oscillation*, at which it will oscillate if given a deflection and then allowed to move on its own. The more deflection in the system, the lower its natural frequency. The degree of vibration isolation provided by the resilient mount depends on the ratio of the driving frequency and the natural frequency. The natural frequency of the resilient mount must be at least twice as low as the driving frequency if any vibration isolation is to be obtained. No vibration isolation will be achieved if the natural frequency of the resilient mount is higher than the driving frequency. If the two frequencies are equal, or nearly equal, the resilient mount will make the situation worse; that is, more vibration will be transmitted than if no resilient mount were used at all.

The amount of deflection of the resilient mount resulting from the dead weight of the supported load is called *static deflection* or *static displacement*. It is quite obvious that a resilient mount must be selected with utmost care, particularly when the frequency of vibration is quite low. The mounting system should be neither overloaded nor underloaded, and it should provide a resonant frequency several times lower than the lowest frequency of vibration to be isolated.

The transmission of vibration from one structure to another can be avoided by interposing a resilient element, called a *vibration isolator*, between the two structures. The vibration isolator can be any of the following:

1. Resilient floor mount (steel spring, air spring, rubber, cork, felt, neoprene, elastomer, fiber glass, precompressed fibrous glass)

2. Resilient ceiling hanger (spring, neoprene, elastomer)

3. Resilient wall isolator (isolation clip, resilient wall brace)

4. Flexible hose (stainless steel, reinforced rubber, molded teflon, flexible butyl)

BIBLIOGRAPHY

Books

Crede, C. E.: *Vibration and Shock Insulation*, John Wiley & Sons, Inc., New York, 1951, 328 pp.

Harris, C. M. (ed.): *Handbook of Noise Control*, McGraw-Hill Book Company, New York, 1957, chaps, 12, 13, 25 to 28, and 30.

Parkin, P. H., and H. R. Humphreys: *Acoustics, Noise and Buildings*, Frederick A. Praeger, Inc., New York, 1958, chaps. 7 and 8.

Beranek, L. L. (ed.): *Noise Reduction*, McGraw-Hill Book Company, New York, 1960, chaps. 20 to 22.

Periodicals

Tutt, R. D., and C. J. Hemond: "Evaluation of Noise Components in Air-distribution Systems," *Noise Control*, January 1957, pp. 10–18.

Allen, C. H.: "Noise from Air-conditioning Fans," *Noise Control*, January 1957, pp. 28–34.

Lemmerman, R. D.: "Air-conditioning and Ventilating Noise Reduction," *Noise Control*, January 1957, pp. 47–51, 62.

Sanders, G. J.: "Noise Reduction in Machinery," *Noise Control*, November 1957, pp. 29–37, 62.

Kodaras, M. J.: "Suppression of Ventilating Noise," *Noise Control*, March 1958, pp. 42–45.

Gerlitz, R. A.: "Reduction of Room Noise Due to Fans," *Noise Control*, May 1958, pp. 21–25.

Wells, R. J.: "Acoustical Plenum Chambers," *Noise Control*, July 1958, pp. 9–15.

Johnson, K. W.: "Vibration Control," *Sound*, May–June 1962, pp. 34-38.

Miller, L. N.: "Controlling Mechanical Noise and Vibration in Buildings," *Architectural and Engineering News*, March 1964, pp. 50–55.

Miller, L. N.: "Isolation of Railroad and Subway Noise and Vibration," *Progressive Architecture*, April 1965, pp. 203–208.

CHAPTER SEVENTEEN

Noise Control in Specific Types of Buildings

The control of environmental noise in any building should start at an early stage in the design process. Recommended methods of environmental noise control were described in Sec. 13.6, covering such important points as the suppression of noise at its source, careful site planning, sensible architectural design by the separation of noisy rooms from noise-sensitive areas, the utilization of masking noise, and the efficient choice of a sound-insulating building construction. Sound-insulating enclosures which can be used in any building were discussed in Chap. 14. Wall and floor constructions with their important architectural-acoustical characteristics are illustrated in Appendixes B and C. The present chapter describes the special requirements of noise control in certain types of buildings.

Noise-control requirements included in building codes, by-laws, standards, etc., contribute fundamentally to effective environmental control. The reasonable trend toward lighter, thinner, and less expensive construction under present conditions could become exaggerated without the restrictions and criteria of the codes and by-laws.

Sound-insulation requirements adopted in the by-laws of municipalities have no value unless they are enforced. This can be done, as in the case of other technical requirements, by withholding or suspending the building permit if inspection of the building plans or of the construction reveals a disregard for the relevant acoustical requirements.

17.1 Auditoriums

The noise control of auditoriums should begin with sensible site planning, by separating the auditorium as much as possible from all exterior and interior noise and vibration sources, such as noisy vehicular traffic, air traffic, subway traffic, parking or loading areas, mechanical equipment, electrical rooms, or workshops (Chap. 13). The importance of locating the auditorium as far away as possible from all potential exterior and interior noise sources cannot be stressed enough, because this has always proved to be the most economical and the most efficient noise-control measure.

The design of a protective buffer zone of rooms between exterior noise sources and auditorium proper will permit the use of less insulative, that is, less expensive, boundary enclosures around the auditorium. Rooms in the buffer zone (lobbies, vestibules, circulation areas, restaurants, bars, offices, etc.) should have sound-absorbing ceilings and if possible carpeted floors. These circulation areas should always be shut off from the auditorium proper by doors. If one auditorium is located next to another (horizontally or vertically), a wall or floor of adequate acoustical performance must be provided between them to permit their simultaneous use.

Whereas in the noise control of residences, offices, hotels, hospitals, restaurants, etc., the use of a continuous, unrecognizable, and not too loud background noise as a masking effect is not only permissible but often even desirable, in auditorium acoustics masking noise is generally undesirable. The ventilating and air-conditioning system for an auditorium should be so designed that the noise level created by the system is 5 to 15 dB below the permissible background-noise level specified in noise criteria levels (Chap. 15). This is necessary in order to prevent mechanical noises from interfering with the intelligibility of speech or the enjoyment of music.

The problem of noise control in auditorium acoustics is directly associated with the provision for adequate loudness because when the background-noise level has been successfully reduced in the room by a certain number of decibels, the subjective loudness of the program material will be automatically increased to the same extent.

A common noise problem in room acoustics is created by the increasingly frequent design of divisible and multipurpose auditoriums (Figs. 17.1 to 17.3). Before designing and selecting the movable partitions of a divisible auditorium, the purposes of the subdivided spaces must be clarified in order to establish the predictable intensity of the various sound programs. If the rooms are to be used for the purposes of verbal instruction only, a moderate degree of sound insulation (STC 40 to 45 dB) will have to be accomplished by the movable partitions. If audio equipment or loudspeakers are to be used, an acoustically more

Fig. 17.1 Plan of a divisible school auditorium.

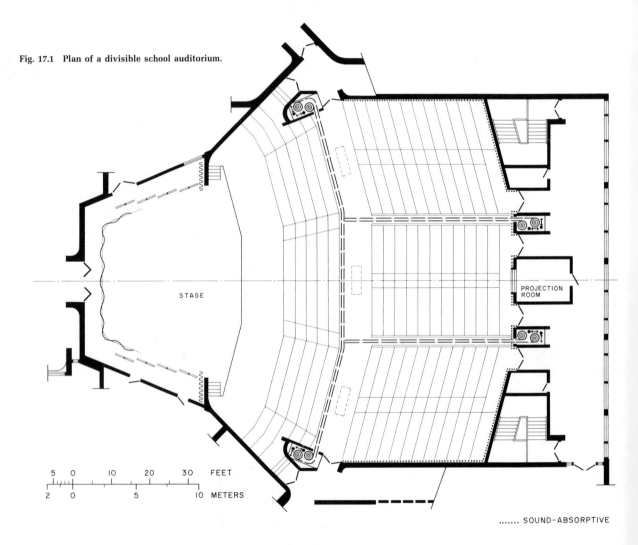

STAGE

PROJECTION ROOM

5 0   10   20   30   FEET

2 0   5   10   METERS

.... SOUND-ABSORPTIVE

DIVISIBLE HIGH-SCHOOL AUDITORIUM, LAPRAIRIE, QUE. (1969)   CAPACITY: 700
LEMAY LECLERC TRAHAN ARCHITECTS, L.L. DOELLE ACOUSTICAL CONSULTANT

PLAN

Fig. 17.2 Interior of the 700-seat divisible auditorium in Fig. 17.1. (Photograph by Bowe Studio.)

Fig. 17.3 Acoustical treatment (slit-resonator absorbers) along the side wall of the divisible auditorium in Fig. 17.2. (Photograph by Bowe Studio.)

efficient partition system (STC 45 to 50 dB) will have to be used to isolate the sound sources. And if any section of the space is selected for the performance of live music, a still higher degree of sound insulation (STC 50 to 60 dB) will be needed. In this particular case of divisible auditoriums, sounds created by the ventilating or air-conditioning system can provide a useful masking noise to drown out undesirable sounds penetrating through the movable partitions, thus reducing the sound-insulation requirements.

Divisible auditoriums also pose additional room-acoustical problems, such as simultaneous reverberation control in the divided and undivided space, provision for loudness in the undivided space through the limited height of the movable-partition opening, elimination of harmful reflections between the untreated movable wall surfaces and opposite walls, and the control of cross talk between divided rooms through ceiling spaces and ventilating ducts.

Today's heavy air traffic often necessitates the design of exceptionally efficient sound-insulating windows and roofs with suspended solid ceilings (Sec. 14.4.2). The installation of a suspended ceiling is now almost indispensible in an auditorium in order to accommodate ventilating, air-conditioning, and electrical services above the room. The elimination of windows is an effective contribution toward the noise control of auditoriums, and with the ventilating and air-conditioning systems now available this should be regarded as a normal design procedure whenever excessive outdoor noises must be excluded.

If an auditorium is subject to vibrations originating from surface or underground trains, nearby bus lines, etc., particular precautions will have to be taken to eliminate these vibrations from the building structure (Sec. 16.4).

17.2 Studios

The difference between the noise control of studios and that of other auditoriums is simply one of degree. All noises from outside and inside the building likely to interfere with use of the studio must be reduced to a particularly low level. It is not a question of what noise levels are comfortable or economical but what levels must be secured if satisfactory broadcasting, telecasting, or recording is to result (Chap. 10).

The recommended noise criteria for various studios were listed in Table 15.2; providing these NC values will require a close consideration of Chap. 14. In addition, particular attention should be given to the design recommendations outlined in Sec. 13.6.4.

In the architectural design of studio buildings the creation of buffer zones around the studio proper is especially advantageous. The juxtaposition of various occupancies in studio buildings also requires the utmost care to avoid unwanted noise transmission through floors.

The suppression of noise originating from ventilating and air-conditioning systems, particularly important in the noise control of studios, has been dealt with in Chap. 16. The installation of noisy ventilating or air-conditioning equipment within about 100 ft (30 m) from the nearest wall or floor of any studio should be avoided.

17.3 Gymnasiums, Swimming Pools, and Bowling Alleys

The activities taking place in these spaces create noises which not only will disturb participants and spectators but may also interfere with the function of nearby rooms as well. The use of a considerable amount of noise-reducing acoustical treatment which will resist mechanical impacts (in gymnasiums) and also withstand humidity (in swimming pools) is imperative.

17.4 Residential Buildings

Residential buildings constructed in quiet rural or suburban districts require a higher degree of sound insulation than those built in noisy areas because noises from outside or from the neighbors will be noticed more readily in quiet than in noisy surroundings. Occupants of apartments who are conditioned to the noisy environment of densely populated areas are generally less concerned about sound insulation than those accustomed to a quiet environment.

Recommended NCs for homes were included in Tables 15.2 and 15.3. The building codes of various countries and progressive building by-laws of federal, provincial, or municipal administrations throughout the world contain noise-control requirements, specifying the desirable sound-insulation values for walls and floors.

The National Building Code of Canada (published in 1970) recommends that in residential buildings walls and floors provide an STC rating of not less than 45 dB between dwelling units in the same building and between a dwelling unit and any space common to two or more dwelling units. Service rooms, or spaces such as storage room, laundry, workshop, building maintenance room, or garage serving more than one dwelling unit, shall be separated from the dwelling unit by a construction providing an STC rating of not less than 45 dB. The sound-insulation requirements of the National Building Code of Canada are not compulsory; they are recommendations. It is left to the responsible authorities of municipalities to make this building code, or parts of it, compulsory if they so wish. The code is, in fact, drafted in the form of a by-law, so that it may be adopted or enacted for legal use by any municipality.

The sound-insulation criteria between dwelling units recommended by the U.S. Federal Housing Administration are based on three grades in order to meet the wide range of existing geographic, environmental, and economic conditions, occupants' demands, and other factors. *Grade I* criteria apply mainly to quiet rural, fully residential, and suburban areas, in certain cases to luxury apartment buildings, and to dwelling units above the eighth floor of a high-rise building. *Grade II* criteria apply to residential buildings built in relatively noisy environments typical of urban and suburban areas; this category covers the majority of residential constructions and should be regarded, therefore, as a basic guide. *Grade III* criteria are minimal requirements applicable to definitely noisy locations, such as downtown areas. In all grades wall constructions and floor-ceiling assemblies between dwelling units should have STC and IIC ratings (discussed and illustrated in Secs. 14.1.6 and 14.2) equal to or greater than the values given in Table 17.1.

In England three grading contours are in use for the sound insulation between dwelling units (Figs. 17.4 and 17.5). *House party-wall grade* is considered for airborne sound insulation between houses. *Grade I* criteria are observed between flats when a higher degree of airborne and structure-borne sound insulation is required. *Grade II* is used between flats when a lower degree of airborne or structure-borne sound insulation is acceptable, according to local needs and conditions. For all three grades a deviation of 1 dB is permitted in the unfavorable direction averaged over the whole frequency range under consideration.

Other countries have adopted grading contours similar to those used in England, but with somewhat different values.

TABLE 17.1   Criteria of Airborne and Impact-sound Insulation between Dwelling Units Recommended by the U.S. Federal Housing Administration

Type of construction	Required sound insulation		
	Grade I	Grade II	Grade III
Walls	STC ⩾ 55	STC ⩾ 52	STC ⩾ 48
Floor-ceiling assemblies	STC ⩾ 55	STC ⩾ 52	STC ⩾ 48
	IIC ⩾ 55	IIC ⩾ 52	IIC ⩾ 48

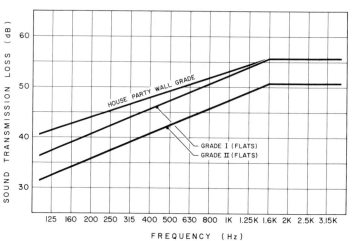

Fig. 17.4 Grading contours for airborne sound insulation in England.

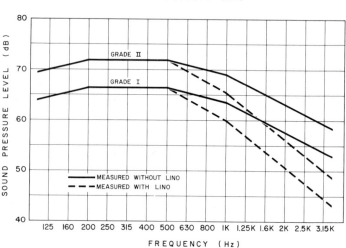

Fig. 17.5 Grading contours for impact-sound insulation in England.

17.5 Hotels and Motels

In the noise control of hotels and motels three types of rooms require attention: (1) public and social rooms, such as dining room, reading room, lounge, ballroom, recreation room, and convention rooms, (2) guest rooms, (3) circulation areas, such as lobby, vestibule, and corridors.

The principal acoustical requirements in the public and social rooms are adequate protection against noise originating from exterior sources or from adjacent rooms and control of noise and reverberation within the rooms themselves. If public rooms have to be subdivided into two or more spaces by movable partitions, the partitions should have an STC rating of 35 to 50 dB, depending on the desired function of the spaces thus provided.

Noise-control problems of guest rooms are identical to those encountered in apartment buildings, since every room of a motel or hotel should be considered as an isolated apartment. For economy hotels and motels an STC rating of 40 to 45 dB is recommended between adjacent rooms and between rooms and corridors. For first-class or luxury hotels and motels the same separation should reach an STC rating of 45 to 50 dB. Direct connection between adjacent guest rooms by doors should be avoided, unless sound-insulating or double doors are installed between the rooms. Particular attention should be paid to the elimination of mechanical noise and cross talk between adjacent occupancies.

Carpeting in all spaces, particularly along corridors and circulation areas, is essential to eliminate the sound of footsteps.

Exterior walls should provide an STC rating of 45 to 60 dB, depending upon local needs and site conditions.

17.6 Schools

The sound control of any educational building requires a consideration of the following:
1. Selection of the site and site planning (Sec. 13.6.3)
2. Room-acoustical design of classrooms, lecture halls, auditorium, gymnasium, music room, audio-visual rooms, etc. (Chaps. 6 to 8)
3. Control of exterior and interior noises throughout the entire building (Chaps. 13 to 16)

Acoustical problems are increasing in educational buildings because of departures from conventional procedures. Recognizing change as an important element in the educational process, planners are incorporating the concept of changeability or flexibility into new educational buildings. This is particularly noticeable in the trend which advocates remarkable freedom in classroom layout through the elimination of doors and permanent partitions. This design concept favors the use of movable partitions, thus providing the possibility of adjusting the size of the classroom to suit momentary space requirements. Figures 17.6 and 17.7 illustrate the plan and the interior of classrooms which are divisible by the use of horizontally sliding dual-coil partitions. These walls have an STC rating of above 43 dB, providing a relatively high degree of acoustical privacy for the occupants in the sectioned-off

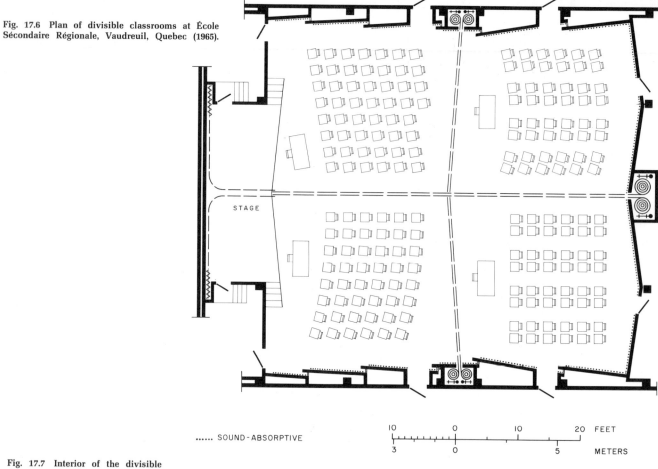

Fig. 17.6 Plan of divisible classrooms at École Sécondaire Régionale, Vaudreuil, Quebec (1965).

STAGE

...... SOUND-ABSORPTIVE

10   0   10   20 FEET

3   0   5 METERS

LABELLE LABELLE MARCHAND GEOFFROY ARCHITECTS, L.L. DOELLE ACOUSTICAL CONSULTANT   PLAN

Fig. 17.7 Interior of the divisible classroom in Fig. 17.6, with the movable partitions (dual-coil walls) in motion.

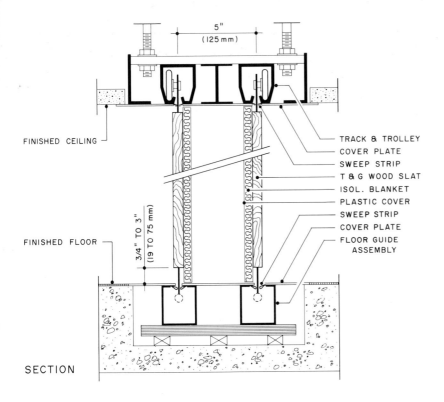

FINISHED CEILING ⎯

5"
(125 mm)

TRACK & TROLLEY
COVER PLATE
SWEEP STRIP
T & G WOOD SLAT
ISOL. BLANKET
PLASTIC COVER
SWEEP STRIP
COVER PLATE
FLOOR GUIDE
ASSEMBLY

FINISHED FLOOR ⎯

3/4" TO 3"
(19 TO 75 mm)

SECTION

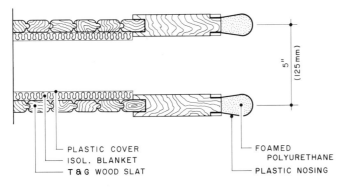

PLAN

PLASTIC COVER
ISOL. BLANKET
T & G WOOD SLAT

5"
(125 mm)

FOAMED
POLYURETHANE
PLASTIC NOSING

Fig. 17.8 Details of the dual-coil movable-partition wall used in the divisible classroom illustrated in Figs. 17.6 and 17.7.

classrooms. Figure 17.8 illustrates details of the movable partition used in the layout.

Figure 17.9 shows the plan of a divisible school auditorium containing two 71-seat revolving lecture halls. Each revolving unit can be hooked up to two demonstration podiums. This layout is particularly suitable for lectures in chemistry or physics, permitting preparation at one demonstration podium while a lecture is being given from the other one.

Figure 17.10 illustrates a team-teaching space in an elementary school consisting of a number of area units. Partitions are completely eliminated from the large space, where several learning groups work simultaneously; the only separation between the area units is a visual one by means of retractable curtains. This highly flexible layout admittedly eliminates the cost of partitions and doors, but on the other hand more

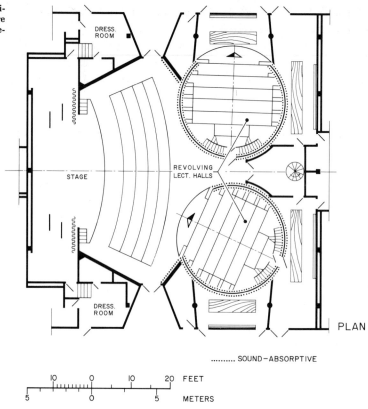

Fig. 17.9 Plan of a divisible 276-seat school auditorium, containing two 71-seat revolving lecture halls, École Sécondaire Polyvalente, Cabano, Quebec (1968).

DRESS. ROOM

STAGE

REVOLVING LECT. HALLS

DRESS. ROOM

PLAN

.... SOUND-ABSORPTIVE

10   0   10   20 FEET
5   0   5 METERS

LABELLE LABELLE MARCHAND GEOFFROY, ARCHITECTS
L.L. DOELLE, ACOUSTICAL CONSULTANT

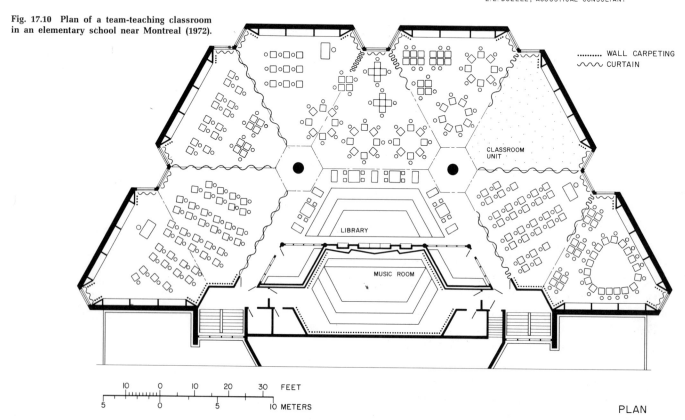

Fig. 17.10 Plan of a team-teaching classroom in an elementary school near Montreal (1972).

.... WALL CARPETING
∿∿∿ CURTAIN

CLASSROOM UNIT

LIBRARY

MUSIC ROOM

10   0   10   20   30 FEET
5   0   5   10 METERS

PLAN

LABELLE LABELLE MARCHAND GEOFFROY ARCHITECTS, L.L. DOELLE ACOUSTICAL CONSULTANT

floor area has to be provided per student than would be necessary in a conventional arrangement with separated classrooms; floor areas have to be carpeted and ceilings lined with sound-absorbing treatment. Team-teaching classrooms in elementary schools challenge the long-established belief that an STC rating of 35 to 45 dB is mandatory between teaching spaces. The standard stereotype classroom layout appears to have lost the battle to team-teaching spaces. Pertinent investigations reveal that the overall visual, thermal, and luminous environment of teaching areas seems to be more important than the degree of acoustical separation between them. The sound of teaching and learning which emerges from the several learning groups of a team-teaching space seems to represent a masking noise that is acceptable to the majority of the occupants.

17.7 Hospitals

A hospital is unquestionably the type of building whose occupants are most affected by noise. The selection of a suitable site must therefore be considered with attention to possible traffic noise from highways, railroads, and airport and to noise originating from parking areas.

Exterior noises are exceeded in number by the interior noises mainly because inherent mechanical units of a hospital are fundamentally noisy. Interior noises are caused by:

1. Mechanical equipment (machinery, boilers, pumps, fans, ventilators, transformers, elevators, and air-conditioning equipment)

2. Operational facilities (plumbing units, refrigerators, ice machines, dishwashers, sterilizers, autoclaves, and housekeeping facilities)

3. Patient service facilities (oxygen tanks, carrier carts, and instrument cases)

4. Personnel activities (staff talk, footsteps in corridors)

5. Patients and visitors

Noise criteria pertaining to hospitals were included in Table 15.2 and Fig. 15.2.

The average STC rating of walls and floors for airborne noise between patient rooms should be about 45 to 50 dB, depending on the importance given to acoustical considerations. Special sound insulation should be provided for maternity and nursery rooms and for the rooms of patients likely to be noisy. An STC rating of about 50 to 55 (sometimes 60) dB is required between rooms whose occupants are particularly susceptible to noise. For walls between patient rooms and corridor an average STC of about 45 dB seems to be satisfactory; in these walls efficient sound-insulating doors should be used. However, a floating floor is seldom required in hospitals.

To achieve the design goals for noise control the requirements outlined in previous chapters should be observed. In addition, attention should be given to the following recommendations:

1. In selecting a site and in site planning, consideration should be given to the distance from exterior noise sources, the effect of nearby high buildings as noise reflectors, nearby traffic conditions (highway grades, traffic volume, traffic lights), and the use of certain buildings as sound barriers.

2. Loading platforms and parking areas (for visitors, staff members, and personnel) should be carefully located, particularly to avoid noise at undesirable times.

3. The mechanical plant should preferably be placed in a separate building.

4. Closed courts should be avoided, unless rooms facing the court are air-conditioned with hermetically sealed fixed windows.

5. Long corridors, as potential noise sources, should be avoided.

6. Doors to opposite rooms should be staggered, and all doors should be fitted with silent closers.

7. Equipment, operational facilities, and patient service facilities should be selected, installed, and operated for minimum noise output. Every effort should be made to substitute resilient material for hard material in each piece of equipment.

Rooms to be used for instructional purposes, conferences, or meetings should be treated so that they provide good acoustical conditions for the intelligibility of speech (Chap. 7).

Virtually all rooms of a hospital should be treated to a greater or lesser extent with sound-absorptive material to reduce the noise level. This acoustical treatment is a supplement to satisfactory insulation between adjacent rooms, not a substitute for it.

Acoustical materials (Chap. 5) should be carefully selected so that they do not interfere with sanitary requirements. Plastic-faced mineral-fiber tiles, metal pan acoustical ceiling with mineral-wool pad, or mineral-wool blankets covered with perforated boards meet these requirements. Floors should be covered with a resilient covering (rubber tile, cork tile, vinyl tile, or linoleum) to reduce impact noises.

17.8 Offices

Practical noise control of offices should include (1) protection against noise from various exterior sources; (2) adequate horizontal and vertical insulation between individual spaces in order to secure speech privacy, that is, speech originating in one office should not be intelligible in an adjacent office; and (3) reasonable noise reduction within a particular office space.

The following are the most common noise sources in offices:

1. Outdoor noise originating from traffic, playgrounds, and arenas

2. Industrial noise associated with manufacturing processes, factory machinery, construction projects, and marshaling yards

3. Mechanical noise caused by heating, ventilating, and air-conditioning systems, plumbing, elevators, escalators, computers, and pneumatic tubes

4. Typical office noise created by speech, circulation on hard floor finishes, opening and closing of doors, and by business machines, tele-printers, typewriters, call systems, and telephones

Recommended noise criteria for offices have been discussed in Secs. 15.2 and 15.4. In order to achieve them, the methods described in Sec. 13.6 and Chap. 16 should be observed. Practical examples of walls and floors to be used between offices are illustrated in Appendixes B and C.

The division of rentable office space by lightweight movable partitions, subsequent to the completion of the building, is becoming increasingly common. The acoustical performance of most of these partitions, erected up to the underside of an acoustically transparent suspended ceiling, seldom exceeds an STC rating of 25 to 30 dB. In most cases this is insufficient unless the background noise is so high that it masks the sounds coming through the lightweight partition.

In the consideration of lightweight, prefabricated, or movable partitions built up to the suspended ceiling, particular attention should be paid to the following:

1. All apertures, gaps, and joints at side wall, floor, and ceiling junctions should be properly sealed.

2. Sound barriers should be provided above the ceiling with a noise-reduction characteristic that will not be diminished by ducts, conduits, and cables installed in the ceiling space.

The noise-reducing effect of acoustical treatment in rooms was discussed in Sec. 13.6.8.

The popular trend to large, undivided *landscaped offices* has created unusual acoustical problems in office design. In an open-plan office full-height partitions cannot be used; therefore spreading noises caused by conversation, typewriters, office machines, etc., will be perceived at a relatively higher level, resulting in a considerable, sometimes disturbing, lack of acoustical privacy. It must be stressed that the direct portion of these noises will travel freely, no matter how much sound-absorbing treatments have been installed in the office or how effective these treatments are. Only the reflected portion of the noise wave will be reduced by the use of floor and wall carpeting, acoustically treated ceiling, etc. It must also be remembered that even a highly sound-absorptive ceiling with, for example, a sound absorption coefficient of 0.70 will absorb 70 percent of the sound energy and will reflect 30 percent of it (Sec. 4.2). While a landscaped office does produce greater functional, physical, aesthetic, environmental, and economical benefits compared to a conventionally compartmented office floor, the achievement of a soundproof interior with satisfactory speech privacy is simply not feasible in the open-plan office. However, the extensive use of acoustical finishes along the room enclosures will create a relatively dead environment that will be acoustically satisfactory to the majority of the occupants.

Figure 17.11 shows the plan of a landscaped office floor, and Fig. 17.12 an interior.

The most important requirements in the acoustical design of landscaped offices are the following:

1. All floor areas should be carpeted in order to absorb airborne noise and to avoid footstep noise. The carpet should be thick and be installed on top of a resilient underlay (Sec. 5.1.4).

2. The entire ceiling should be treated with a highly sound-absorptive material, since the sound absorption coefficient of any surface falls off when the sound wave approaches at grazing incidence, as it does along the ceiling. For this reason a ceiling type that features sound-absorptive vertical baffles is preferable to a simple horizontal ceiling.

3. The total area of window glazing should not exceed 40 percent

Fig. 17.11 Plan of a landscaped office in the Area Headquarters Building of the Canadian National Railways, London, Ontario. (1969. Staff design of the Engineering Department and Department of Research and Development of the Canadian National Railways. L. L. Doelle, acoustical consultant.)

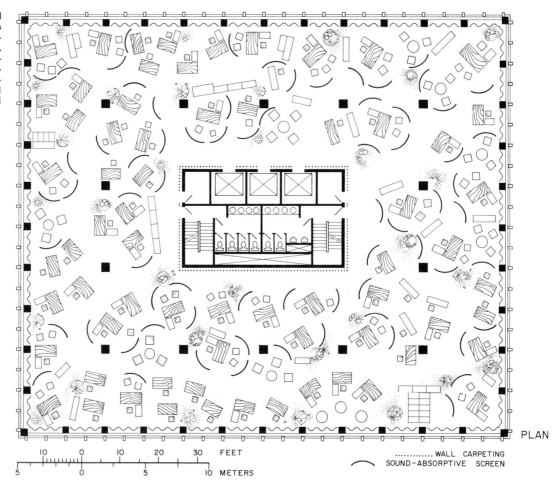

PLAN

FEET

METERS

.... WALL CARPETING
⌒ SOUND-ABSORPTIVE SCREEN

Fig. 17.12 Interior of the landscaped office shown in Fig. 17.11. (Photograph by Canadian National Railways.)

PLAN

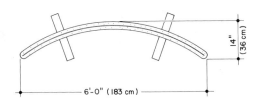

6'-0" (183 cm)

14" (36 cm)

ELEVATION

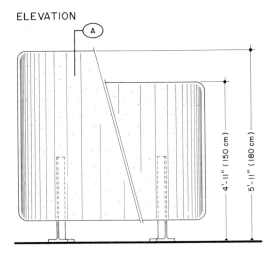

A

4'-11" (150 cm)

5'-11" (180 cm)

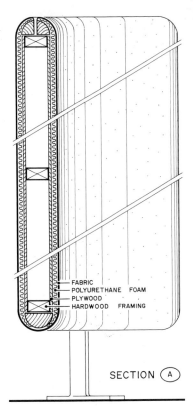

FABRIC
POLYURETHANE FOAM
PLYWOOD
HARDWOOD FRAMING

SECTION A

Fig. 17.13 Two types of sound-absorptive screen (room divider) used in the landscaped office illustrated in Figs. 17.11 and 17.12.

of the exterior wall area, viewed from inside the office space. Sound-absorptive drapery should be used along the entire fenestrated walls.

4. All wall surfaces surrounding the office space should be lined with a carpet of high sound absorption (Sec. 5.1.4).

5. Room dividers (screens), providing visual separation between work stations or certain office areas, need have only a reasonable amount of sound insulation since spreading noise waves, particularly at low frequencies, will bend around their edges anyway. All exposed surfaces of these screens must be treated with a sound-absorptive material (Fig. 17.13).

6. The distribution of moderately noisy office equipment (typewriters, telephones) should be as uniform as possible all over the office space. Noisy office equipment (electric adding, addressing, billing machines, etc.) should be concentrated into specific areas of the office space, surrounded with a maximum amount of sound-absorptive treatment, and visually separated from the rest of the office.

7. The noise of air-handling systems should be reasonably but not overly reduced (about NC 35 to 40) since landscaped offices need a relatively high masking noise level.

8. If the background noise created by the air-handling system is not sufficiently high or uniform, electronically controlled masking noise can be produced with a noise generator and amplifier that feeds loudspeakers properly located along the ceiling.

9. Floor areas designated for executives or conference corners, etc., should be generously surrounded with sound-absorptive finishes and visually separated from the rest of the floor area by the use of screens, room dividers, etc.

Fig. 17.14 Close-up of a work station in the landscaped office of Canadian National Railways (Figs. 17.11 and 17.12). The view shows elements of acoustical importance: floor carpeting, acoustically treated ceiling, sound-absorptive screen, upholstered furniture, bookshelves, and plants. (Photograph by Canadian National Railways.)

10. In spite of their negligible acoustical value, plants and flowers should be distributed in the office space because of their purely psychoacoustically quieting effect.

Figure 17.14 illustrates a work station of the landscaped office shown in Figs. 17.11 and 17.12.

17.9 Museums and Libraries

In museums and libraries every reasonable effort should be made to provide the quiet environment essential for studying or reading or contemplating works of art. This suggests the use of a reasonable amount of sound-absorbing materials along the boundary surfaces in order to reduce the RT to a minimum and to lessen any noise within the room created by dropping a book, closing a door, coughing, and talking.

Recommended NCs for libraries were listed in Table 15.2.

17.10 Restaurants and Cafeterias

The acoustical problem in restaurants and cafeterias is simply one of reducing reverberation and noise, mostly created within these rooms or in adjacent spaces, such as kitchen and service rooms.

In more expensive restaurants, elements of the room decoration (draperies, carpets, wall panelings, and lighting fixtures) contribute to sound absorption. In addition, the use of acoustical treatment along available (mostly ceiling) surfaces should be considered. To achieve the required degree of noise reduction in cafeterias, it is important to give acoustical treatment to the ceilings of the dining, serving, and all adjacent areas. Using a sound lock between dining space and kitchen is always advantageous to exclude kitchen noise from the dining area.

In restaurants and cafeterias acoustical materials should be used which can withstand humidity, can be cleaned easily, and can be painted repeatedly.

Table 15.2 shows the recommended NCs for restaurants.

17.11 Airports

The major function of a large city airport is to provide adequate facilities for the transport of people and freight. However, a large number of additional services must also be provided both for the airlines and for their customers (executive, clerical, and engineering operation offices, ticket counters, shops, lunch counters and restaurants, maintenance, baggage, and cargo handling areas). Since the activities of most of these occupancies require either direct speech or telephone conversation, the acoustical criteria for noise control within these areas should be established with the intent of securing adequate speech privacy.

With commercial supersonic air traffic practically at our doorstep, the acoustical environment of airports is becoming far more critical, seriously affecting passengers and employees as well as residents of the surrounding neighborhoods.

Aircraft noise, its control, and effect upon town planning have been discussed in Secs. 13.3.3 and 13.6.2.

17.12 Industrial Buildings

The high levels of industrial noise sources clearly indicate the necessity for an effective noise control in particular industries. In the noise control of industrial buildings the requirements are the following:

1. To provide an acceptable acoustical environment for the individual workers (machine operators) who produce the noise

2. To facilitate speech communication among operators to the required degree

3. To protect other workers or office employees, either close to the noise source or at some other location within the same building

4. To prevent the transmission of noise into adjacent buildings or into the surrounding community

Workmen can be protected by suppressing the noise at the source with the use of a sound-reducing enclosure (screening) around the machine making the noise or by introducing sound-absorbent materials into the noisy space. If after all these measures are taken the noise level is still above a tolerable degree, the workers should protect their hearing by means of earmuffs or earplugs. In conjunction with the use of noise-reducing enclosures around noisy machines, it must be noted that the operator of the offending equipment is seldom critical about the noise produced by the machine under his control; furthermore, he often relies upon the noise it generates to check its efficiency and performance.

Considerable noise reduction can be achieved in noisy industrial buildings by a sensible architectural layout, by the separation of noisy areas from spaces requiring quiet, and by subsequent organization (Chap. 13).

Screens, such as a high wall or a building between noise source and the area requiring protection, can be useful. The screen must be as close as possible to the noise source (Fig. 13.10).

The provision for adequate speech intelligibility, the protection of employees working within the boundaries of the noisy building, and the confinement of the disturbing noises within their legitimate premises can be accomplished by using suitable sound-insulating enclosures, described in Chap. 14. It is important to consider the frequency distribution of the offending noise so that suitable enclosures can be selected with effective sound insulation at these critical frequencies.

17.13 Audiometric Rooms and Sound Laboratories

Used for audiometry and for acoustical measurements and research, these rooms are practical applications of discontinuous construction. They were discussed briefly and illustrated in Sec. 14.4.5. Their design and construction constitute special problems of architectural acoustics.

BIBLIOGRAPHY

Books

Beranek, L. L. (ed.): *Noise Reduction*, McGraw-Hill Book Company, New York, 1960, chaps. 23 to 25.
Hayes, A. S.: *Language Laboratory Facilities*, U.S. Government Printing Office, Washington, D.C., 1963, 119 pp.
Chapman, D.: *Design for Educational Television: Planning for Schools with Television*, Educational Facilities Laboratories, New York, May 1963, 96 pp.
Hines, W. A.: *Noise Control in Industry*, Business Publications Ltd., London, 1966, 197 pp.

Periodicals

Content, E. J.: "Sound Control in Libraries," *Architectural Record*, November 1946, p. 121.
"School Acoustics," *Architectural Forum*, October 1953, pp. 188, 224.
Parkin, P. H., and E. F. Stacy: "Recent Research on Sound Insulation in Houses and Flats," *J. RIBA*, July 1954, pp. 372–376.
Purcell, J. B. C.: "Acoustics in Dwellings," *Architectural Record*, September 1955, pp. 229–232.
Hardy, H. C.: "A Guide to Office Acoustics," *Architectural Record*, February 1957, pp. 235–240.
Snow, W. B.: "Noise Control in Recording, Television, and Motion-picture Studios," *Noise Control*, May 1957, pp. 19–22.
Lane, R. N.: "Noise Control in Schools," *Noise Control*, July 1957, pp. 27–34.
Goodfriend, L. S.: "Noise Control in Civic Buildings," *Noise Control*, July 1957, pp. 38–42, 60.
Lane, R. N.: "Planning for Noise Control in Church Buildings," *Noise Control*, January 1958, pp. 50–51, 56.
Cavanaugh, W. J., and N. Doelling: "Noise Control Techniques for Motels," *Architectural Record*, April 1958, pp. 231–234.

Mikeska, E. E.: "Noise in the Modern Home," *Noise Control*, May 1958, pp. 38–41, 52.

Williams, L. J.: "Some Industrial Noise Problems and Their Solution," *Noise Control*, January 1959, pp. 36–38, 72–73.

Stacy, E. F.: "The Control of Noise in Factory Buildings," *Insulation*, July–August 1959, pp. 223–226.

Doelle, L. L.: "Sound Insulation in Dwellings," *Canadian Architect*, November 1959, pp. 61–63.

King, J.: "The Sound of Change in the American Schoolhouse," *Architectural Record*, July 1962, pp. 147–149.

Newman, R. B.: "Some Common Sense for School Acoustics," *Architectural Record*, July 1962, pp. 154–155.

Hardy, H. C.: "Introduction to School Acoustics," *Sound*, January–February 1963, pp. 9–11.

Fitzroy, D.: "Classrooms in Use," *Sound*, January–February 1963, pp. 16–18.

Farrell, W. R.: "Sound Isolation between Teaching Spaces," *Architectural Record*, October 1963, pp. 229–232.

Northwood, T. D.: "Sound Insulation and the Apartment Dweller," *J. Acoust. Soc. Am.*, April 1964, pp. 725–728.

McGuinness, W. J.: "Residential Noise Control," *Progressive Architecture*, July 1964, p. 18.

Ford, R. D., P. Lord, and A. W. Walker: "Offices with High Sound Insulation," *Applied Acoustics*, January 1968, pp. 21–28.

Scholes, W. E., and P. H. Parkin: "The Insulation of Houses against Noise from Aircraft in Flight," *Applied Acoustics*, January 1968, pp. 37–46.

Pohl, J. G.: "Artificial Sound Blankets in Modern School Planning," *Architectural Science Review*, June 1968, pp. 61–66.

Anstey, B.: "Noise at Airports," *The Architect and Building News*, January 1 and 15, 1969, pp. 46–49; January 29, 1969, pp. 36–37; February 13, 1969, pp. 52–53.

Waller, R. A.: "Office Acoustics: Effect of Background Noise," *Applied Acoustics*, April 1969, pp. 121–130.

Powell, J. A., and D. M. Harman: "A Design Guide: Information Required for the Acoustic Design of Offices," *Applied Acoustics*, April 1969, pp. 137–145.

Pile, J.: "Burolandschaft ('Office Landscaping')," *The Canadian Architect*, June 1969, pp. 39–60.

Hirtle, P. W., and R. Pirn: "Acoustics without Walls," *Architectural and Engineering News*, February 1970, pp. 38–39.

Lord, P.: "The Results of Application of Simple Acoustic Principles to Low Cost Housing with a View to Reducing Loss of Comfort Due to Noise," *Applied Acoustics*, April 1970, pp. 145–160.

Digests and Reports

Fitzroy, D., and J. L. Reid: *Acoustical Environment of School Buildings*, Educational Facilities Laboratories, New York, 1963, 128 pp.

Goodfriend, L. S., and R. L. Cardinell: *Noise in Hospitals*, U.S. Department of Health, Education, and Welfare Publications 930-D-11, Washington, D.C., 1963, 130 pp.

Northwood, T. D.: *Sound Insulation in Office Buildings*, National Research Council, Ottawa, Canadian Building Digest 51, March 1964, 4 pp.

Divisible Auditoriums, Educational Facilities Laboratories, New York, May 1966, 48 pp.

Northwood, T. D., H. B. Dickens, and A. T. Hansen: Noise Control in Residential Buildings, National Research Council, Ottawa, Technical Paper 230, February 1967, 46 pp.

Execution

The attention given to acoustical requirements of a building while it is still in the preliminary design stage should continue during the process of detailing and specification. And once the job is under construction, several acoustical details will require constant supervision on the site until the building is completed.

A sensible approach to the architectural design and construction of a project with acoustical control in mind will increase construction costs only negligibly. However, acoustical correction after the completion of a project, that is, after the building has been put to use, is always very expensive and is usually associated with considerable inconvenience.

Architectural detail drawings and specifications should indicate design elements which have acoustical significance, giving their acoustical characteristics or criteria. The following acoustical properties of design elements should be included in detail drawings or specifications:

1. Sound absorption coefficients of acoustical treatments at standard frequencies, or at least at mid-frequency

2. Weights (specific densities) of isolation blankets both in sound-absorbing and in sound-insulating constructions

3. STC ratings of wall, floor, door, or window constructions in acoustically sensitive areas

4. INR or IIC values of floor constructions in noise-sensitive areas

5. Noise-attenuation values of suspended acoustical ceilings where a partition wall separating acoustically critical areas is built up to the suspended ceiling only

6. Maximum permissible background-noise levels (NC levels) in acoustically important rooms when unoccupied but with the ventilating or air-conditioning system in full operation

Acoustical characteristics of materials or building constructions (α, TL, STC, IIC, etc., values) used in drawings or specifications should be based on test results published or issued by accredited acoustical laboratories.

If there is any doubt about the acoustical property or efficiency of a planned or built design element, it is important to refer to the test method which is considered acceptable in identifying the critical acoustical property of the material or construction in question. For example:

1. When a particular enclosure (wall, floor, door, or window) must have a certain STC rating, it is necessary to state that this particular rating must be achieved when the enclosure under consideration is tested in accordance with the ASTM E90-66T standard, "Laboratory Measurement of Air-borne Sound Transmission Loss of Building Partitions."

2. When the STC rating of an enclosure has to be tested on the site, it is necessary to indicate that the test must be conducted to conform with the ASTM E336-67T standard, "Measurement of Air-borne Sound Insulation in Buildings."

3. When an acoustically critical movable partition is not a tested commercial product of a reputable manufacturer, it should be rated according to the recommendations of the National School Supply and Equipment Association, "Testing Procedures for Measuring Sound Transmission Loss through Operable Walls."

Detailing, Specification, and Supervision

4. If there is any doubt about the noise attenuation of a suspended-ceiling construction, it should be specified that this particular property be tested in accordance with the Method of Test AMA-1-II-1967, recommended by the Acoustical and Insulating Materials Association, "Ceiling Sound Transmission Test by the Two-room Method."

5. If the STC value of an existing wall or floor is noticeably reduced by flanking transmission, for example, by noise transmission through mechanical ducts (cross talk), the critical enclosure should be tested on the site with an approved method of test.

6. When noise created by components of mechanical equipment seems to exceed the permissible value or the reduction of mechanical noise appears to be inadequate, the necessary test should be conducted in accordance with various test methods recommended by the American Society of Heating, Refrigerating and Air-conditioning Engineers.

Acoustically critical details of a project should be systematically and carefully supervised to make sure that the detail drawings and specifications have been properly interpreted by the contractor. Such critical details are the following:

1. Caulkings around the periphery of dry-wall partitions

2. Horizontal and vertical mortar joints in sound-insulating masonry walls

3. The presence of uninterrupted air space in multiple partitions, free from short-circuiting elements, pieces of mortar, penetrating cables, ducts, etc.

4. Noise baffles above partition walls which are built up to the underside of a suspended ceiling only

5. Packing and caulking around holes or gaps in sound-insulating enclosures

6. Separation of floating floors from the supporting structural floor and from surrounding walls

7. The specific density (weight) of isolation blankets used in sound-absorptive and sound-insulating constructions, etc.

Not infrequently, during the construction of a project, the contractor is unable to supply in time a particular material specified for a detail of acoustical importance. In such cases the purpose of supervision is to advise on the feasibility of a reasonable and acceptable substitution. In acoustical design there is a considerable latitude for flexibility; the same performance can be often achieved in several ways, by the application of different materials.

In completed buildings important noise-control characteristics, such as NC levels, STC and IIC values, etc., should be checked in critical instances by conducting acoustical measurements.

BIBLIOGRAPHY

Periodicals

Kodaras, M. J.: "Specifications, Performance, Testing," *Applied Acoustics*, April 1968, pp. 143–150.

Waller, R. A.: "Economics of Sound Reduction in Buildings," *Applied Acoustics*, July 1968, pp. 205–213.

CHAPTER NINETEEN

Duranig the design and construction of an auditorium, large or small, the architect is obviously anxious to make a preliminary evaluation, as early as possible, of the predictable acoustical qualities of the room. There are several methods available for this purpose, which, if applied with precision at the outset, can assess the acoustical performance with a reasonable degree of engineering accuracy.

Checking the Acoustical Performance of Auditoriums

19.1 During Design

The floor plans and sections of an auditorium offer a good opportunity for establishing the paths of sound rays traveling from source to listeners. It has been described in Sec. 4.1 how these sound rays are reflected from the boundary surfaces at an angle that is equal to the angle of incidence (law of reflection). This simple *graphic analysis* of the propagation of sound in rooms will be useful:

1. To check whether the supply of direct sound from source to all parts of the seating area is satisfactory, that is, whether the seating area is adequately ramped or raked and the sound source sufficiently elevated (Sec. 6.2)

2. To make sure that a sufficient amount of short-delayed reflected sound has been provided for the entire seating area, in particular for the remote seats (Sec. 6.2)

3. To trace surfaces liable to produce acoustical defects, such as echoes, corner echoes, flutter echoes, long-delayed reflections, sound concentrations, or acoustical shadows (Sec. 6.5)

Analyzing the paths of sound waves beyond the first and second reflections is unimportant because of the loss of sound energy after several reflections.

Another simple method of checking the acoustical qualities of an auditorium during the design stage consists of *calculating the reverberation time*. The small lecture hall shown in Fig. 19.1 has been used to illustrate a sample calculation of the RT at 500 Hz, as given in Table 19.1. The seats in this lecture hall consist of heavily upholstered theater chairs; capacity audience has been assumed for the calculation. The reverberation time for a simplified calculation is given by the following formula (Sec. 4.5):

$$
RT = \begin{cases} \dfrac{0.05V}{A + xV} & \text{English system} \\[2ex] \dfrac{0.16V}{A + xV} & \text{metric system} \end{cases}
$$

Figures 19.2 and 19.3 illustrate the interior of the lecture hall detailed in Fig. 19.1 and used in the sample RT calculation.

A third method of checking the room-acoustical qualities of an auditorium consists of *model tests*, which normally use various alternatives of the *optical* or *wave* methods. In the first case, conditions of geometrical acoustics are assumed using wavelengths that are extremely small compared to the dimensions of the model. In the second case, calculations are based on wavelengths reduced in the same proportion as the dimensions of the model.

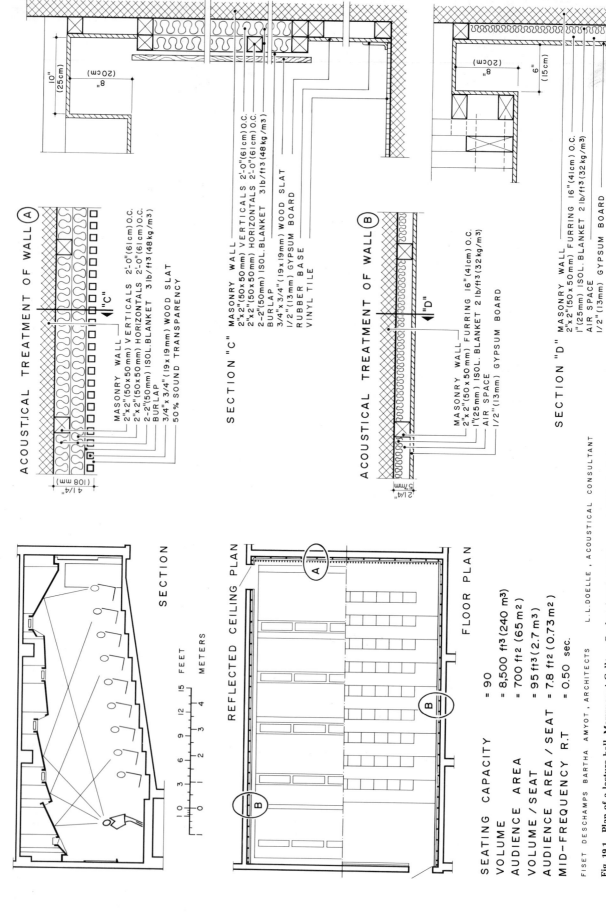

ACOUSTICAL TREATMENT OF WALL (A)

MASONRY WALL
2"x 2"(50x50mm) VERTICALS 2'-0"(61cm) O.C.
2"x 2"(50x50mm) HORIZONTALS 2'-0"(61cm) O.C.
2-2"(50mm) ISOL.BLANKET 3 lb/ft3 (48kg/m3)
BURLAP
3/4" x 3/4" (19x19mm) WOOD SLAT
50 % SOUND TRANSPARENCY

SECTION "C"   MASONRY WALL
2"x 2"(50x50 mm) VERTICALS 2'-0"(61cm) O.C.
2"x 2"(50x50 mm) HORIZONTALS 2'-0"(61cm) O.C.
2-2"(50mm) ISOL.BLANKET 3 lb/ft3 (48kg/m3)
BURLAP
3/4" x 3/4" (19x19mm) WOOD SLAT
1/2" (13mm) GYPSUM BOARD
RUBBER BASE
VINYL TILE

ACOUSTICAL TREATMENT OF WALL (B)

MASONRY WALL
2"x 2"(50 x 50mm) FURRING 16"(41cm) O.C.
1"(25mm) ISOL. BLANKET 2 lb/ft3 (32kg/m3)
AIR SPACE
1/2" (13mm) GYPSUM BOARD

SECTION "D"   MASONRY WALL
2"x 2"(50x50mm) FURRING 16"(41cm) O.C.
1"(25mm) ISOL. BLANKET 2 lb/ft3 (32 kg/m3)
AIR SPACE
1/2" (13mm) GYPSUM BOARD

SECTION

REFLECTED CEILING PLAN

FLOOR PLAN

SEATING CAPACITY	= 90
VOLUME	= 8,500 ft3 (240 m3)
AUDIENCE AREA	= 700 ft2 (65 m2)
VOLUME / SEAT	= 95 ft3 (2.7 m3)
AUDIENCE AREA / SEAT	= 7.8 ft2 (0.73 m2)
MID-FREQUENCY R.T	= 0.50 sec.

FISET DESCHAMPS BARTHA AMYOT, ARCHITECTS   L.L.DOELLE, ACOUSTICAL CONSULTANT

Fig. 19.1 Plan of a lecture hall, Marymount College, Quebec (1967), used in sample RT calculation.

Fig. 19.2 Front view of the 90-seat lecture hall illustrated in Fig. 19.1, used in sample RT calculation. (Photograph by Legare & Kedl.)

Fig. 19.3 Rear view of the lecture hall illustrated in Fig. 19.1, with wood-slatted acoustical treatment along the wall opposite the podium. (Photograph by Legare & Kedl.)

19.2 During Construction and after Completion

Before being declared complete and ready for use, every auditorium should undergo certain tests to make sure that it has no acoustical defects which could impair its usefulness. These tests will enable the architect to take immediate measures for the acoustical correction of the auditorium if it proves to be necessary.

In simple cases the room can be checked for echoes or flutter echoes by producing a sharp clap at the location of the sound source and then listening to the response. A person with an acute ear will also detect the reverberation characteristics of the room simply by listening to a performance in the room.

TABLE 19.1 Sample RT Calculation of a Lecture Hall (See Fig. 19.1)

Surface	Area Sq ft	Area Sq m	α_{500}	$S\alpha$ Sq ft	$S\alpha$ Sq m
Floor:					
Occupied area, upholstered seats	700	65	0.80	560	52
Unoccupied area, vinyl on wood	192	17	0.05	10	1
Walls:					
Rear, wood slats, detail A	120	11	0.50	60	5
Rear, gypsum with air space, section B	72	7	0.10	7	0.5
Side, gypsum, detail B	900	83	0.10	90	8
Front, gypsum on masonry	240	22	0.02	5	0.5
Ceiling:					
Suspended gypsum boards	1,030	95	0.12	123	11
Total absorption				855	78

$$RT_{500} = \begin{array}{l} \dfrac{0.05 \times 8,500}{855} = 0.50 \text{ sec} \quad \text{English system} \\[2ex] \dfrac{0.16 \times 240}{78} = 0.50 \text{ sec} \quad \text{metric system} \end{array}$$

In medium-sized and large auditoriums however, particularly if importance is attached to good acoustics, a more precise quantitative and qualitative evaluation of the acoustical properties is necessary. This evaluation can consist of (1) speech-intelligibility testing, (2) test performances, (3) objective measurements of room-acoustical properties.

The intelligibility within a room used for speech can be determined by *articulation* or *intelligibility testing*. A speaker on the stage or platform reads a number of words, phrases, or sentences or a number of meaningless monosyllables, and listeners at various parts of the seating area write down or repeat what they think they hear. The percentage of the words correctly recorded is called percent articulation or percent intelligibility. The term *articulation* is used when the speech material consists of meaningless syllables or fragments; the word *intelligibility* is applied when the speech material consists of complete words, phrases, or sentences.

Before an auditorium of particular acoustical importance comes into regular use, carefully planned *test performances* should be held to test the room subjectively for major acoustical faults, such as echoes, flutter echoes, incorrect RT, unusual lack of low-frequency sounds, room resonance, etc. Any defect which may be found can then be further investigated and probably corrected before the official opening of the auditorium, and while the building contractor is still on the site.

During construction and after completion of an auditorium several acoustical characteristics, such as RT, diffusion, balance of high, middle, and low frequencies, sound pressure level, and noise level, can be *objectively measured* or detected by instruments, thus providing a precise quantitative evaluation of the acoustical performance of the room.

Reverberation-time measurements during the construction of a radio or television studio might suggest certain adjustments or modifications in the planned acoustical treatment of the room. Acoustical measurements in completed radio studios will reveal whether any change is required in the acoustical treatment.

BIBLIOGRAPHY

Book

Newman, R. B., and W. J. Cavanaugh: "Acoustics," in J. H. Callender (ed.), *Timer-saver Standards*, 4th ed., McGraw-Hill Book Company, New York, 1966, pp. 623–625.

Periodicals

Nordlund, B., T. Kihlman, and S. Lindblad: "Use of Articulation Tests in Auditorium Studies," *J. Acoust. Soc. Am.*, July 1968, pp. 148–156.

"Scale Model Acoustic Studies," *The Architect and Building News*, April 10, 1969, pp. 77–78.

Day, B., and R. J. White: "A Study of Acoustic Field in Landscaped Offices with the Aid of a Tenth-scale Model," *Applied Acoustics*, July 1969, pp. 161–183.

Knudsen, V. O.: "Model Testing of Auditoriums," *J. Acoust. Soc. Am.*, February 1970, pp. 401–407.

Jordan, V. L.: "Acoustical Criteria for Auditoriums and Their Relation to Model Techniques," *J. Acoust. Soc. Am.*, February 1970, pp. 408–412.

Watters, B. G.: "Instrumentation for Acoustic Modeling," *J. Acoust. Soc. Am.*, February 1970, pp. 413–418.

Veneklasen, P. S.: "Model Techniques in Architectural Acoustics," *J. Acoust. Soc. Am.*, February 1970, pp. 419–423.

Appendixes

Table A.1 lists *sound absorption coefficients* of common building materials, acoustical materials, and room contents (audience, seats, etc.). It will be useful when making simple RT calculations.

The absorption coefficients are given for six representative frequencies, that is, for 125, 250, 500, 1000, 2000, and 4000 Hz, these being the most important in general acoustical design practice. Values of absorption coefficients below and above this frequency region are of use to acoustical experts only.

Sound absorption coefficients of standard acoustical materials, generally published in manufacturers' pamphlets, are, as a rule, not included in Table A.1. The inclusion of a few commercial acoustical materials does not necessarily mean that they are endorsed in any way; they merely constitute typical examples of their kind.

APPENDIX A

Sound Absorption Coefficients

TABLE A.1 Sound Absorption Coefficients of Building Materials, Acoustical Materials, and Room Contents

Description	Frequency, Hz						Source[°]
	125	250	500	1000	2000	4000	
Acoustical plaster, average	0.07	0.17	0.50	0.60	0.68	0.66	8
Acoustic steel deck, 6-in. (150-mm) ribs	0.58	0.64	0.71	0.63	0.47	0.40	7
Acoustone space tile, 32 in. (81 cm) OC, per unit	0.22	0.81	1.88	2.28	2.16	1.83	7
Air, per 1,000 cu ft volume, relative humidity 50%				0.9	2.9	7.4	6
Per 100 cu m volume, relative humidity 50%				0.3	0.9	2.4	6
Audience, in upholstered seats, per unit floor area	0.39	0.57	0.80	0.94	0.92	0.87	2
Unoccupied, well-upholstered seating, per unit floor area	0.19	0.37	0.56	0.67	0.61	0.59	2
Unoccupied, leather-covered upholstered seating, per unit floor area	0.15	0.25	0.36	0.40	0.37	0.35	8
Wooden pews, occupied, per unit floor area	0.37	0.44	0.67	0.70	0.80	0.72	8
Musician, with seat and instrument, per person	4.0	8.5	11.5	14.0	13.0	12.0	3
Brick, exposed, unglazed, unpainted	0.03	0.03	0.03	0.04	0.05	0.07	1
Carpet, heavy, on concrete	0.02	0.06	0.14	0.37	0.60	0.65	1
Heavy, on 40-oz (1.35 kg per sq m) hair felt or foam rubber	0.08	0.24	0.57	0.69	0.71	0.73	1
Concrete block, unpainted	0.36	0.44	0.31	0.29	0.39	0.25	1
Painted	0.10	0.05	0.06	0.07	0.09	0.08	1
Concrete, poured, unpainted	0.01	0.01	0.02	0.02	0.02	0.03	2
Fabrics, medium velour, 14 oz (0.48 kg per sq m), draped to half area	0.07	0.31	0.49	0.75	0.70	0.60	1
Floors, concrete or terrazzo	0.01	0.01	0.015	0.02	0.02	0.02	1
Linoleum, vinyl, rubber, or cork tile on concrete	0.02	0.03	0.03	0.03	0.03	0.02	1
On subfloor	0.02	0.04	0.05	0.05	0.10	0.05	3
Wooden	0.15	0.11	0.10	0.07	0.06	0.07	1
Wooden platform, with air space beneath	0.40	0.30	0.20	0.17	0.15	0.10	2
Geocoustic tile, 32 in. (81 cm) OC, per unit	0.13	0.74	2.35	2.53	2.03	1.73	4
Glass, heavy plate	0.18	0.06	0.04	0.03	0.02	0.02	1
Ordinary window	0.35	0.25	0.18	0.12	0.07	0.04	1
Gypsum board ½ in. (13 mm), on 2- by 4-in. (50- by 100-mm) stud, 16 in. (41 cm) OC	0.29	0.10	0.05	0.04	0.07	0.09	1
Plaster, gypsum or lime, smooth finish, on brick	0.013	0.015	0.02	0.03	0.04	0.05	1
On concrete block	0.12	0.09	0.07	0.05	0.05	0.04	2
On lath	0.14	0.10	0.06	0.04	0.04	0.03	1
On lath, over air space, or on studs	0.30	0.15	0.10	0.05	0.04	0.05	3
Plywood, ¼ in. (6 mm) over 3-in. (75-mm) air space, 1-in. (25-mm) glass-fiber backing	0.60	0.30	0.10	0.09	0.09	0.09	5
Soundblox unit, type B, 8-in. (20-cm) thick, painted	0.74	0.57	0.45	0.35	0.36	0.34	4
Wood panel, ⅜ to ½ in. (10 to 13 mm), over 2- to 4-in. (50- to 100-mm) air space	0.30	0.25	0.20	0.17	0.15	0.10	2

[°] 1, Acoustical and Insulating Materials Association; 2, L. L. Beranek; 3, P. H. Parkin and H. R. Humphreys; 4, P. G. Geiger and R. N. Hamme; 5, National Research Council of Canada; 6, C. M. Harris; 7, manufacturer's claim; 8, estimated.

Sound-insulation Values of Walls

Figures B.1 to B.9 include a number of typical *wall constructions* with pertinent architectural-acoustical data. The STC ratings indicated at each wall construction represent average values, somewhat on the conservative side, derived from test results issued by leading authorities in the field of acoustical testing and research. These values can be regarded as guidelines in architectural design practice. Most of the information shown in Figs. B.1 to B.9 was published in *A Guide to Air-borne, Impact, and Structure-borne Noise Control in Multi-family Dwellings*, National Bureau of Standards, Washington, D.C., 1967, and by the National Research Council of Canada, Ottawa, in the Building Research Note entitled *Transmission Loss of Plasterboard Walls*, 1968. It must be stressed that in practice the STC ratings may fall somewhat short of the values shown in the figures, due to poor workmanship or unpredictable and invisible paths of flanking transmission.

These illustrations also exemplify the manner in which the overall acoustical performance of walls is affected by various components and their physical characteristics, such as number and thickness of layers, width of air space between the layers, the use of isolation blanket or resilient attachment, spacing and rigidity of studs, etc.

The wall constructions shown in Figs. B.1 to B.9 can be grouped in the following way:

1. Masonry walls (Fig. B.1)
2. Lightweight walls
   2.1 Single-leaf assemblies (Fig. B.2)
   2.2 Multiple-leaf assemblies:
      Wood-stud partitions with 16-in. (41-cm) spacing (Fig. B.3)
      Wood-stud partitions with 24-in. (61-cm) spacing (Fig. B.4)
      Staggered wood-stud partitions (Fig. B.5)
      Metal-stud partitions with 16-in. (41-cm) spacing (Fig. B.6)
      Metal-stud partitions with 24-in. (61-cm) spacing (Fig. B.7)
      Staggered metal-stud partitions (Fig. B.8)
      Studless partitions (Fig. B.9)

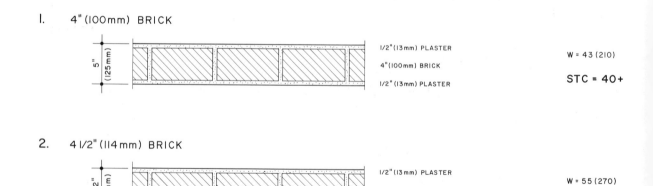

1. 4" (100mm) BRICK

5" (125mm)

1/2"(13mm) PLASTER
4"(100mm) BRICK
1/2" (13mm) PLASTER

W = 43 (210)

STC = 40+

2. 4 1/2" (114mm) BRICK

5 1/2" (140mm)

1/2"(13mm) PLASTER
4 1/2"(114mm) BRICK
1/2"(13mm) PLASTER

W = 55 (270)

STC = 42

Fig. B.1 Sound-insulation values of masonry walls: W, weight in pounds per square foot (kilograms per square meter); STC, sound transmission class rating in decibels.

3. 9" (23 cm) BRICK

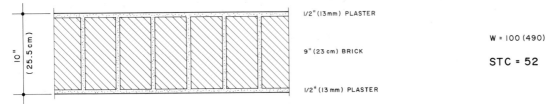

1/2" (13 mm) PLASTER

9" (23 cm) BRICK

1/2" (13 mm) PLASTER

W = 100 (490)

STC = 52

4. 12" (30.5 cm) BRICK

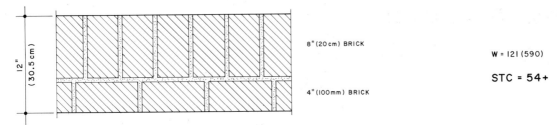

8" (20 cm) BRICK

4" (100 mm) BRICK

W = 121 (590)

STC = 54+

5. CAVITY BRICK

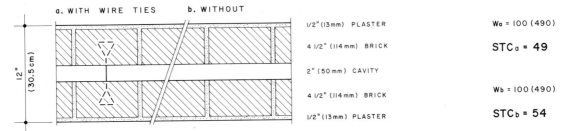

a. WITH WIRE TIES   b. WITHOUT

1/2" (13 mm) PLASTER

4 1/2" (114 mm) BRICK

2" (50 mm) CAVITY

4 1/2" (114 mm) BRICK

1/2" (13 mm) PLASTER

W_a = 100 (490)

STC_a = 49

W_b = 100 (490)

STC_b = 54

6.

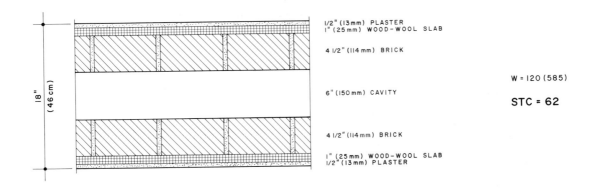

1/2" (13 mm) PLASTER
1" (25 mm) WOOD-WOOL SLAB

4 1/2" (114 mm) BRICK

6" (150 mm) CAVITY

4 1/2" (114 mm) BRICK

1" (25 mm) WOOD-WOOL SLAB
1/2" (13 mm) PLASTER

W = 120 (585)

STC = 62

7. 4" (100 mm) HOLLOW GYPSUM BLOCK

1/2" (13 mm) PLASTER

4" (100 mm) GYPSUM BLOCK

1/2" (13 mm) PLASTER

W = 23.5 (115)

STC = 40+

Fig. B.1 (continued)   Sound-insulation values of masonry walls: W, weight in pounds per square foot (kilograms per square meter); STC, sound transmission class rating in decibels.

8. 24" (61 cm) STONE

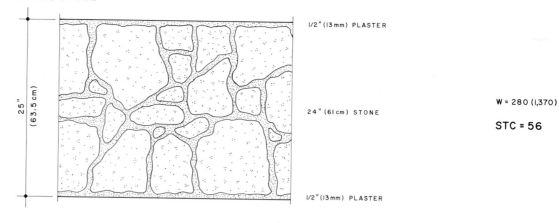

1/2" (13mm) PLASTER

24" (61 cm) STONE

1/2" (13mm) PLASTER

25" (63.5 cm)

W = 280 (1,370)

STC = 56

9. 6" (150mm) CONCRETE

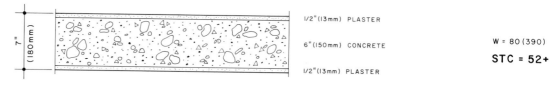

1/2" (13mm) PLASTER

6" (150mm) CONCRETE

1/2" (13mm) PLASTER

7" (180mm)

W = 80 (390)

STC = 52+

10. 6" (150mm) HOLLOW DENSE CONCRETE BLOCK

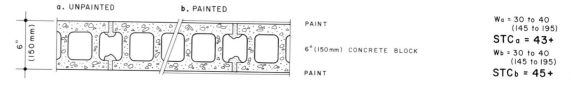

a. UNPAINTED   b. PAINTED

PAINT

6" (150mm) CONCRETE BLOCK

PAINT

6" (150mm)

Wₐ = 30 to 40 (145 to 195)

STCₐ = 43+

W_b = 30 to 40 (145 to 195)

STC_b = 45+

11. 8" (20 cm) HOLLOW DENSE CONCRETE BLOCK

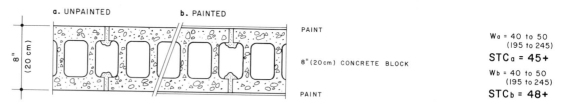

a. UNPAINTED   b. PAINTED

PAINT

8" (20 cm) CONCRETE BLOCK

PAINT

8" (20 cm)

Wₐ = 40 to 50 (195 to 245)

STCₐ = 45+

W_b = 40 to 50 (195 to 245)

STC_b = 48+

12.

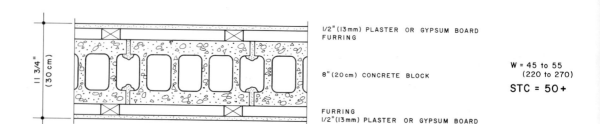

1/2" (13mm) PLASTER OR GYPSUM BOARD
FURRING

8" (20 cm) CONCRETE BLOCK

FURRING
1/2" (13mm) PLASTER OR GYPSUM BOARD

11 3/4" (30 cm)

W = 45 to 55 (220 to 270)

STC = 50+

Fig. B.1 (continued)   Sound-insulation values of masonry walls: W, weight in pounds per square foot (kilograms per square meter); STC, sound transmission class rating in decibels.

13. GYPSUM WALLBOARD

a. 3/8" (10 mm)   b. 1/2" (13 mm)   c. 5/8" (16 mm)

Wa = 1.6 (8) STCa = 26
Wb = 2.1 (10) STCb = 28
Wc = 2.7 (13) STCc = 29

14. TWO LAYERS OF GYPSUM WALLBOARD

1/2" (13 mm) GYPSUM BOARD
1/2" (13 mm) GYPSUM BOARD

1" (25 mm)

W = 4.6 (22)
STC = 31

15. GYPSUM SANDWICH PANEL

a. WITHOUT   b. WITH LEAD

2 1/4" (57 mm)

1/2" (13 mm) GYPSUM BOARD
1/8" (3 mm) LEAD
1" (25 mm) GYPSUM COREBOARD
5/8" (16 mm) GYPSUM BOARD

Wa = 10 (49)
STCa = 34+
Wb = 17 (83)
STCb = 40+

16. SOLID PLASTER

a. WITHOUT   b. WITH 3/4" (19 mm) CHANNEL

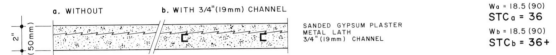

2" (50 mm)

SANDED GYPSUM PLASTER
METAL LATH
3/4" (19 mm) CHANNEL

Wa = 18.5 (90)
STCa = 36
Wb = 18.5 (90)
STCb = 36+

Fig. B.2 Sound-insulation values of lightweight walls with single-leaf assemblies: W, weight in pounds per square foot (kilograms per square meter); STC, sound transmission class rating in decibels.

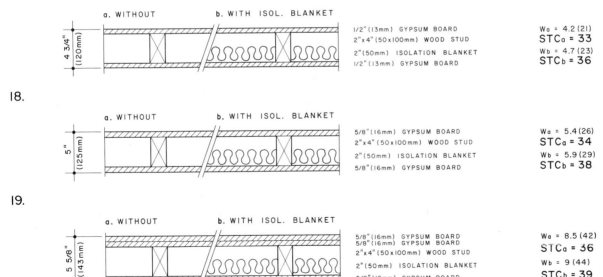

17.

a. WITHOUT   b. WITH ISOL. BLANKET

4 3/4" (120 mm)

1/2" (13 mm) GYPSUM BOARD
2"x4" (50x100mm) WOOD STUD
2" (50 mm) ISOLATION BLANKET
1/2" (13 mm) GYPSUM BOARD

Wa = 4.2 (21)
STCa = 33
Wb = 4.7 (23)
STCb = 36

18.

a. WITHOUT   b. WITH ISOL. BLANKET

5" (125 mm)

5/8" (16 mm) GYPSUM BOARD
2"x4" (50x100mm) WOOD STUD
2" (50 mm) ISOLATION BLANKET
5/8" (16 mm) GYPSUM BOARD

Wa = 5.4 (26)
STCa = 34
Wb = 5.9 (29)
STCb = 38

19.

a. WITHOUT   b. WITH ISOL. BLANKET

5 5/8" (143 mm)

5/8" (16 mm) GYPSUM BOARD
5/8" (16 mm) GYPSUM BOARD
2"x4" (50x100mm) WOOD STUD
2" (50 mm) ISOLATION BLANKET
5/8" (16 mm) GYPSUM BOARD

Wa = 8.5 (42)
STCa = 36
Wb = 9 (44)
STCb = 39

Fig. B.3 Sound-insulation values of wood-stud partition walls with 16-in. (41-cm) spacings: W, weight in pounds per square foot (kilograms per square meter); STC, sound transmission class rating in decibels.

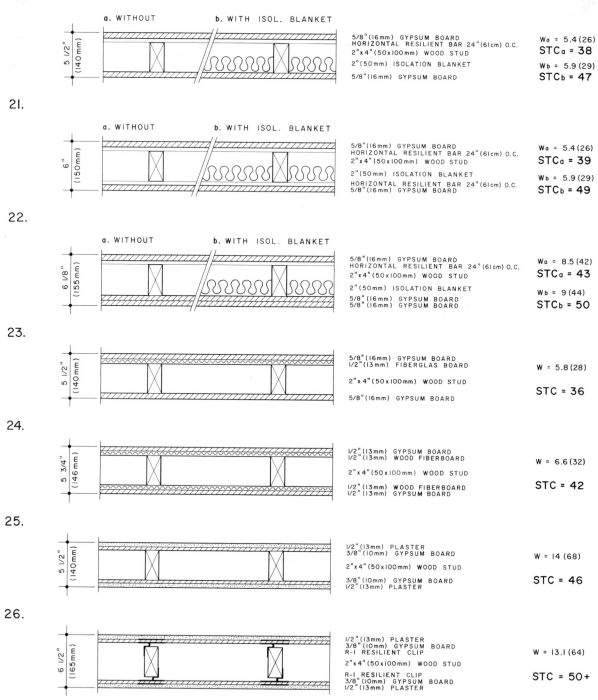

Fig. B.3 (continued) Sound-insulation values of wood-stud partition walls with 16-in. (41-cm) spacings: W, weight in pounds per square foot (kilograms per square meter); STC, sound transmission class rating in decibels.

27.

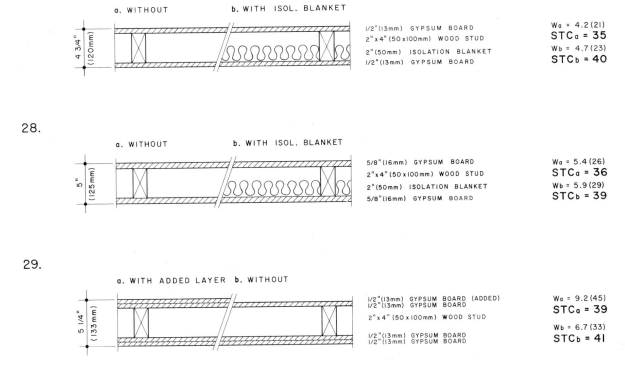

1/2"(13mm) GYPSUM BOARD	Wa = 4.2(21)
2"x4"(50x100mm) WOOD STUD	STCa = 35
2"(50mm) ISOLATION BLANKET	Wb = 4.7(23)
1/2"(13mm) GYPSUM BOARD	STCb = 40

28.

5/8"(16mm) GYPSUM BOARD	Wa = 5.4(26)
2"x4"(50x100mm) WOOD STUD	STCa = 36
2"(50mm) ISOLATION BLANKET	Wb = 5.9(29)
5/8"(16mm) GYPSUM BOARD	STCb = 39

29.

1/2"(13mm) GYPSUM BOARD (ADDED)	Wa = 9.2(45)
1/2"(13mm) GYPSUM BOARD	STCa = 39
2"x4"(50x100mm) WOOD STUD	
	Wb = 6.7(33)
1/2"(13mm) GYPSUM BOARD	STCb = 41
1/2"(13mm) GYPSUM BOARD	

Fig. B.4 Sound-insulation values of wood-stud partition walls with 24-in. (61-cm) spacings: W, weight in pounds per square foot (kilograms per square meter); STC, sound transmission class rating in decibels.

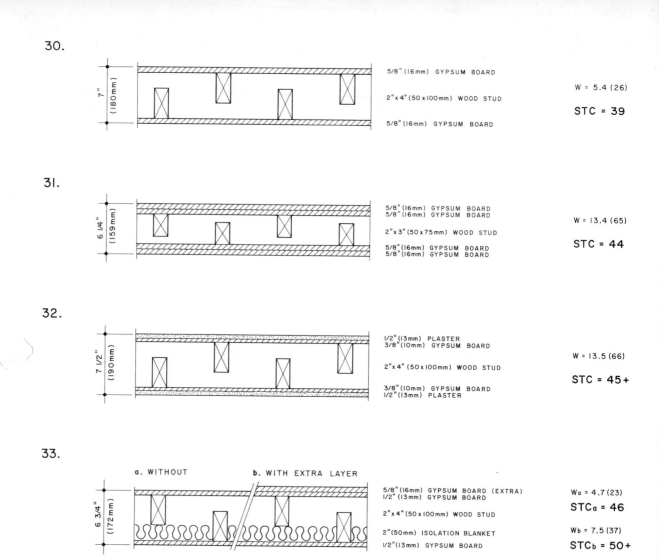

30.

7" (180mm)

5/8" (16mm) GYPSUM BOARD

2"x4" (50x100mm) WOOD STUD

5/8" (16mm) GYPSUM BOARD

W = 5.4 (26)

STC = 39

31.

6 1/4" (159mm)

5/8" (16mm) GYPSUM BOARD
5/8" (16mm) GYPSUM BOARD

2"x3" (50x75mm) WOOD STUD

5/8" (16mm) GYPSUM BOARD
5/8" (16mm) GYPSUM BOARD

W = 13.4 (65)

STC = 44

32.

7 1/2" (190mm)

1/2" (13mm) PLASTER
3/8" (10mm) GYPSUM BOARD

2"x4" (50x100mm) WOOD STUD

3/8" (10mm) GYPSUM BOARD
1/2" (13mm) PLASTER

W = 13.5 (66)

STC = 45+

33.

6 3/4" (172mm)

a. WITHOUT   b. WITH EXTRA LAYER

5/8" (16mm) GYPSUM BOARD (EXTRA)
1/2" (13mm) GYPSUM BOARD

2"x4" (50x100mm) WOOD STUD

2" (50mm) ISOLATION BLANKET

1/2" (13mm) GYPSUM BOARD

W_a = 4.7 (23)

STC_a = 46

W_b = 7.5 (37)

STC_b = 50+

Fig. B.5 Sound-insulation values of staggered wood-stud partition walls with 8-in. (20-cm) spacings: W, weight in pounds per square foot (kilograms per square meter); STC, sound transmission class rating in decibels.

34.

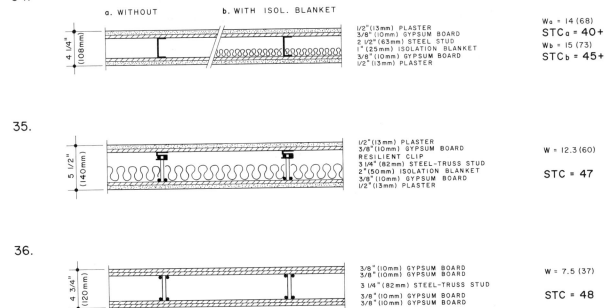

a. WITHOUT   b. WITH ISOL. BLANKET

4 1/4" (108mm)

1/2"(13mm) PLASTER
3/8"(10mm) GYPSUM BOARD
2 1/2"(63mm) STEEL STUD
1"(25mm) ISOLATION BLANKET
3/8"(10mm) GYPSUM BOARD
1/2"(13mm) PLASTER

W$_a$ = 14 (68)
STC$_a$ = 40+
W$_b$ = 15 (73)
STC$_b$ = 45+

35.

5 1/2" (140mm)

1/2"(13mm) PLASTER
3/8"(10mm) GYPSUM BOARD
RESILIENT CLIP
3 1/4"(82mm) STEEL-TRUSS STUD
2"(50mm) ISOLATION BLANKET
3/8"(10mm) GYPSUM BOARD
1/2"(13mm) PLASTER

W = 12.3 (60)

STC = 47

36.

4 3/4" (120mm)

3/8"(10mm) GYPSUM BOARD
3/8"(10mm) GYPSUM BOARD
3 1/4"(82mm) STEEL-TRUSS STUD
3/8"(10mm) GYPSUM BOARD
3/8"(10mm) GYPSUM BOARD

W = 7.5 (37)

STC = 48

Fig. B.6   Sound-insulation values of metal-stud partition walls with 16-in. (41-cm) spacings:
W, weight in pounds per square foot (kilograms per square meter); STC, sound transmission
class rating in decibels.

37.

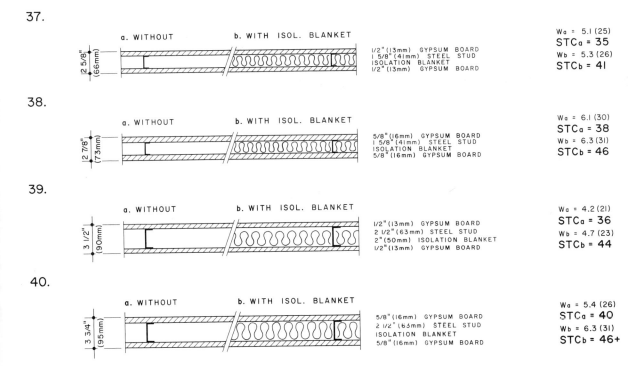

a. WITHOUT   b. WITH ISOL. BLANKET

2 5/8" (66mm)

1/2"(13mm) GYPSUM BOARD
1 5/8"(41mm) STEEL STUD
ISOLATION BLANKET
1/2"(13mm) GYPSUM BOARD

W$_a$ = 5.1 (25)
STC$_a$ = 35
W$_b$ = 5.3 (26)
STC$_b$ = 41

38.

a. WITHOUT   b. WITH ISOL. BLANKET

2 7/8" (73mm)

5/8"(16mm) GYPSUM BOARD
1 5/8"(41mm) STEEL STUD
ISOLATION BLANKET
5/8"(16mm) GYPSUM BOARD

W$_a$ = 6.1 (30)
STC$_a$ = 38
W$_b$ = 6.3 (31)
STC$_b$ = 46

39.

a. WITHOUT   b. WITH ISOL. BLANKET

3 1/2" (90mm)

1/2"(13mm) GYPSUM BOARD
2 1/2"(63mm) STEEL STUD
2"(50mm) ISOLATION BLANKET
1/2"(13mm) GYPSUM BOARD

W$_a$ = 4.2 (21)
STC$_a$ = 36
W$_b$ = 4.7 (23)
STC$_b$ = 44

40.

a. WITHOUT   b. WITH ISOL. BLANKET

3 3/4" (95mm)

5/8"(16mm) GYPSUM BOARD
2 1/2"(63mm) STEEL STUD
ISOLATION BLANKET
5/8"(16mm) GYPSUM BOARD

W$_a$ = 5.4 (26)
STC$_a$ = 40
W$_b$ = 6.3 (31)
STC$_b$ = 46+

Fig. B.7   Sound-insulation values of metal-stud partition walls with 24-in. (61-cm) spacings:
W, weight in pounds per square foot (kilograms per square meter); STC, sound transmission
class rating in decibels.

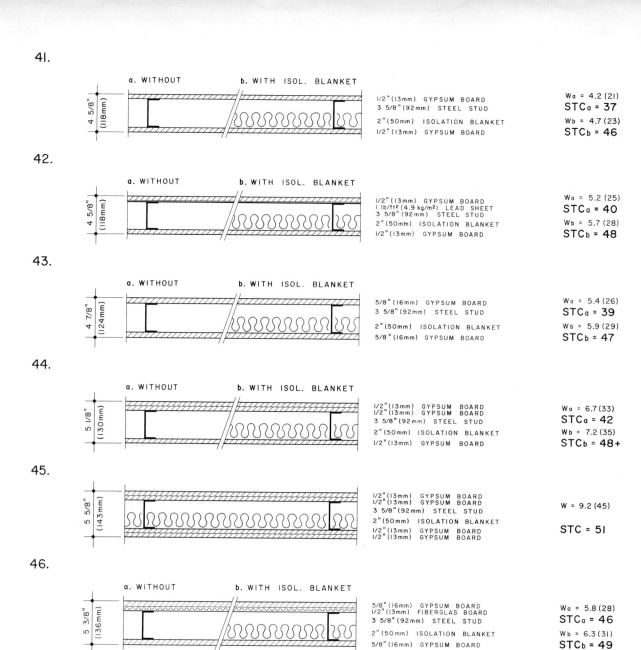

41.

a. WITHOUT   b. WITH ISOL. BLANKET

1/2"(13mm) GYPSUM BOARD
3 5/8"(92mm) STEEL STUD
2"(50mm) ISOLATION BLANKET
1/2"(13mm) GYPSUM BOARD

Wa = 4.2 (21)
STCa = 37
Wb = 4.7 (23)
STCb = 46

42.

a. WITHOUT   b. WITH ISOL. BLANKET

1/2"(13mm) GYPSUM BOARD
1 lb/ft² (4.9 kg/m²) LEAD SHEET
3 5/8"(92mm) STEEL STUD
2"(50mm) ISOLATION BLANKET
1/2"(13mm) GYPSUM BOARD

Wa = 5.2 (25)
STCa = 40
Wb = 5.7 (28)
STCb = 48

43.

a. WITHOUT   b. WITH ISOL. BLANKET

5/8"(16mm) GYPSUM BOARD
3 5/8"(92mm) STEEL STUD
2"(50mm) ISOLATION BLANKET
5/8"(16mm) GYPSUM BOARD

Wa = 5.4 (26)
STCa = 39
Wb = 5.9 (29)
STCb = 47

44.

a. WITHOUT   b. WITH ISOL. BLANKET

1/2"(13mm) GYPSUM BOARD
1/2"(13mm) GYPSUM BOARD
3 5/8"(92mm) STEEL STUD
2"(50mm) ISOLATION BLANKET
1/2"(13mm) GYPSUM BOARD

Wa = 6.7 (33)
STCa = 42
Wb = 7.2 (35)
STCb = 48+

45.

1/2"(13mm) GYPSUM BOARD
1/2"(13mm) GYPSUM BOARD
3 5/8"(92mm) STEEL STUD
2"(50mm) ISOLATION BLANKET
1/2"(13mm) GYPSUM BOARD
1/2"(13mm) GYPSUM BOARD

W = 9.2 (45)

STC = 51

46.

a. WITHOUT   b. WITH ISOL. BLANKET

5/8"(16mm) GYPSUM BOARD
1/2"(13mm) FIBERGLAS BOARD
3 5/8"(92mm) STEEL STUD
2"(50mm) ISOLATION BLANKET
5/8"(16mm) GYPSUM BOARD

Wa = 5.8 (28)
STCa = 46
Wb = 6.3 (31)
STCb = 49

47.

1/2"(13mm) GYPSUM BOARD
1/2"(13mm) MINERAL FIBERBOARD
3 5/8"(92mm) STEEL STUD
1/2"(13mm) MINERAL FIBERBOARD
1/2"(13mm) GYPSUM BOARD
1/2"(13mm) GYPSUM BOARD

W = 8.2 (40)

STC = 52

Fig. B.7 (continued) Sound-insulation values of metal-stud partition walls with 24-in. (61-cm) spacings: W, weight in pounds per square foot (kilograms per square meter); STC, sound transmission class rating in decibels.

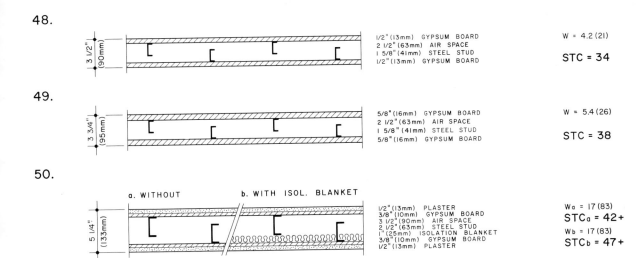

48.

1/2"(13mm) GYPSUM BOARD
2 1/2"(63mm) AIR SPACE
1 5/8"(41mm) STEEL STUD
1/2"(13mm) GYPSUM BOARD

W = 4.2 (21)

STC = 34

49.

5/8"(16mm) GYPSUM BOARD
2 1/2"(63mm) AIR SPACE
1 5/8"(41mm) STEEL STUD
5/8"(16mm) GYPSUM BOARD

W = 5.4 (26)

STC = 38

50.

a. WITHOUT   b. WITH ISOL. BLANKET

1/2"(13mm) PLASTER
3/8"(10mm) GYPSUM BOARD
3 1/2"(90mm) AIR SPACE
2 1/2"(63mm) STEEL STUD
1"(25mm) ISOLATION BLANKET
3/8"(10mm) GYPSUM BOARD
1/2"(13mm) PLASTER

Wa = 17 (83)
STCa = 42+
Wb = 17 (83)
STCb = 47+

Fig. B.8 Sound-insulation values of staggered metal-stud partition walls with 8-in. (20-cm) spacings: W, weight in pounds per square foot (kilograms per square meter); STC, sound transmission class rating in decibels.

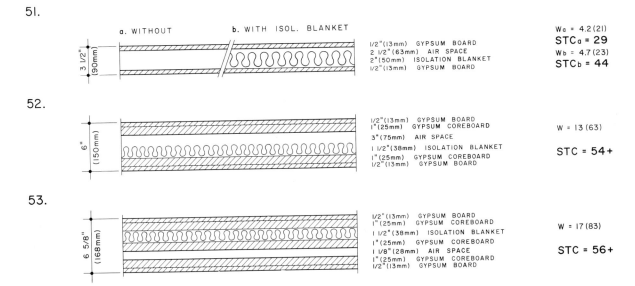

51.

a. WITHOUT   b. WITH ISOL. BLANKET

1/2"(13mm) GYPSUM BOARD
2 1/2"(63mm) AIR SPACE
2"(50mm) ISOLATION BLANKET
1/2"(13mm) GYPSUM BOARD

Wa = 4.2(21)
STCa = 29
Wb = 4.7(23)
STCb = 44

52.

1/2"(13mm) GYPSUM BOARD
1"(25mm) GYPSUM COREBOARD
3"(75mm) AIR SPACE
1 1/2"(38mm) ISOLATION BLANKET
1"(25mm) GYPSUM COREBOARD
1/2"(13mm) GYPSUM BOARD

W = 13 (63)

STC = 54+

53.

1/2"(13mm) GYPSUM BOARD
1"(25mm) GYPSUM COREBOARD
1 1/2"(38mm) ISOLATION BLANKET
1"(25mm) GYPSUM COREBOARD
1 1/8"(28mm) AIR SPACE
1"(25mm) GYPSUM COREBOARD
1/2"(13mm) GYPSUM BOARD

W = 17 (83)

STC = 56+

Fig. B.9 Sound-insulation values of studless partition walls: W, weight in pounds per square foot (kilograms per square meter); STC, sound transmission class rating in decibels.

APPENDIX C

Sound-insulation Values of Floors

Figures C.1 to C.4 include a number of typical *floor constructions* with pertinent architectural-acoustical data. The STC and IIC ratings indicated at each floor construction have been derived from test results issued by leading authorities in the field of acoustical testing and research. Most of the information shown in Figs. C.1 to C.4 was published in *A Guide to Air-borne, Impact, and Structure-borne Noise Control in Multi-family Dwellings,* National Bureau of Standards, Washington, D.C., 1967. It should be noted that in practice both STC and IIC ratings may fall somewhat short of the values shown in the figures, due to poor workmanship or unpredictable and invisible paths of flanking transmission. In addition, resiliently suspended ceilings in field installations seldom perform as effectively as they do in testing laboratories unless flanking paths are eliminated or at least minimized.

These illustrations also exemplify how the overall acoustical performance of floors is affected by various components and their physical characteristics, such as resilient floor finish, resilient or rigid floor supports, number and thickness of various layers, the use of isolation blankets in cavities, resilient ceiling attachments, spacing of joists, etc.

The floor constructions shown in Figs. C.1 to C.4 can be grouped in the following way:

1. Cast-in-place concrete floors (Fig. C.1)
2. Precast concrete floors (Fig. C.2)
3. Wood-joist floors (Fig. C.3)
4. Steel-joist floors (Fig. C.4)

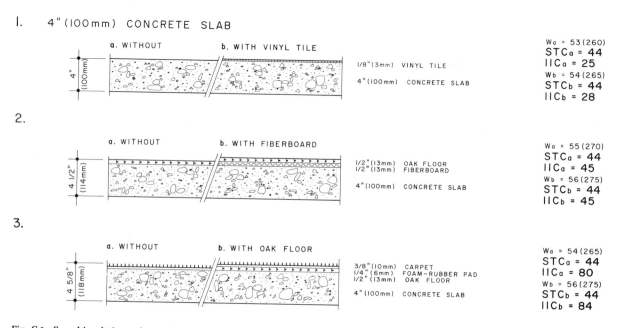

Fig. C.1 Sound-insulation values of cast-in-place concrete floors: W, weight in pounds per square foot (kilograms per square meter); STC, sound transmission class rating in decibels; IIC, impact insulation class rating.

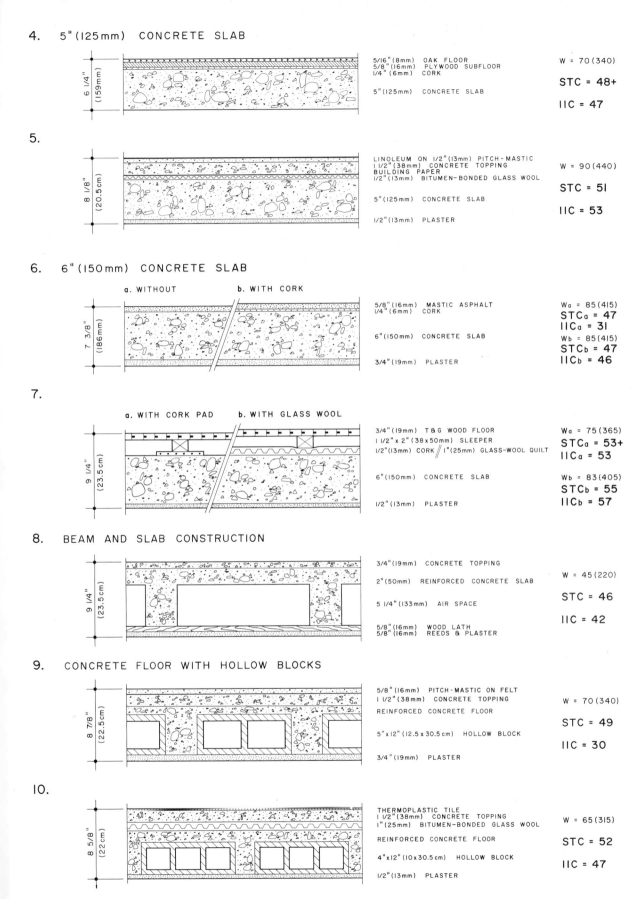

4.   5" (125mm) CONCRETE SLAB

6 1/4" (159mm)

5/16" (8mm)   OAK FLOOR
5/8" (16mm)   PLYWOOD SUBFLOOR
1/4" (6mm)   CORK
5" (125mm)   CONCRETE SLAB

W = 70 (340)

STC = 48+

IIC = 47

5.

8 1/8" (20.5cm)

LINOLEUM ON 1/2" (13mm) PITCH-MASTIC
1 1/2" (38mm)   CONCRETE TOPPING
BUILDING PAPER
1/2" (13mm)   BITUMEN-BONDED GLASS WOOL

5" (125mm)   CONCRETE SLAB

1/2" (13mm)   PLASTER

W = 90 (440)

STC = 51

IIC = 53

6.   6" (150mm) CONCRETE SLAB

a. WITHOUT   b. WITH CORK

7 3/8" (186mm)

5/8" (16mm)   MASTIC ASPHALT
1/4" (6mm)   CORK
6" (150mm)   CONCRETE SLAB
3/4" (19mm)   PLASTER

Wa = 85 (415)
STCa = 47
IICa = 31
Wb = 85 (415)
STCb = 47
IICb = 46

7.

a. WITH CORK PAD   b. WITH GLASS WOOL

9 1/4" (23.5cm)

3/4" (19mm)   T&G WOOD FLOOR
1 1/2" x 2" (38 x 50mm) SLEEPER
1/2" (13mm) CORK // 1" (25mm) GLASS-WOOL QUILT

6" (150mm)   CONCRETE SLAB

1/2" (13mm)   PLASTER

Wa = 75 (365)
STCa = 53+
IICa = 53
Wb = 83 (405)
STCb = 55
IICb = 57

8.   BEAM AND SLAB CONSTRUCTION

9 1/4" (23.5cm)

3/4" (19mm)   CONCRETE TOPPING

2" (50mm)   REINFORCED CONCRETE SLAB

5 1/4" (133mm)   AIR SPACE

5/8" (16mm)   WOOD LATH
5/8" (16mm)   REEDS & PLASTER

W = 45 (220)

STC = 46

IIC = 42

9.   CONCRETE FLOOR WITH HOLLOW BLOCKS

8 7/8" (22.5cm)

5/8" (16mm)   PITCH-MASTIC ON FELT
1 1/2" (38mm)   CONCRETE TOPPING
REINFORCED CONCRETE FLOOR

5" x 12" (12.5 x 30.5 cm) HOLLOW BLOCK

3/4" (19mm)   PLASTER

W = 70 (340)

STC = 49

IIC = 30

10.

8 5/8" (22cm)

THERMOPLASTIC TILE
1 1/2" (38mm)   CONCRETE TOPPING
1" (25mm)   BITUMEN-BONDED GLASS WOOL
REINFORCED CONCRETE FLOOR

4" x 12" (10 x 30.5 cm) HOLLOW BLOCK

1/2" (13mm)   PLASTER

W = 65 (315)

STC = 52

IIC = 47

Fig. C.1 (continued)   Sound-insulation values of cast-in-place concrete floors: W, weight in pounds per square foot (kilograms per square meter); STC, sound transmission class rating in decibels; IIC, impact insulation class rating.

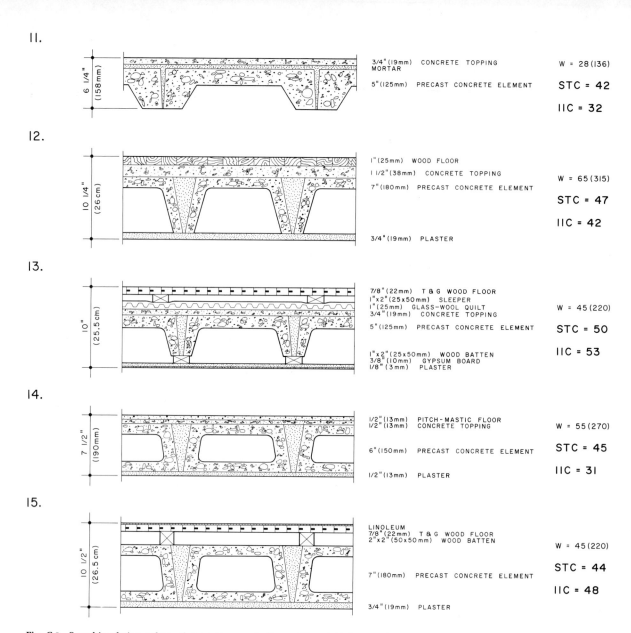

11.

6 1/4" (158mm)

3/4" (19mm) CONCRETE TOPPING MORTAR

5" (125mm) PRECAST CONCRETE ELEMENT

W = 28 (136)

STC = 42

IIC = 32

12.

10 1/4" (26 cm)

1" (25mm) WOOD FLOOR

1 1/2" (38mm) CONCRETE TOPPING

7" (180mm) PRECAST CONCRETE ELEMENT

3/4" (19mm) PLASTER

W = 65 (315)

STC = 47

IIC = 42

13.

10" (25.5 cm)

7/8" (22mm) T & G WOOD FLOOR
1"x2" (25x50mm) SLEEPER
1" (25mm) GLASS-WOOL QUILT
3/4" (19mm) CONCRETE TOPPING

5" (125mm) PRECAST CONCRETE ELEMENT

1"x2" (25x50mm) WOOD BATTEN
3/8" (10mm) GYPSUM BOARD
1/8" (3mm) PLASTER

W = 45 (220)

STC = 50

IIC = 53

14.

7 1/2" (190mm)

1/2" (13mm) PITCH-MASTIC FLOOR
1/2" (13mm) CONCRETE TOPPING

6" (150mm) PRECAST CONCRETE ELEMENT

1/2" (13mm) PLASTER

W = 55 (270)

STC = 45

IIC = 31

15.

10 1/2" (26.5 cm)

LINOLEUM
7/8" (22mm) T & G WOOD FLOOR
2"x2" (50x50mm) WOOD BATTEN

7" (180mm) PRECAST CONCRETE ELEMENT

3/4" (19mm) PLASTER

W = 45 (220)

STC = 44

IIC = 48

Fig. C.2 Sound-insulation values of precast concrete floors: W, weight in pounds per square foot (kilograms per square meter); STC, sound transmission class rating in decibels; IIC, impact insulation class rating.

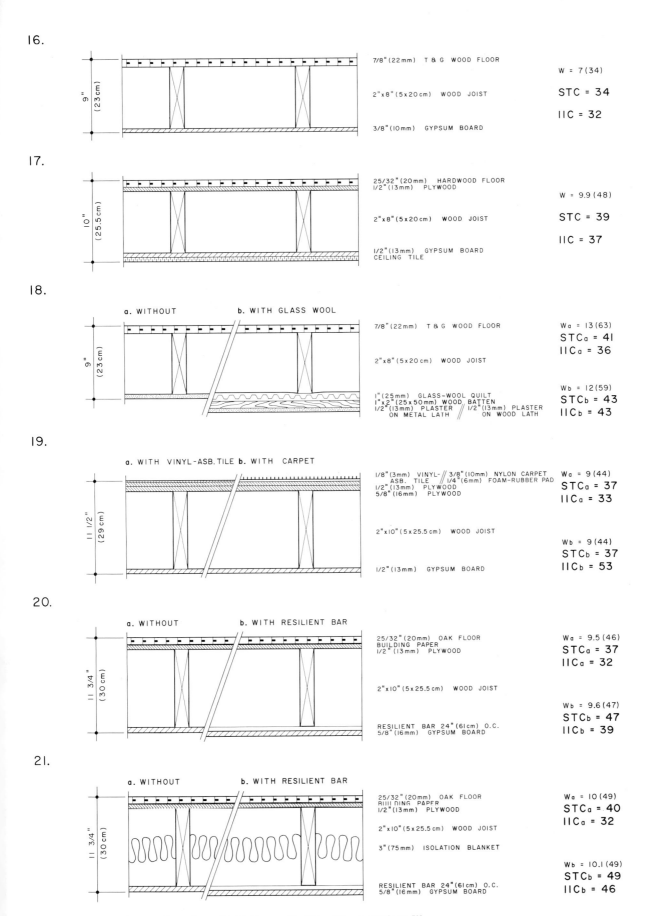

16.

7/8"(22mm) T & G WOOD FLOOR

2"x8"(5x20cm) WOOD JOIST

3/8"(10mm) GYPSUM BOARD

9" (23cm)

W = 7(34)

STC = 34

IIC = 32

17.

25/32"(20mm) HARDWOOD FLOOR
1/2"(13mm) PLYWOOD

2"x8"(5x20cm) WOOD JOIST

1/2"(13mm) GYPSUM BOARD
CEILING TILE

10" (25.5cm)

W = 9.9(48)

STC = 39

IIC = 37

18.

a. WITHOUT   b. WITH GLASS WOOL

7/8"(22mm) T & G WOOD FLOOR

2"x8"(5x20cm) WOOD JOIST

1"(25mm) GLASS-WOOL QUILT
1"x2"(25x50mm) WOOD BATTEN
1/2"(13mm) PLASTER   1/2"(13mm) PLASTER
ON METAL LATH   ON WOOD LATH

9" (23cm)

Wa = 13(63)
STCa = 41
IICa = 36

Wb = 12(59)
STCb = 43
IICb = 43

19.

a. WITH VINYL-ASB.TILE b. WITH CARPET

1/8"(3mm) VINYL-// 3/8"(10mm) NYLON CARPET
ASB. TILE // 1/4"(6mm) FOAM-RUBBER PAD
1/2"(13mm) PLYWOOD
5/8"(16mm) PLYWOOD

2"x10"(5x25.5cm) WOOD JOIST

1/2"(13mm) GYPSUM BOARD

11 1/2" (29 cm)

Wa = 9(44)
STCa = 37
IICa = 33

Wb = 9(44)
STCb = 37
IICb = 53

20.

a. WITHOUT   b. WITH RESILIENT BAR

25/32"(20mm) OAK FLOOR
BUILDING PAPER
1/2"(13mm) PLYWOOD

2"x10"(5x25.5cm) WOOD JOIST

RESILIENT BAR 24"(61cm) O.C.
5/8"(16mm) GYPSUM BOARD

11 3/4" (30cm)

Wa = 9.5(46)
STCa = 37
IICa = 32

Wb = 9.6(47)
STCb = 47
IICb = 39

21.

a. WITHOUT   b. WITH RESILIENT BAR

25/32"(20mm) OAK FLOOR
BUILDING PAPER
1/2"(13mm) PLYWOOD

2"x10"(5x25.5cm) WOOD JOIST

3"(75mm) ISOLATION BLANKET

RESILIENT BAR 24"(61cm) O.C.
5/8"(16mm) GYPSUM BOARD

11 3/4" (30cm)

Wa = 10(49)
STCa = 40
IICa = 32

Wb = 10.1(49)
STCb = 49
IICb = 46

Fig. C.3 Sound-insulation values of wood-joist floors with 16-in. (41-cm) spacings: W, weight in pounds per square foot (kilograms per square meter); STC, sound transmission class rating in decibels; IIC, impact insulation class rating.

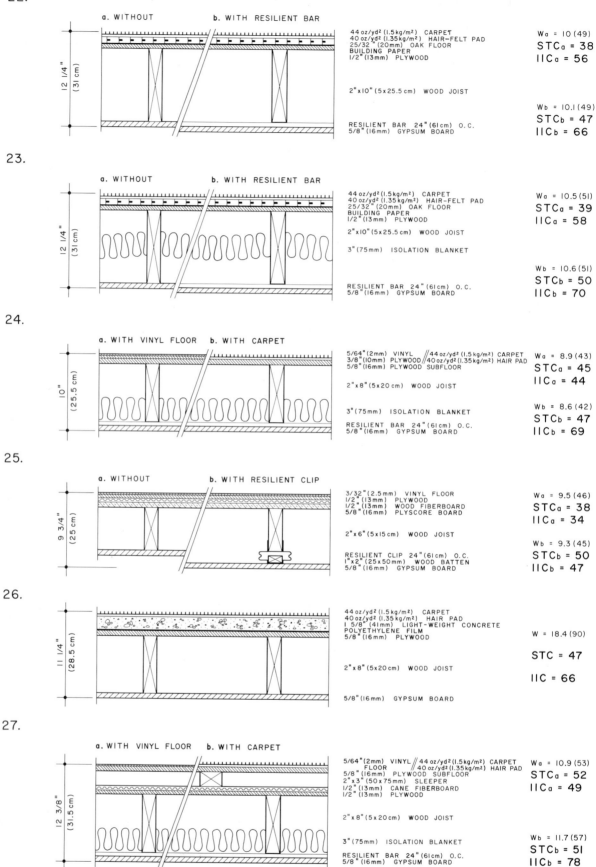

22.

a. WITHOUT   b. WITH RESILIENT BAR

12 1/4" (31 cm)

44 oz/yd² (1.5kg/m²) CARPET
40 oz/yd² (1.35kg/m²) HAIR-FELT PAD
25/32" (20mm) OAK FLOOR
BUILDING PAPER
1/2" (13mm) PLYWOOD

2"x10" (5x25.5 cm) WOOD JOIST

RESILIENT BAR 24" (61cm) O.C.
5/8" (16mm) GYPSUM BOARD

W_a = 10 (49)
STC_a = 38
IIC_a = 56

W_b = 10.1 (49)
STC_b = 47
IIC_b = 66

23.

a. WITHOUT   b. WITH RESILIENT BAR

12 1/4" (31 cm)

44 oz/yd² (1.5kg/m²) CARPET
40 oz/yd² (1.35kg/m²) HAIR-FELT PAD
25/32" (20mm) OAK FLOOR
BUILDING PAPER
1/2" (13mm) PLYWOOD

2"x10" (5x25.5 cm) WOOD JOIST

3" (75mm) ISOLATION BLANKET

RESILIENT BAR 24" (61cm) O.C.
5/8" (16mm) GYPSUM BOARD

W_a = 10.5 (51)
STC_a = 39
IIC_a = 58

W_b = 10.6 (51)
STC_b = 50
IIC_b = 70

24.

a. WITH VINYL FLOOR   b. WITH CARPET

10" (25.5 cm)

5/64" (2mm) VINYL // 44 oz/yd² (1.5kg/m²) CARPET
3/8" (10mm) PLYWOOD / 40 oz/yd² (1.35kg/m²) HAIR PAD
5/8" (16mm) PLYWOOD SUBFLOOR

2"x8" (5x20 cm) WOOD JOIST

3" (75mm) ISOLATION BLANKET
RESILIENT BAR 24" (61cm) O.C.
5/8" (16mm) GYPSUM BOARD

W_a = 8.9 (43)
STC_a = 45
IIC_a = 44

W_b = 8.6 (42)
STC_b = 47
IIC_b = 69

25.

a. WITHOUT   b. WITH RESILIENT CLIP

9 3/4" (25 cm)

3/32" (2.5mm) VINYL FLOOR
1/2" (13mm) PLYWOOD
1/2" (13mm) WOOD FIBERBOARD
5/8" (16mm) PLYSCORE BOARD

2"x6" (5x15 cm) WOOD JOIST

RESILIENT CLIP 24" (61cm) O.C.
1"x2" (25x50mm) WOOD BATTEN
5/8" (16mm) GYPSUM BOARD

W_a = 9.5 (46)
STC_a = 38
IIC_a = 34

W_b = 9.3 (45)
STC_b = 50
IIC_b = 47

26.

11 1/4" (28.5 cm)

44 oz/yd² (1.5kg/m²) CARPET
40 oz/yd² (1.35kg/m²) HAIR PAD
1 5/8" (41mm) LIGHT-WEIGHT CONCRETE
POLYETHYLENE FILM
5/8" (16mm) PLYWOOD

2"x8" (5x20 cm) WOOD JOIST

5/8" (16mm) GYPSUM BOARD

W = 18.4 (90)

STC = 47

IIC = 66

27.

a. WITH VINYL FLOOR   b. WITH CARPET

12 3/8" (31.5 cm)

5/64" (2mm) VINYL // 44 oz/yd² (1.5kg/m²) CARPET
FLOOR / 40 oz/yd² (1.35kg/m²) HAIR PAD
5/8" (16mm) PLYWOOD SUBFLOOR
2"x3" (50x75mm) SLEEPER
1/2" (13mm) CANE FIBERBOARD
1/2" (13mm) PLYWOOD

2"x8" (5x20 cm) WOOD JOIST

3" (75mm) ISOLATION BLANKET

RESILIENT BAR 24" (61cm) O.C.
5/8" (16mm) GYPSUM BOARD

W_a = 10.9 (53)
STC_a = 52
IIC_a = 49

W_b = 11.7 (57)
STC_b = 51
IIC_b = 78

Fig. C.3 (continued)   Sound-insulation values of wood-joist floors with 16-in. (41-cm) spacings: W, weight in pounds per square foot (kilograms per square meter); STC, sound transmission class rating in decibels; IIC, impact insulation class rating.

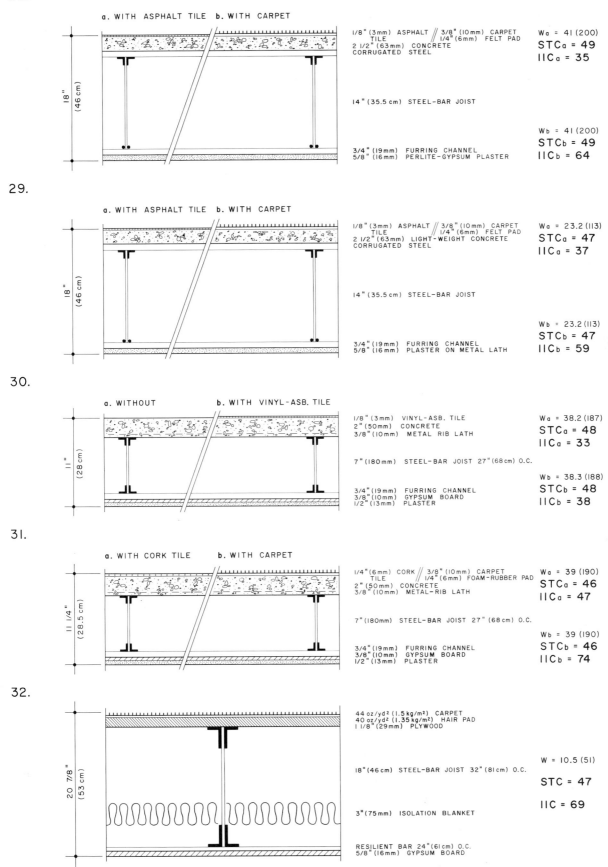

28.

a. WITH ASPHALT TILE b. WITH CARPET

18" (46 cm)

1/8" (3mm) ASPHALT // 3/8" (10mm) CARPET
TILE // 1/4" (6mm) FELT PAD
2 1/2" (63mm) CONCRETE
CORRUGATED STEEL

Wa = 41 (200)
STCa = 49
IICa = 35

14" (35.5 cm) STEEL-BAR JOIST

3/4" (19mm) FURRING CHANNEL
5/8" (16mm) PERLITE-GYPSUM PLASTER

Wb = 41 (200)
STCb = 49
IICb = 64

29.

a. WITH ASPHALT TILE b. WITH CARPET

18" (46 cm)

1/8" (3mm) ASPHALT // 3/8" (10mm) CARPET
TILE // 1/4" (6mm) FELT PAD
2 1/2" (63mm) LIGHT-WEIGHT CONCRETE
CORRUGATED STEEL

Wa = 23.2 (113)
STCa = 47
IICa = 37

14" (35.5 cm) STEEL-BAR JOIST

3/4" (19mm) FURRING CHANNEL
5/8" (16mm) PLASTER ON METAL LATH

Wb = 23.2 (113)
STCb = 47
IICb = 59

30.

a. WITHOUT   b. WITH VINYL-ASB. TILE

11" (28 cm)

1/8" (3mm) VINYL-ASB. TILE
2" (50mm) CONCRETE
3/8" (10mm) METAL RIB LATH

Wa = 38.2 (187)
STCa = 48
IICa = 33

7" (180mm) STEEL-BAR JOIST 27" (68cm) O.C.

3/4" (19mm) FURRING CHANNEL
3/8" (10mm) GYPSUM BOARD
1/2" (13mm) PLASTER

Wb = 38.3 (188)
STCb = 48
IICb = 38

31.

a. WITH CORK TILE   b. WITH CARPET

11 1/4" (28.5 cm)

1/4" (6mm) CORK // 3/8" (10mm) CARPET
TILE // 1/4" (6mm) FOAM-RUBBER PAD
2" (50mm) CONCRETE
3/8" (10mm) METAL-RIB LATH

Wa = 39 (190)
STCa = 46
IICa = 47

7" (180mm) STEEL-BAR JOIST 27" (68cm) O.C.

3/4" (19mm) FURRING CHANNEL
3/8" (10mm) GYPSUM BOARD
1/2" (13mm) PLASTER

Wb = 39 (190)
STCb = 46
IICb = 74

32.

20 7/8" (53 cm)

44 oz/yd² (1.5 kg/m²) CARPET
40 oz/yd² (1.35 kg/m²) HAIR PAD
1 1/8" (29mm) PLYWOOD

W = 10.5 (51)

18" (46 cm) STEEL-BAR JOIST 32" (81cm) O.C.

STC = 47

IIC = 69

3" (75mm) ISOLATION BLANKET

RESILIENT BAR 24" (61cm) O.C.
5/8" (16mm) GYPSUM BOARD

Fig. C.4 Sound-insulation values of steel-joist floors: W, weight in pounds per square foot (kilograms per square meter); STC, sound transmission class rating in decibels; IIC, impact insulation class rating.

APPENDIX D   Books[1]

Knudsen, V. O., and C. M. Harris: *Acoustical Designing in Architecture*, John Wiley & Sons, Inc., New York, 1950, 457 pp.

Bruel, P. V.: *Sound Insulation and Room Acoustics*, Chapman & Hall, Ltd., London, 1951, 275 pp.

Ingerslev, F.: *Acoustics in Modern Building Practice*, The Architectural Press, London, 1952, 290 pp.

Beranek, L. L.: *Acoustics*, McGraw-Hill Book Company, New York, 1954, 481 pp.

Conturie, L.: *L'Acoustique dans les bâtiments*, Éditions Eyrolles, Paris, 1955, 284 pp.

Burris-Meyer, H., and L. S. Goodfriend: *Acoustics for the Architect*, Reinhold Publishing Corporation, New York, 1957, 126 pp.

Harris, C. M. (ed.): *Handbook of Noise Control*, McGraw-Hill Book Company, New York, 1957, 1184 pp.

Parkin, P. H., and H. R. Humphreys: *Acoustics, Noise and Buildings*, Frederick A. Praeger, Inc., New York, 1958, 331 pp.

Beranek, L. L. (ed.): *Noise Reduction*, McGraw-Hill Book Company, New York, 1960, 752 pp.

Moore, J. E.: *Design for Good Acoustics*, The Architectural Press, London, 1961, 91 pp.

Armagnac, M. R.: *L'Isolation acoustique dans le bâtiment*, Ampère, Paris, 1962.

Noise: The Wilson Report, Her Majesty's Stationery Office, London, July 1963, 235 pp.

Furrer, W.: *Room and Building Acoustics and Noise Abatement*, Butterworth & Co. Ltd., London, 1964, 226 pp.

Raes, A. C.: *Isolation sonore et acoustique architecturale*, Éditions Chiron, Paris, 1964, 383 pp.

Doelle, L. L.: *Acoustics in Architectural Design*, Bibliography 29, National Research Council, Ottawa, 1965, 543 pp.

Close, P. D.: *Sound Control and Thermal Insulation of Buildings*, Reinhold Publishing Corporation, New York, 1966, 502 pp.

Newman, R. B., and W. J. Cavanaugh: "Acoustics," in J. H. Callender (ed.), *Time-saver Standards*, 4th ed., McGraw-Hill Book Company, New York, 1966, pp. 609–648.

Hines, W. A.: *Noise Control in Industry*, Business Publications Ltd., London, 1966, 197 pp.

Purkis, H. J.: *Building Physics: Acoustics*, Pergamon Press, London, 1966, 141 pp.

Berendt, R. D., G. E. Winzer, and C. B. Burroughs: *A Guide to Air-borne, Impact, and Structure-borne Noise Control in Multi-family Dwellings*, U.S. Department of Housing and Urban Development, Washington, D.C., September 1967.

Lamoral, R.: *Problèmes d'acoustique des salles et des studios*, Éditions Chiron, Paris, 1967, 189 pp.

Rettinger, M.: *Acoustics*, Chemical Publishing Company, Inc., New York, 1968, 386 pp.

Day, B. F., R. D. Ford, and P. Lord (eds.): *Building Acoustics*, Elsevier Publishing Company Ltd., New York, 1969, 120 pp.

Lawrence, A.: *Architectural Acoustics*, Elsevier Publishing Company Ltd., Barking, London, 1970, 225 pp.

General Bibliography

[1] Entries are listed in chronological order because it is believed this will be more helpful to the reader than an alphabetical arrangement.

Index